RĀMĀYAṆAM

Volume 1

RĀMĀYAṆAM

Volume 1

Dushyanth Sridhar

HarperCollins *Publishers* India

First published in India by HarperCollins *Publishers* 2024
4th Floor, Tower A, Building No. 10, DLF Cyber City,
DLF Phase II, Gurugram, Haryana – 122002
www.harpercollins.co.in

2 4 6 8 10 9 7 5 3

Front cover illustration: Seeking consent to accompany them to the Daṇḍaka forests, Lakṣmaṇa performs prapatti at the feet of Rāma and Sītā
Back cover illustration: As Viśvāmitra looks on, Rāma and Lakṣmaṇa fight the rākṣasas led by Tāṭakā

P-ISBN: 978-93-6213-603-9
E-ISBN: 978-93-6213-076-1

Typeset in 12/15 Minion Pro at
Manipal Technologies Limited, Manipal

Printed and bound at
Thomson Press (India) Ltd

tasmai śrī-gurave namaḥ
I offer obeisance to (my) Śrī Guru(s):

Villivalam *Śrī Nārāyaṇa Yatīndra Mahādeśikan*
(45th Pontiff of *Śrī Ahobila Maṭha)*

Nāvalpākkam Śaṭhakopa Rāmānuja Tātācārya
(Chevalier of the Légion d'honneur and Padma Bhushan awardee)

Setlur *Śrīvatsāṅkācārya*

Nelvoy *Soumyanārāyanācārya*

Villur *Karuṇākarācārya*

Devanārvilāgam *Sāranāthācārya*

Contents

Preface

'*Kūjantaṃ Rāma Rāmeti*' is the verse that has filled my ears since childhood. My journey with Rāma and the Rāmāyaṇam has been nothing short of a spiritual cruise since then. Rāmāyaṇa reminds me of Vālmīki, a maharṣi and a poet of the highest order, whose presentation of Rāma and Sītā's life history is plain truth. It is thus referred to as itihāsa, making it integral to Bhārata's history.

To keep associating the Rāmāyaṇa with the word 'myth' is gross injustice. Our ācāryas have placed the Rāmāyaṇa alongside the Vedas, the Upaniṣads, the Bhagavad Gītā and Bramhā Sūtras, giving it the respect and prominence, it deserves. But it is made grander and unambiguous with the exquisite commentaries it has received in the last millennium. The famous ones include Tattvadīpikā of Maheśvara Tīrtha, Bhūṣaṇa of Govindarāja, Dharmakūṭa of Tryaṃbaka Makhin, Amṛtakataka of Mādhava Yogī, Tilaka of Nāgeśa Bhaṭṭa and Śiromaṇi of Vaṃsīdhara Śivasahāya.

No English retelling of the Rāmāyaṇa, to the best of my knowledge, has covered the purpose of pairing the original with its commentaries, as much as this book does. Mahābhārata, Harivaṃśa and Purāṇas—such as Viṣṇu, Bhāgavata, Matsya, Vāyu, Kūrma, Agni, Śiva, Skanda, Padma, Nāradīya and Viṣṇudharmottara—have dealt with Rāma's life history as well. So have three other texts—the Adbhuta, Adhyātma and Ānanda Rāmāyaṇas. Poet extraordinaires and consummate dramatists in different time periods have either recreated the entire scripture or some portions of it. Kālidāsa's Raghuvaṃśa, Bhoja's Rāmāyaṇacampū, Kumāradāsa's Jānakīharaṇa, Abhinanda's Rāmacarita, Bhatti's Rāvaṇavadha, Bhavabhūti's Uttararāmacarita, Pravaraṣeṇa's Setukāvya, Kṣemendra's Rāmāyaṇamañjarī are noted works. Some lesser-known texts like Bhāsa's Pratimā nāṭaka and Abhiṣeka nāṭaka, Yaśovarman's Rāmābhyudaya and Bhimata's Svapnadaśānana are equally beautiful.

Interesting aspects of the above works have been incorporated in this book in a way that there is no digression from Vālmīki's text. The contribution of ācāryas through stotras have been vital in the preservation of the philosophical content in the Rāmāyaṇa. Vedānta Deśika's Raghuvīra gadya, Abhaya pradāna sāra, Haṃsa Sandeśa, Pādukā sahasra; commentaries by Nampiḷḷai and Periyavāccāṉ Piḷḷai; Madhva's Tātparyanirṇaya and Rāghavendra's Rāmacāritra mañjarī; Bhattathiri's Nārāyaṇīya and Śūrpaṇakhā pralāpa; Appayyadīkṣita's Rāmāyaṇa tātparya sāra saṅgraha and many such works have accomplished this task.

This book has borrowed the views of such ācāryas as and when required. We have known that Bhārata is a potpourri of multiple religions, languages and cultures. A Rāmāyaṇa version advocating Jain tenets, and another teaching Buddhist aphorisms are well-known. The ancient works in the Tamil language such as the Puṟanāṉūṟu, Iḷaṅkōvaṭikaḷ's Cilappatikāra, Nālāyira Divya Prabandha of the Āḻvārs, Commentaries by Nampiḷḷai, Periavācchān Piḷḷai; Manavāḷa Māmuni; Kamban's Rāmāvatāra and Aruṇācala's Rāma Nāṭaka have been inspired by Vālmīki's Rāmāyaṇa. So have other magnificent Rāmāyaṇa versions like Molla's in Telugu, Eḻutthacchan's in Malayalam, Tulasīdāsa's in Awadhi, Kṛttivāsa's in Bengali, Torave's in Kannada, Balarāma's in Odia, Kākāvin's in Javanese. The compositions of Annamayya, Purandaradāsa, Gopaṇṇā, Veṅkaṭakavi, Tyāgarāja and Muddusvāmidīkṣita on Rāma all exude bhakti.

The reader is likely to find some elements inspired by these monumental works in this book. Authors like Tirukkudantai Āndavan, Paravākottai Āndavan, C. Rājagopālācārī, V.S. Śrīnivāsa Śāstrī, V. Rāghavan, R.K. Nārāyaṇan, Kamalā Subrahmaṇyan have been my companions all through. This book has evolved under the benevolent influence of this galaxy of texts, and the blessings of their authors. An uncompromising attention to detail and a touch of creative originality have helped me dovetail certain loose ends in the narration.

I am indebted to my friends who have enhanced this book with their expertise:

- Latha Rengachari for the script editing
- Keshav for the creative drawings
- Upasana Govindarajan for the sculpture drawings
- T S Krishnan for the inscription data
- Dr Jayashree Saranathan for the Rāmāyaṇam dates' data

Well-wishers are aplenty. These patrons truly deserve a mention:

- Daya and Sridhar, Mumbai
- Krittika and Rajesh, Maryland
- Nimmy and Srikanth, Dallas
- Radhika and Seshadri, Sacramento
- Naresh Murali, San Jose (in memory of Kandalla Murali)

HarperCollins, above all, for having found merit in my writing, and taking it to readers across the globe.

1
Recognizing the Divine Chronicler

Two years had passed since the paṭṭābhiṣeka. One fine day, Sītā walked towards Rāma, who noticed her golden-hued body fairer now, bosoms enlarged and an added beauty converging then on her belly. She sat next to him and kept looking at his bright Sūrya-like face that would make the lotuses of this vaṃśa blossom.

A rakṣaka interrupted their conversation hesitantly and announced that Vasiṣṭha's śiṣya had arrived and sought an audience with the rājā. Instantly, Rāma, the one who always treated well-read persons honourably, rose from his seat and greeted his guest. He enquired of the ṛṣi daṃpati and requested the reason for his visit. The śiṣya of Vasiṣṭha read aloud the ṛṣi daṃpati's message to Rāma from the letter: 'You are blessed to have Sītā as your wife. She is treated as the daughter of Bhūmi and is the source of delight to her father, Janaka, who treats joy and sorrow unequivocally. She is the daughter-in-law of the Sūrya vaṃśa that is renowned for its contribution to the society at large. And yes, I am her spiritual advisor. With Sītā by your side, satisfy your subjects for that is the matchless treasure handed over to you in your vaṃśa.'

Hearing this, Rāma looked at Sītā with a beam of happiness, and asked the śiṣya if there were any words of advice from the universally revered Arundhatī. The śiṣya nodded affirmatively and continued, 'Rāma, fulfil whatever Sītā asks for.' Rāma was surprised that Arundhatī knew of Sītā's pregnancy even before anyone else did, but quickly realized that when the mind travels faster than wind, a woman's mind travelled the fastest. The śiṣya pronounced blessings on the divya daṃpati and left the chamber.

Rāma held Sītā's hand and led her to the gallery of paintings depicting the events of their life together as a couple.

She looked at each one of them in awe, especially the one where a little Rāma with an elephant-like gait was running towards the welcoming arms of his father who loved him more than anybody else. While on the one hand, she frowned at the fierce-eyed Śūrpanakhā advancing towards Rāma, on the other, she laughed at the painting of Hanūmān who played several pranks to keep the rākṣasas of Lankā on their toes. A certain painting held Sītā's eyes, and Rāma walked closer to look at what mesmerized the love of his life. It was a scene in the forests adorned with the āśramas of selfless ṛṣis. He observed that great tranquillity prevailed in such places and that the ṛṣis there regarded hospitality as their supreme objective. She looked intently at one ṛṣi and asked if Rāma knew who he was. 'Vālmīki,' exclaimed Rāma. 'The one who is born of a termite-hill, is it?' asked Sītā. Rāma nodded in agreement, and she asked to know more about the ṛṣi.

2

From Hunter to Ṛṣi-Vālmīki

Rāma sat on the bed and Sītā advanced towards his broad-chest to rest her head, but found his ornaments sharp and piercing. Rāma removed them and put them aside. He then began narrating Vālmīki's life.

In childhood, Vālmīki was called Hārit. Once, while he was playing, he saw a peacock spread its feathers and cry out. He joined the peacock in making a raucous noise, disturbing his father, Varuṇa ṛṣi, who was at that time in discussion with Sanaka and his brothers—Sananda, Sanātana and Sanatkumāra. Unable to tolerate this tumult, Sanaka pronounced a curse on Hārit, saying that he would spend a considerable time as a niṣāda who would enjoy such noises. Eventually during his routine task of foraging for wood for the ṛṣi's yajña, Hārit befriended the sons of niṣādas. The time spent with them increased by the day and their influence was evident in his food habits, dress and language. He married a huntress, lived in their habitat and produced children. To support his familial needs, he became a dacoit, seizing the possessions of wayfarers in the forest.

During one such dacoity, he held the saptarṣis as hostages. While they requested him to free them from his clutches, and advised him not to indulge in such sinful activities, the saptaṛṣis warned Hārit that since one's pāpas could neither be shared nor be washed away, he would find no one to share his sins with. The dacoit confidently claimed that his family would share the punishment accorded to his accrued pāpas. To validate his claim, he ran to his dwelling and called out to his son. When asked if he would take on himself the pāpas of his father, his son asked, 'If a rājā's general catches you while you are seizing jewellery from travellers, who will the punishment be meted to?' and the father said, 'to me'. The son gave a sarcastic smile while the niṣāda got his answer. Irritated, confused, shocked and angry, he returned to the place where he had met the saptaṛṣis and requested them for spiritual emancipation. They took him into their fold and said, 'The way out is to recite the name of Rāma.'

Hearing this, Sītā immediately asked, 'Āryaputra, so was Hārit enlightened by the ṛṣis at the time of your birth? And now I remember that we had visited his āśrama during our exile. Didn't we?' Rāma replied, 'Yes, when I was almost one, Hārit was enlightened.' Sītā chuckled, 'So while you enlighten others, why don't you enlighten me?' and rose from the bed only to be pulled down by Rāma onto his lap. He noticed that pregnancy had made her more delicate and fragile. He asked, 'Will you tell me of your desires so that I can fulfil them?' 'I shall ask but I am eager to hear Hārit's story leading to his enlightenment. And you didn't confirm whether we visited his āśrama,' Sītā quipped.

Rāma said, 'Patience, Sītā. You cannot have answers to all questions at one go.'

He continued, 'Hārit thanked the ṛṣis for teaching him the mantra that could help him transcend the material realm. At the same time, he expressed his inability to recite anything from memory. The ṛṣis, who understood his problem, asked him to keep repeating the word, Rāma. Soon, Hārit sat for dhyāna and repeated the word Rāma. He eventually got so involved that he forgot to drink water and consume food. Bereft of sleep and other activities he sat like a piece of stone. Well, even like a log of wood.

'Over the years, termites built a little mound around and over him.

Little did Hārit realize this and continued meditating on Rāma. Bramhā[1], amazed at this tapasyā of Hārit, travelled to the spot and sprinkled divine waters on the termite-hill. The mound slowly crumbled to reveal a puny, yet resplendent, personality. Hārit opened his eyes and saluted Bramhā. While Hārit repented for his past actions, Bramhā asked him to contemplate on our life. Bramhā said, 'Since you arose from the ant-hill, which is the Valmīka, you shall be called Vālmīki, henceforth. And to the descendants of Bhṛgu, you shall be known as Rukṣa.'

'And yes,' Rāma exclaimed, 'We, along with Lakṣmaṇa, had the opportunity to visit his āśrama. He was living in Citrakūṭa on the banks of Mandākinī and later shifted to the banks of Gaṅgā just before Bharata could visit us in Citrakūṭa. He is worthy of everyone's respect and is a personification of true wisdom.'

---

1 In Saṃskṛta, though written as Brahmā and Brāhmaṇa, it is pronounced as Bramhā and Brāmhaṇa by most sampradāyas. Adhering to this norm, we have used the latter format, though a section of scholars prefer the former.

Sītā observed that she was spotted on Bhūmi, while Vālmīki arose from Valmīka, anthills, which were regarded as Bhūmi's ears.[2] Hence, she was his sister. Sītā said, 'I wish to visit the holy tapasyā groves on the banks of Gaṅgā where the violent beasts eat the nīvāra offerings and not the meat of other animals. The daughters of the ṛṣis are my friends. In the mornings, the ṛṣis with the upavīta will bathe in Gaṅgā and offer arghya. Watching that will be so satisfying. I shall take a plunge in the rivers whose waters are purifying, gladdening and cooling.'

Rāma said, 'So be it.' She was pleased to hear this and reclined on his chest. Rāma said to himself, 'She is the very mūrti of prosperity in my house. She is the brush of nectar that brightens my eyes. It is her touch that cools my body like the thick candana paste. Her hands that have embraced me are as soft as the pearl strings. Everything about her is so pleasing, but for the separation that is unbearable. May that never happen.'

That night passed in peace.

---

2 Taittiriya Brāmhana, 1.1.3.

3

A Rājā Spurns His Wife, Protects His Vaṃśa

Bhadra, one among the ten informers who used to inform Rāma of the happenings in the Kosalā province, sought permission to meet him. The rakṣaka informed Rāma of Bhadra's arrival and Rāma asked him to be allowed to enter.

Bhadra walked in, saluted the rājā and said, 'The prajā talk about your heroic deeds and are in all praise of you, but ...'

Rāma said, 'Don't hesitate. Like an ācārya who should be determined to correct his śiṣya, a rājā must be open to any adverse comments.'

Bhadra continued, 'They do not approve of your accepting the rānī who lived in the captivity of a rākṣasa. They believe that they will need to suffer similar conduct in their wives as the public follows what their rājās do.'

On hearing this baseless allegation slandering his wife, Rāma swooned. Rāma said to himself, 'It is this Sītā who lived in the prison of Lankā and her tapasyā that is still praised by the ṛṣis all over the universe. But this allegation is troubling me. How can I disregard it? I can either choose to ignore these vicious comments or abandon my dear wife forever. My mind is very turbulent, and I am unable to choose the right path.'

For the rājās of Sūrya vaṃśa, a spotless reputation was their biggest wealth. But wasn't Sītā's reputation and respect even greater? Sītā was born to suffer for no fault of hers, and seeking justice for her was always futile.

Rāma summoned his brothers to his chamber. The brothers reached and offered their praṇāmas to Rāma. They were shocked to see Rāma's swollen eyes and puffy cheeks. Lakṣmaṇa murmured to Bharata that he had seen his brother in this state when Rāma was in search of Sītā in Daṇḍaka forests[1] and hearing this, slowly their faces started turning pale. Rāma said, 'O Arundhatī, O Vasiṣṭha, O venerable Viśvāmitra, O all-absorbing Agni, O Janaka-the learned, O Sugrīva, O gentle and scholarly Hanūmān, O Vibhīṣaṇa! You have all been insulted by this non-virtuous Rāma! What right have I to pollute such virtuous names by just articulating them, I being such an ungrateful villain?'

---

1 Spread across the Indian states of Chhattisgarh, Maharashtra, Odisha and Andhra Pradesh.

He then looked at his brothers and said, 'You three are my possessions. You are my very life. I am just a caretaker of this rājya. But when it comes to practice, as mentioned in the śāstras, you three are the most deserved. You need to guide me on how to handle the lightning that has now struck my life.'

Rāma informed his brothers of the infamy circulating amongst the prajā and strongly felt that if not remedied at once it would bring disrepute. While the brothers were shocked and speechless, Rāma continued, 'I have always followed the right path. But my act of accepting Sītā is viewed as a blot on our virtuous vaṃśa, like a mirror that will look unclear when clouded by vapour. When a slick of oil is on water, it starts spreading all over and likewise, my stained reputation shall also permeate every house. Every minute that I live with this I feel as if I am slaughtering the glorious reputation garnered by our ancestors. Like a majestic elephant when chained to the post gets irritated and would want to get rid of it, so do I want to be rid of this ill-fame.'

In anguish, Rāma rolled on the floor seeking consolation but the ultimate solace-giver, Sītā, was the one he was to banish. He lamented, 'O rānī, who sprang from the sacrificial ground and brought joy to Bhūmi! You brought fame to the vaṃśa of Janaka and you are respected by Vasiṣṭha, Arundhatī and Agni. O my dear companion in the forest! O, the one of moderate speech! How is it that one of your grace has to meet with such a vidhi? By your presence, the worlds gain holiness but unholy are the words of people with regard to you. You helped even the world of devas since your abduction ended their miseries caused by the rākṣasas, but today you fall as a helpless victim! I need to relinquish Sītā who is now pregnant with my child just as many years ago, I had to abandon the rājya and its oceans for my father.

I am aware that she is completely innocent. But, in my view, a blot on our vaṃśa is more overpowering than the truth. People call the shadow of Bhūmi falling on Candra a blemish. Is it? No. It is a lie. Everyone knows that it is no blemish but they continue to believe that it is the truth.'

'O Lakṣmaṇa!' Rāma continued, 'Ascend the chariot driven by Sumantra. Take Sītā into the woods and leave her beyond the boundaries of our rājya. I am saying this because tomorrow, no one should accuse the throne of pronouncing a judgement that is a travesty, an eyewash. At the same time, I want to fulfil her wish to stay amidst the āśramas of ṛṣis adept in tapasyā. I have chosen the āśrama of Vālmīki, who lives on the banks of river Tamasā.[2] He is a ṛṣi of great tapasyā and bhakti. He was also a great friend of our father, and we visited him in Citrakūṭa, during our exile in the forests. His āśrama is equidistant from our rājya and that of Janaka, our father-in-law. Above all, other ṛṣis pay regular visits to his āśrama and discuss the qualities of paramātmā. It will be best suited for Sītā's stay, especially during her pregnancy.'

Lakṣmaṇa, with eyes soaked in tears, lifted his head and said, 'O Rāghava! The stool that supports your lotus-like feet adorned with

2 Tributary of Ganga with a length of over 250 kilometres. Flows through the Indian states of Madhya Pradesh and Uttar Pradesh.

holy sandals is gold-plated and studded with gems from the crowns of those rājās who offered their praṇāmas to you, having surrendered to your valour. You are respected by all for your auspicious attributes. It is said that adherence to dharma will become weaker as we cross successive yugas, starting from krita yuga. But in tretā yuga, where dharma encounters troubled times, we, the prajā, feel that we still continue to live in krita yuga only because of your administration as a rājā that ensures fairness to all. But now the manner in which you are treating Sītā, the rānī who is an embodiment of virtues, is indeed deplorable. You know what she means to our vaṃśa, especially when she is now carrying the light of our vaṃśa in her womb. Please don't commit this grave mistake by being victim to malicious comments. People will be malicious but hasty judgements could cast a blot on your character.'

Rāma, with a determined face, heard Lakṣmaṇa and said, 'Any resistance on your part will cause me extreme displeasure. I swear to you by my feet which you have worshipped for long, and also my life which you have for long protected, that whosoever speaks out to pacify me in any manner while I speak, shall be considered inimical to me. If you will act at my command, then take away Sītā from me, as a mark of respect for my word, this very day.'

Lakṣmaṇa stood speechless. He couldn't agree with the rājā's decree, for that would amount to disrespecting his mother-like Sītā, nor could he disagree for that would go against the old adage that the wishes of elders were unquestionable. Like Paraśurāma who obeyed his father Jamadagni's command without a second thought and killed his mother as if he were killing an enemy, Lakṣmaṇa kept in mind that he had to carry out the wish of his brother, Rāma. He showed the face of a true warrior, but his eyes revealed the agony of a loving son. Bharata murmured to him, 'This will remain a blot on Rāma's rule, but the rule carried out at the behest of his pādukās was flawless. I feel that the Bhūmi beneath is shaking to indicate that she is unable to see her daughter Sītā suffer.'

4

Sītā's Abandonment

Sumantra, summoned by Lakṣmaṇa, had by then arrived. He was asked to harness speedy horses to the best of the chariots and equip the chariot with a splendid seat for Sītā. He said, 'Sītā, at the command of the rājā, needs to be taken to the āśrama of the pious ṛṣis.' Sumantra accepted the order in complete reverence and decided that the pregnant rānī should not receive a single jolt during the journey, unaware that she was to receive the biggest shock yet when the journey ended.

Meanwhile, Lakṣmaṇa entered Sītā's quarters and said, 'Make haste! The rājā has approved of your desire to visit the āśramas of ṛṣis. Please ascend the chariot that is ready for you.'

Sītā readily agreed and gathered jewels and clothes that could be given as presents to the daughters of the ṛṣis. She was delighted at the very thought of driving through the pleasant countryside and felt indebted to Rāma for being the wish-yielding kalpaka tree but was unaware that he was, in reality, the tree with sharp sword-like leaves, called asitapatra.

Rāma heard the sound of the chariot leaving the main road of Ayodhyā. As the sound receded, Rāma's pain increased and he said to himself, 'I have discarded the ornament of my house, the one who used to recline on my chest and is now heavy with child, just like a protected offering in a yajña that is ruthlessly cast off to the animals.'

Sītā noticed that her right eye was throbbing and so was her right thigh. Sensing that these were inauspicious nimitta, she prayed for the welfare of her husband, brothers-in-law and mothers-in-law. How selfless of her that she did not pray for herself!

While she got down from the chariot, the waters of Gaṅgā that had risen above the banks were pleading to Lakṣmaṇa to not desert this woman of impeccable character.

Sumantra was reminded of a similar scene several years ago when he had driven Rāma, Sītā and Lakṣmaṇa, at the command of the then royal rānī. To his dismay, the scene seemed incomplete without Rāma.

Sītā was ferried across Gaṅgā to the other bank by Lakṣmaṇa. After alighting from the boat, Lakṣmaṇa, in a choked voice, informed her of all that had transpired. Like a creeper that shed all its flowers on being hit by a calamitous wind, Sītā fell on Bhūmi like the daughter seeking solace on her mother's lap. Lakṣmaṇa immediately brought some water from Gaṅgā to sprinkle on her. Her awakening was more painful than her falling unconscious on the ground. Sītā said, 'There is no fault in you, Lakṣmaṇa! You obey your elder brother's command, just as Viṣṇu obeys Indra's words. It is my misfortune. I shall not drown myself in the Gaṅgā as I am carrying the light of the vaṃśa. And my dying will only cast aspersion on Rāma's regime, as a time when unhappiness abounded and women committed suicide. Moreover, how could I fall into Gaṅgā waters, brought down by your ancestors to redeem people of their pāpas?'

Sītā continued with her words of wisdom, wishing that Rāma treat all his prajā impartially for that would bestow the highest honours on him and added that she would act as per his commands for he was her love, family and ācārya. She asked Lakṣmaṇa to look at her belly to make him realize the stage and state in which she had been deserted. Refusing to obey, Lakṣmaṇa wailed in a loud voice, 'I have never looked above your feet. I shall not do so now. I can't bear to see you separated from Rāma, who is still inseparable from you in your thoughts,' and left the place.

Sītā couldn't believe that Lakṣmaṇa was also leaving her. Indeed, how cruel is karma that it snatches away a husband from a wife when she yearns to be with him the most! Sītā was now standing all alone in the forest. Stones would have melted on hearing her wails, had they the ears to hear and the heart to feel. Hearing her cries, the peacocks stopped dancing, the trees shed flowers as if they were in tears and the deer that had been chewing grass stopped. She said to herself, 'He has looked after the welfare of everyone at all times and he couldn't have imagined treating me like this. I must have sinned in an earlier life to deserve this sudden, forceful and unbearable treatment. This must be the explanation: It is said that to a rājā, his rājya is his first wife. But when he came to the forest with me earlier, the rājya, who was his first consort, was deprived of living with him. Feeling offended, and resenting my presence, she must have banished me now. Many tapasvinīs in the past have sought my refuge when their husbands were tortured by rākṣasas. Today, I need to seek refuge at their feet when Rāma is still a glorious rājā.

'O Rāma! Vaivasvata has stated that it is the rājā's duty to protect all classes of people in different stages of their life. I am a tapasvinī who is

even now entitled to your protection as a subject. After the birth of your son, I shall sit and meditate on Sūrya with a steady mind. I shall seek the boon of being your wife yet again, in my next birth.'

Vālmīki, who could sense bad nimitta, stepped out of his āśrama and saw a lady in distress close by. He walked towards her and recognized her as Sītā. He praised her father and father-in-law for their commitment towards their subjects. He also acknowledged the fact that Rāma was instrumental in annihilating the rākṣasas who were a hindrance to the ṛṣis. But also added that he was upset and that there was no justification for the treatment Rāma had meted out to her.

Moved by her humility and compassion, he offered her asylum in his āśrama. He also promised that all birth rituals for her child would be performed by him. 'Think of this as your father's house in a different deśa,' said Vālmīki as he welcomed Sītā to his āśrama.

He said, 'You are blessed to live on the banks of Tamasā that dispels the internal darkness.

'The tapasvinīs here shall bring you all the seasonal flowers, fruits and grains that you shall require for worship. While talking to them, you shall slowly lose your grief and eventually become a happy person. Spend your free time watering the plants with utmost love and care for that will train you to nurture your children later.'

She was shown her room and given a deer's skin, which would keep insects away, to sleep on. She slept like a child with no hatred towards Rāma and proved again how forgiving she was.

5

Nārada Acknowledges the Greatest amongst Men

The next morning, Vālmīki's śiṣyas saw Nārada arriving. While Nārada holding his veenā, called Mahatī, was crossing the river, Vālmīki's śiṣyas quickly collected flowers to be strewn on his path.

Nārada at the Undavalli Caves in Vijayawada (Andhra Pradesh) sculpted in the Viṣṇukuṇḍina dynasty (5th-7th century CE)

One śiṣya said, 'He is the greatest of all munis who meditates on the paramātmā. In tapasyā, he attempts to understand the qualities of the paramātmā. He undertakes severe vratas like cāndrāyana and kṛcchra to drive away pāpas that may be impediments to acquiring knowledge. He also spends a considerable time reciting the Vedas and researching on their purport. Therefore, his biggest asset is his tapasyā.'

Another śiṣya interrupted, 'He preaches what he practises. The sole reason for this being his

bhakti towards the supreme Nārāyaṇa for that is the essence of learning of all branches of knowledge.'

While the two śiṣyas were discussing this, one little boy asked, 'Why is he called Nārada?' On hearing this, the first śiṣya said, 'He is the one who helps us get rid of nescience by bestowing knowledge about the jīvātmā and paramātmā.' The second śiṣya continued, 'Here comes the greatest of all speakers, Nārada, to meet our ācārya who is a tapasvī of the highest order.'

Vālmīki stood at the entrance to receive Nārada. He washed Nārada's feet and invited him into the āśrama. He sat only after Nārada was seated. With folded hands, he went near Nārada and asked questions that had recently troubled him in the light of recent unprecedented events. He said, 'O ṛṣi of supreme knowledge! I am delighted to welcome you, the possessor of all auspicious qualities, and look forward to listening to your words of wisdom. I am sure that you are the most qualified to answer my questions. At present,

- who on this Bhūmi interacts with all classes of people without any feeling of superiority, thereby ensuring a heartfelt association?
- who is the one with a brave heart that treats joy and sorrow in a similar fashion, rises with a braver heart to face his detractors?
- who is the one who knows the concept of bhakti and prapatti completely?
- is there someone who remembers a small help extended to him throughout his life but forgets any harm meted to him instantly?

- who is the one who, at all times, sticks to the path of truth and always speaks it?
- is there someone who is ready to abandon anything and anybody in order to keep the promise made to the poor and the needy?
- who is the one who attaches immense value to character and follows the rules of his vaṃśa?
- is there a person who understands what is good in the long run for his subjects?
- is there someone who has learnt all branches of knowledge religiously?
- is he also the same person who practises that which he has learnt?
- who is the one who, at all times, assumes a pleasing face with a demeanour captivating almost everyone?
- is there someone who is courageous enough to stand by his decisions?
- who is the one who controls his anger and expresses it only when the situation warrants it?
- who is the one whose effulgence is matchless?
- who is the one who chooses to notice only the good within a person, thereby leaving no room for jealousy?
- is there someone whose righteous anger makes the devas tremble, and which makes even his loved ones jittery?'

Nārada was glad to see the excitement on Vālmīki's face as he posed these questions. He was happy that the questions were about a person who would be the protagonist of the world's most revered work. Nārada said, 'Finding even one of these qualities in a person is tough while you have asked for sixteen such qualities in one person. I took this little time to think. It ought to have been an arduous task. But we are blessed to live in the times of a personality who possesses not only these qualities, but much more.'

Vālmīki could not guess whom Nārada was hinting at, and was all ears to know the name. Nārada said, 'He is respected by one and all. He is an embodiment of valour and physical perfection.

He is intelligent. All his actions conform to rules. He is eloquent. He annihilates enemies who undermine humanity. His ability to listen, understand, remember, contemplate and practise what he is convinced about makes him an honest man. He is the one with long arms, a śaṅkha-shaped throat and a broad chest. He performs his duties and protects his subjects. He is adept in all branches of knowledge. His patience is comparable to Bhūmi's forbearance of humanity. He is as forgiving as a mother is to her children. He is matchless, indeed,' Nārada sighed.

Vālmīki smilingly responded, 'I will offer all the prowess gathered from my tapasyā at your feet to know that single name.'

Nārada said, 'Rāma of the Ikṣvāku vaṃśa.'

6
A Foretelling of the Itihāsa

It was customary for Vālmīki to go to Gaṅgā every day, but the meeting with Nārada delayed his routine and hence, he decided to go to Tamasā. After having prostrated twice at the feet of Nārada who left for Satyaloka, Vālmīki, accompanied by his śiṣyas, started for the river. Her waters were crystal clear. A delighted Vālmīki offered his noon arghya. With immense satisfaction, Vālmīki walked along the Tamasā with his śiṣya Bharadvāja beside him, enjoying nature's scenic beauty. He saw a pair of birds on a tree, making love.

Bharadvāja asked, 'O ṛṣi! Can you please tell me about these birds?' Vālmīki patted Bharadvāja on the back and said, 'I am fortunate to have a śiṣya like you, who is vigilant and inquisitive. These are the krauñca birds which live together. Even while sleeping, the female rests her beak between the mandibles of the male. If they are separated even for a moment, they keep calling to the other for union, and die if the partner is late. That call of the bird hurts any lover undergoing separation.'

Suddenly, he saw the red-headed male krauñca bird fall from the branch of the tree with a wail. Hit by an arrow, he was bleeding profusely. The female bird cried aloud and this separation during their love play caused severe anguish to Vālmīki. The sorrow coupled with anger aroused severe emotions in him. He choked and as the sorrow made its way through his throat, it was transformed into letters.

In all, thirty-two letters reached the tip of his tongue and he uttered, 'O niṣāda, who awaits calamity very soon, your unworthy attitude was seen when you shot and killed one of the birds while they were making love. As a result, you shall be eternally unhappy.' A furious Vālmīki walked away with Bharadvāja.

After a few yards, he spoke in a melancholic tone, 'I shouldn't have uttered such words of hate. He is a niṣāda and has only done his daily work. I should have exercised caution and restraint, and desisted from making such hateful pronunciations on the poor man.'

He asked Bharadvāja to quickly check if the niṣāda had left and to his dismay, the śiṣya exclaimed, 'Ṛṣi, I don't see the niṣāda, or the birds.'

Vālmīki said, 'I am not surprised now. Did you notice while I spoke, the letters were numbered, and the lines flowed in a rhythm? Each part had eight letters, and, in all, the verse had thirty-two. I have heard my ācārya say that this format is the anuṣṭup metre, one of the seven reins that hold the horses of Sūrya's chariot. I am sure there is something more to this incident, but I am unable to decipher what it means. Hope I get a stalwart to reveal the purport.'

The duo traced their path to the āśrama with an obedient Bharadvāja contemplating on his ācārya's composition while carrying a pot filled with water on his shoulder.

They entered to find Bramhā seated on a wooden plank lined with a thin layer of darbha grass and a haṃsa seated by his feet. The unexpected arrival of Nārada earlier and Bramhā now, coupled with the hunting incident, confused Vālmīki. He instantly prostrated at Bramhā's feet. Like a tortoise that keeps its limbs concealed, so did Vālmīki keep his mind, senses and heart under control. He sat on the floor in utmost humility after doing a pradakṣiṇā around Bramhā.

Bramhā said, 'After Rāvaṇa's death and the subsequent paṭṭābhiṣeka of Rāma, I was asked by Rāma to have his biography written in verse. It was to be a poem which, on reading, would ignite in the reader the urge to seek mokṣa.

'A rākṣasa called Śaṅkukarṇa, also known as Akampana, escaped from the hands of Rāma during the battle at Janasthāna. He reared a male krauñca bird that was traumatizing the travellers in the forest. A niṣāda, immensely blessed by Rāma, came into the scene. The niṣāda killed the rākṣasa in front of your eyes and received the curse in return.'

Vālmīki interposed, 'Have I cursed the scion of Sūrya vaṃśa? I couldn't have been crueller.'

Bramhā smilingly remarked, 'Do not worry. Your uttering was not a curse, but a blessing. You said, "O consort of Lakṣmī! You have separated Rāvaṇa, who had indecent intentions towards Sītā, from his consort Mandodarī, even as they were making love. You shall remain blessed and for years together live in fame and prosperity."

'This, indeed, was a benediction on Rāma through the niṣāda. My son, Nārada, using the nuances of grammar, interpreted your uttering thus, "O rājā of Lanka, who is adorned with the red crown, you have separated Rāma from Sītā, who is virtue personified, while they were together. This act of yours is condemnable and this shall become the theme of a work that will be unparalleled in religious literature."

'But I see this verse of yours as a condensed form of the work you will be writing. It goes like this, "O consort of Lakṣmī! You shall live for years together and your fame will be eternal. You had forsaken your rājya to keep your father's promise and left for the woods for fourteen years. You freed the ṛṣis of their fears by defeating the rākṣasas and you relieved Sugrīva of his cunning brother Vāli. You rescued Sītā from Rāvaṇa's clutches and forsook her to uphold the duties of an unbiased rājā."'

7

A Blessed Poet and His Epic Task

Bramhā looked at a petrified Vālmīki, who said, 'O Bramhā! The most respected one! What should I do?'

Bramhā replied, 'You need to write the biography of Rāma in great detail, omitting nothing. I shall bless you with the ability to see every incident in Rāma's life as if you were seeing it in person. No word of yours shall be untrue. As long as the mountains survive and the rivers flow, your work shall exist. And only as long as your work exists, the mountains and rivers shall remain.'

Bramhā directs Vālmīki to compose the Rāmāyaṇam, in Banteay Chhmar Temple (Cambodia) sculpted in the Khmêr dynasty (12th–13th century CE)

Vālmīki was overwhelmed and asked, 'Sir! What should I call this work?' Bramhā thought for a while and said, 'You are writing of the scion of Sūrya vaṃśa. Just as Sūrya's rays travel northwards during uttarāyaṇa and southwards during dakṣiṇāyana, the path traced by Rāma, his descendants shall be Rāmāyaṇa.'

Vālmīki repeated the name with deep fervour, 'Rāma of Rāmāyaṇa. Rāma in Rāmāyaṇa. Rāmāyaṇa. Sounds beautiful.'

Bramhā said, 'It sounds more beautiful when you, the poet, utter the name, and it is as beautiful as that kokila's call in spring which displaces all other sounds.'

Vālmīki noticed two women enter the āśrama. While one wore a spotless white saree, the other was draped in a lustrous yellow saree. The former said, 'I am Sarasvatī, the one endowed with an incessant flow of words. I shall be at your fingertips to help create a monumental work.'

The latter said, 'I am Sāvitrī, also known as Gāyatrī, and hailed as the best among poetic metres. I shall help you to effortlessly induce each of my twenty-four letters in every thousandth verse of yours, thereby making this work sacrosanct.'

Vālmīki thanked the devatās and after sipping water, sat facing the east to start on his task of giving this world a holy śāstra.

Meanwhile Bramhā, who left the āśrama with Sarasvatī and Sāvitrī, stopped outside Sītā's chamber for a moment and offered his praṇāmas. His wives, who were amazed by his gesture, asked Bramhā for the reason. He said, 'While I am regarded as the creator, she is my mother who has inspired me. I was born from Nārāyaṇa's navel and I chose the lotus as my seat since that is my mother's abode too. I use the haṃsa as my vehicle to mimic my mother's gait. I sport the japamāla made of tulasī wood for she lives in it.'

'"Like mother, like son," is it?' Sarasvatī intervened. She added, 'And how come you don't learn how not to be lethargic from her?' Bramhā gave her a sarcastic stare and said, 'Yes, I must learn from your mother-in-law.' The trio laughed and left.

Nārada entered the āśrama with his veeṇā and a small wooden box. Vālmīki welcomed him and offered a seat. He asked, 'O ṛṣi! What are you carrying in this box?' Nārada said that he was carrying the śālagrāma, to be worshipped every day, and mentioned that he would be in Vālmīki's āśrama for two reasons—one to listen to the great work, Rāmāyaṇa, being composed and secondly to be of moral support to Sītā. Nārada asked Vālmīki to begin his work by praying to his family mūrti, Jaladhivarṇa, and the ṛṣi consented.

Sarasvatī seated on Bramhā's lap in Hoysalesvara Temple (Karnataka) sculpted in the Hoysāla dynasty (12th century CE)

8

Daśaratha: A Glorious Rājya and Its Virtuous Rājā

Vaivasvata once desired to build a province that was perfect.[1] So was born Kosalā that stood on the banks of river Sarayū.[2] Sarayū was clean-looking, sweet to taste and cool to bathe in. Haṃsas from the lake of Mānasa would fly with their little ones to Kosalā and slowly walk through the streets of Ayodhyā[3], its rājadhānī, where they would wait to catch a glimpse of the women walking. In the meantime, the little haṃsas would cry for their mothers and, surprisingly, would be fed by the grazing buffaloes secreting milk in memory of their calves. And before the haṃsas came back to check on their little ones, they would have dozed off while the slow winds sang a scriptless lullaby. Any traveller to this nagarī would wait to smell the smoke from the palasā sticks used in agnihotra emanating from the houses. Buoyed by the prosperity that flooded the nagarī,

1 Taittiriya Aranyaka, 1.27.

2 Tributary of Ganga with a length of over 350 kilometres. Flows through the Indian states of Uttarakhand and Uttar Pradesh.

3 A city in the Indian state of Uttar Pradesh.

the rājās of Sūrya vaṃśa drove away the troublesome rākṣasas with just their fearsome glances, without needing to wage a war.

In Ayodhyā ruled a rājā called Daśaratha. In his regime, there was neither a person to give alms nor one to receive any, for every prajā had everything that he could wish for. An oft-repeated anecdote describing this prosperity talks of a learned brāmhaṇa in Ayodhyā who had once invited his childhood friend from Kamboja. The friend was welcomed with Vaidika chants, given a good seat, his feet were washed and he was served delicious food. He was surprised at the affluence and asked his host about the secret behind his prosperity. The brāmhaṇa, who resided in Kosalā, said, 'I once asked Lakṣmī as to why the ones trained in Vedas were largely penniless. She divulged that her sympathy was for the dull-headed ones and not for the brāmhaṇas who had always driven her away. She illustrated how she was sent away from the samudra when Agastya drank its waters, hurt when Bhṛgu kicked Viṣṇu's chest and indeed left homeless when Atri plucked the lotuses, her favourite abode, for his daily rituals. I quipped that the houses in Ayodhyā were always open for her. And this is the secret of my prosperity.' The two friends chuckled with mirth.

Daśaratha was well-versed in the Vedas and that knowledge helped him cultivate good practices in his subjects. This deep knowledge put him at par with bramharṣis who called him a rājarṣi. He protected Ayodhyā like the devas took care of Amarāvatī. Like his forefathers, Daśaratha, too, believed in levying one sixth of his subjects' earnings as taxes. Like Sūrya that drains a lot more water from the seas in summer, stores it in clouds and gives it back as pure water during monsoons, so did the rājās of Sūrya vaṃśa give back plentifully to their subjects. Most administrative decisions were kept secret. Daśaratha played the role of not only a rājā but also that of a father who protected his subjects from danger. He never spared anyone who committed crimes against women, the young, old and the disabled. He was, hence, aptly called Dharmarājā. His ability in driving made him Daśaratha, the one adept in the 'ten directions'. His valour was much lauded, and that made Indra seat Daśaratha beside him on his throne as a mark of respect and garland him with the fragrant pārijāta flowers. His regime was regarded safer than the strife-ridden regime of Indra, the unfairly oppressive regime of Varuṇa and the fear-instilling regime of Vāsuki.

A council of good mantris assisted the rājā in being a good administrator who thought, spoke and acted correctly always. Adhering to the number eight prescribed by Vaivasvata, the mantris were:

- Dṛṣṭi, who ensured a flawless completion of developmental works
- Jayanta, who successfully expanded boundaries
- Vijaya, who emerged victorious in battles
- Siddhārtha, who acquired what was required
- Arthasādhaka, who was capable of managing the treasury
- Aśoka, who ensured people were without worries
- Mantrapālā, who protected secrets
- Sumantra, who advised on political matters

The desire to have a son as a torchbearer of the vaṃśa was growing by the day within this rājā who already possessed all forms of wealth. Without a son to carry his vaṃśa forward, Daśaratha's life was like a song without a rhythm, a friendship without respect, well-prepared food without ājya.

While he was lost in this thought, his mantri, Sumantra, arrived. He learnt of the rājā's anguish and said, 'I have heard from the Sanatkumāras that you will obtain sons of great valour by the grace of Ṛṣyaśṛṅga.'

9
Aśvamedha and Gaining Nārāyaṇa's Attention

Nārada interrupted Vālmīki's narrative and asked who Ṛṣyaśṛṅga was. Vālmīki said, 'Kaśyapa had a son called Vibhāndaka. Vibhāndaka and his wife, Kumudinī, had a son. This boy, at birth, had an unusual growth resembling the horn of a ṛśya deer on his scalp. He was thus called Ṛṣyaśṛṅga. He lost his mother at a very young age. His life revolved around attending to his father's needs, learning the Vedas and observing bramhacarya.

'In the deśa, Daśaratha and Kausalyā had a daughter called Sāntā, who was adopted by Romapāda, the rājā of Aṅga. A severe drought struck the Aṅga province. When consulted, the learned men asked Romapāda to invite Ṛṣyaśṛṅga to assist in putting an end to the drought. Ṛṣyaśṛṅga, impelled by divine providence, came out of his āśrama[1] to see the courtesans of Aṅga camping nearby. Unfamiliar with women and their ways, he was mesmerized by their appearance and followed them all the way to Aṅga.

1 Kigga, a village in the Indian state of Karnataka.

Ṛṣyaśṛṅga in Mathura Government Museum (Uttar Pradesh) sculpted in the Kuṣāṇ dynasty (2nd century CE)

'His arrival brought spells of rain. While people rejoiced, the elated rājā welcomed Ṛṣyaśṛṅga with praṇāmas. The rājā requested that he marry Sāntā. The ṛṣi assented gracefully.' Vālmīki continued with his work in all sincerity.

On hearing the words of Sumantra, Daśaratha obtained the permission of Vasiṣṭha and left for Aṅga. He offered his praṇāmas to Romapāda and requested that he take Sāntā and Ṛṣyaśṛṅga to Ayodhyā for a greater scheme. Upon Romapāda's consent, the daṃpati arrived in Ayodhyā with great fanfare.

Realizing that the rājya's prosperity would be enhanced by performing the Aśvamedha[2], Daśaratha resolved to perform this yajña which would eradicate all pāpas. Performing this yajña was no ordinary affair, and that was the reason why very few rulers undertook to perform it. The materials and men specifically required for the yajña were brought together. These included a yellow rope which was twelve units long, four kinds of water based on their sources, four erudite ṛtviks, four learned brāmhaṇas and a horse. The northern banks of Sarayū, which was less inhabited, was the location chosen for the Aśvamedha.

During the first year of the yajña when the horse was let loose, Vasiṣṭha managed the rājya as Daśaratha was engaged in tapasyā. At the year-end, Daśaratha requested that the rituals begin. Invitations were sent to the rājās of Mithilā, Kāśī, Kekayā, Aṅga, Sindhu-Sauvīra[3],

2 Taittiriya Brāmhana, 3.8.1.

3 Covers the states of Punjab and Sindh in Pakistan.

Saurāṣṭra and Drāviḍa for the yajña. All the rituals associated with Aśvamedha were followed by the ṛtviks, led by Ṛṣyaśṛṅga. Invitees were fed without any discrimination throughout this period. While the horse was tied to a post, a vedikā was constructed with eighteen bricks arranged in sets of three in order to give it the shape of a golden-winged Garuḍa, as mentioned in the Śuklayajur vedā. At the end of this yajña, Daśaratha gave away gifts to the ṛtviks. The rājās conducted this yajña as prescribed by Bramhā who once performed this in Kañcī on a hill held up by elephants in order to seek the grace of the supreme Nārāyaṇa.[4] Kausalyā, with three golden needles, drew lines on the horse's body from right to left. An attendant assisted her in taking the fat from its abdomen which was then offered in the yajña. Ṛtviks obtained the remaining parts of the horse and with appropriate mantras offered them to the yajña again. The other two wives of the rājā stayed back with Kausalyā.

Vālmīki paused for a minute and said, 'O Nārada! While the rājā is seeking a son, isn't it barbaric to sacrifice a horse?'

Nārada said, 'A pertinent question you have asked. But this killing is rendered painless through recitation of mantras that make the horse numb. Moreover, when a rājya needs an able administrator, a single sacrifice cannot amount to cruelty. This is not just to please the devas but also to annihilate some of the impeding pāpas.'

Vālmīki appeared unconvinced by the explanation. He nevertheless continued writing.

The devas, under the leadership of Bramhā and Śiva, marched to kṣīrasāgara, the abode of the supreme Nārāyaṇa, where the oceanic waters resembled milk. On hearing their prayers, he who rested on the white-hued Ananta, opened his lotus petal-like eyes and asked, 'Are all the devas doing well? Has the arrogance of the rākṣasas been crushed by the mighty vajra of Indra? Have the principles of administration, as taught by Bṛhaspati, been followed?'

The devas said, 'Emboldened by the boons bestowed by Bramhā, Rāvaṇa is mistreating the brāmhaṇas and the Gandharvas. While

---

4 Varadaraja Swami Temple in Kanchipuram in the Indian state of Tamil Nadu.

Sūrya is ordered to prevent Rāvaṇa's skin from tanning, Vāyu is asked to blow gently so as not to dishevel Rāvaṇa's hair.'

Without further delay, they said, 'We plead with you to annihilate the evil forces as we perform prapatti at your lotus-like feet. You are the only one capable of driving our fears away.'

On hearing the worried words of the devas, Nārāyaṇa, who was draped in yellow silk, and whose vehicle was Garuḍa, the Veda incarnate, was very concerned. Well aware of Daśaratha's excellent qualities, Nārāyaṇa, who holds the Sudarśana, Pāñcajanya and Kaumodakī, decided to be born as the son of Daśaratha, in order to address the fears of the devas. Nārāyaṇa, illuminated by the brilliance of his teeth with the most accurate of pronunciations said, 'I am aware of the sufferings the world is undergoing at the hands of Rāvaṇa. It is my duty to destroy these evil forces. I will not need a reminder just as fire wouldn't need the wind to fan it.'

10

The Boon of Parenthood

Daśaratha requested Ṛṣyaśṛṅga to commence the putrakāmeṣṭi, as the Aśvamedha had concluded.

The expert in Atharva Veda commenced the yajña and the offerings meant for the yajña were placed on a cane mat. In the following days, chatuṣṭoma, ukthya and atirātra were performed. At the end, Ṛṣyaśṛṅga said, 'Do not worry. You will have four sons of the highest calibre to protect your subjects.'

Into the vedikā walked an extraordinary person, dark-complexioned, clad in red clothes and with soft hair all over his body. In his arms, he carried a large, brilliant gold jar covered with a silver lid, containing pāyasa. This combination of metals indicated the debts owed to devas which would be cleared by donating gold and debts due to the forefathers which could be cleared by donating silver. This person directed the rājā to distribute the pāyasa amongst his principal wives.

The rājā, who received it with humility, honoured Ṛṣyaśṛṅga and Sāntā for the successful completion of the yajña. The rājā reached the apartments of the rānīs. He asked the maids to get four golden cups

Daśaratha in the putrakāmeṣṭi yajña in Hazara Rama Temple (Karnataka) sculpted in the Vijayanagara dynasty (15th century CE)

to match the number uttered by Ṛṣyaśṛṅga and Sanatkumāras. The maids brought the cups as ordered by the rājā. He poured half the pāyasa in the first cup meant for Kausalyā, foremost of the rānīs. He subsequently poured half of the remaining pāyasa in the second cup meant for Sumitrā. From the remaining portion, half was poured in the third cup meant for Kaikeyī, the youngest of the rānīs. Daśaratha cleared the remaining portion into the last cup contemplating on whom to give that to. If he were to give it to Kaikeyī, Sumitrā's share would have matched hers. If he were to give it to Kausalyā, he would have to face the wrath of Kaikeyī.

He handed each of them their portions of the pāyasa. While Kausalyā and Kaikeyī consumed their shares with reverence, Sumitrā waited for the both of them to finish. Daśaratha, who witnessed Sumitrā's magnanimity in letting the other two rānīs enjoy older sons, thought her eligible for the last cup. He decided to give her the last portion and thus, Sumitrā consumed the pāyasa twice.

The rānīs who felt that their foetuses were their real ornaments slowly abandoned their metal ornaments which now seemed

burdensome. Toned and glowing, their bodies now bore all the proud marks of impending motherhood.

11

Peerless Rājakumāras Are Born

After dwelling in Daśaratha's mind for three months and in Kausalyā's womb for nine months, in the month of Viṣṇu, also called Caitra, and in the nakṣatra of Punarvasu, a son was born to Kausalyā.[1] This child was replete with auspicious marks, such as exceptionally long arms and a voice resembling the sound of a kettledrum. From the womb of Kaikeyī was born a son when the Puṣya nakṣatra was in the ascendant,[2] while Sumitrā gave birth to valiant twins in the āsleśa nakṣatra.[3]

The streets of Ayodhyā were strewn with the powder of gems brought from various rājyas. The prajā danced with joy while the rājā sent various gifts to them. The brāmhaṇas were delighted to see cows of superior quality arrive in their backyards.

---

1 9 January, 5114 BCE, Parābhava saṃvatsara, Caitra, Śuklapakṣa, Navami tithi, Punarvasu, Monday, 12.10 p.m.

2 10 January, 5114 BCE, Parābhava saṃvatsara, Caitra, Śuklapakṣa, Navami tithi, Puṣya, Tuesday.

3 10 January, 5114 BCE, Parābhava saṃvatsara, Caitra, Śuklapakṣa, Daśamī tithi, Āśleṣā, Tuesday.

Aśauca, the period of impurity arising out of the birth or death of a family member that doesn't allow performing of vaidika rituals, was followed. This period for the kṣatriyas lasted for twelve days. As it got over, on the thirteenth day after the first son's birth, Daśaratha performed the naming ceremony for his newly born sons.[4] Vasiṣṭha arrived on request and looked at Kausalyā's son. He said, 'This child bears all the characteristics of a complete man. His eyes exude mercy while his arms spell valour. The brilliance of his face is as cool as

4 *Asminaṃśa Catuṣṭayena Bhagavān Vaṃśejaniśta Prabhu: Kliṣṭām Vīkṣya Vasundharām Atibalairbhraśtair Mahārākṣasa: Rāma: Lakṣmaṇa Samyutotha Bharata Śatrughnayuktastviti Dvandvaṃ Viṣṇubhujāyugadvayatulā Murjasvalāṃ Yadyayou*
Sarala copper plate inscription from the Cola dynasty (11th century CE) refers to the birth of Daśaratha's sons

Candra's rays. He is to charm the world with his qualities. I shall call him Rāma, the name that shall bestow auspiciousness.'

He now looked at the son of Kaikeyī and said, 'This child shall be Bharata, the one who will bear an unwanted burden, when everyone else refuses.' Kaikeyī, who was anxious to know the reason that would cause the burden, was prompted by Daśaratha not to delve into the subject. It wasn't appropriate to question a bramharṣi, especially their upādhyāya.

Looking at the sons of Sumitrā, Vasiṣṭha said, 'Here are the two who will serve the other two. This boy will be called Lakṣmaṇa, the one armoured with prosperity, and the other boy will be Śatrughna, the one who will annihilate forces that impede growth.' Sumitrā gleamed with happiness. Daśaratha asked, 'What brings Sumitrā so much happiness?' She replied, 'Beloved! Didn't Vasiṣṭha speak of Lakṣmaṇa as the one who is adorned with the armour of servitude and of Śatrughna as the one who will annihilate forces that impede bhakti?' The rājā's earlier conviction that she deserved two portions of the pāyasa was only reinforced by her mature response.

While Vasiṣṭha was about to leave the apartment, Daśaratha requested to speak to him in private and took him to the temple of Nārāyaṇa, their family mūrti. Daśaratha's ancestors had been worshipping this mūrti since the days of Ikṣvāku. With rakṣaka guarding the gateway, Daśaratha took Vasiṣṭha to the hall where the mūrti's bathing rituals were performed and said, 'O Sir! Will you be able to draw the horoscope of Rāma and brief me about his future?' Vasiṣṭha said, 'As an upādhyāya, I am duty-bound to do so and I shall do as you ask, but as a ṛṣi, my only request to you is to not distress yourself by worrying about anything I foretell.' Daśaratha nodded in acceptance and waited for Vasiṣṭha to draw the positions of the astronomical bodies during Rāma's birth.

Vasiṣṭha said, 'Born in the month of Caitra, he will be eloquent. He will bring happiness to his relatives and will walk with his head straight. Born on navami, the ninth day from amāvasya, he will be famous, powerful and unfazed by the strongest of enemies. Born in the Punarvasu nakṣatra, he will be patient and adept in dance. Born in the fourth quarter of the nakṣatra, his looks will overshadow any flaw. Sūrya is exalted in the meśa rāśi thereby making him a strong warrior while Aṅgāraka is exalted in makara rāśi, making him the rājā of forests. Śani in tula rāśi and Bṛhaspati in karkata rāśi will make him a wealthy monarch. Finally, Śukra in meena rāśi will make him a custodian of many rājyas. In simple words, he will be an invincible rājā. Bṛhaspati and Candra are found together. So, he will value friendship. Ketu is the neighbour to Bṛhaspati and Candra. Rāma has narrowly escaped the kemadruma yoga that is known to cause calamities. The only worry I see is the separation from his wife as Aṅgāraka is exalted in the seventh house from the karkata.' Daśaratha's face glowed when he heard that his son would be invincible but dimmed when the ṛṣi hinted at a familial separation.

As infants in individual cradles, Lakṣmaṇa and Śatrughna cried without a break, until they were placed in Rāma and Bharata's cradles, respectively. Attachment among the brothers grew by the day. Like fragrance that is inseparable from the Tulasī leaves, so was Lakṣmaṇa's love for Rāma and Śatrughna's for Bharata. Vasiṣṭha performed the upanayana ceremony for the rājakumāras and through tutors, trained them in archery and other relevant arts. While all the four rājakumāras were talented, Rāma emerged the most glorious. Daśaratha loved Rāma beyond any metrics. He could feel his ātmā loitering in Rāma's body while Rāma could feel the same in Lakṣmaṇa's, thereby proving the smṛti injunction that speaks of the father's ātmā reverberating in his son and of the eldest brother who is to be treated like one's father.[5] Rāma resembled Viṣṇu while Lakṣmaṇa followed him like Ananta, the serpent. Śatrughna was intently watching for any dangers like Sudarśana, the discus, while Bharata waited to announce Rāma's arrival like the Pāñcajanya, the conch.

5 Brihadaranyaka Upanishad, 6.4.8.

12

A Rite of Passage

One day, Daśaratha summoned the ṛtviks to discuss the vivāha of his sons. While they had just commenced, the gatekeeper announced the arrival of Viśvāmitra. The rājā, who deemed this an auspicious nimitta, rose out of respect for the bramharṣi. He was duly welcomed and offered a seat covered with darbha. Daśaratha was known to make promises in a hurry and then to repent at leisure. He thus said, 'Like a traveller in a desert who comes across an oasis, I am blessed by your presence. I shall do, as you desire. I swear.'

Viśvāmitra said, 'To attain spiritual betterment, I have been performing yajña. Two rākṣasas have been trying to hamper the yajña. I have tried my best to stop them. The yajña has almost reached its completion. During pūrṇāhuti, I shall be busy with the rituals with no time to combat the rākṣasas. I will need your help for ten nights.'

When Viśvāmitra finished, Daśaratha reached for his bow and quiver of arrows. He held them firmly and said, 'Ṛṣi! I shall follow you to the forests and drive those rākṣasas away. They will not trouble you anymore.'

Viśvāmitra smiled, and said, 'I am capable of killing these rākṣasas. But I have vowed neither to curse nor kill anyone during the yajña. So, I have come to you.'

Before Viśvāmitra could continue further, Daśaratha said, 'I shall march with my cavalry to kill these rākṣasas. I am duty bound to protect bramhaṛṣis like you.'

Viśvāmitra sighed and said, 'Daśaratha! The two rākṣasas Mārīca and Subāhu are appointed by the tyrant Rāvaṇa to impede the yajñas. And you know well that Rāvaṇa is invincible and so are his appointed rākṣasas. I will need a powerful warrior to fight them.'

When Viśvāmitra uttered this, Vasiṣṭha was puzzled as Daśaratha was one of the most valiant rājās the vaṃśa had seen. Finding someone more powerful would be arduous, he thought. Viśvāmitra noted Vasiṣṭha's reaction and wanting to end this surprise, said, 'Rāma.'

While this name made Vasiṣṭha smile, it gave Daśaratha the shock of his life. He was stupefied. This teary-eyed rājā momentarily forgot that he was a kṣatriya, a descendent of the Sūrya vaṃśa and the rājā of Ayodhyā.

Viśvāmitra continued, 'Give me the eldest of your sons. I need your son Rāma who is valorous and adheres to righteousness. These two rākṣasas are puffed up with a pride that augurs their destruction at the hands of the ever-humble and honest Rāma. Like the oceans that use clouds as intermediaries to moisten Bhūmi, like Sūrya who employs Aruṇa to dispel darkness ahead of his own appearance, I would suggest that you avail yourself of the invincible Rāma's kaiṅkarya to help your subjects like me in distress.'

Daśaratha stood unconvinced. Viśvāmitra, who took notice of this, continued, 'Rājā, both of us are equally interested in Rāma's welfare. But there is a difference in our approach. You enjoy the riches of life and you spend your leisure time hunting. You performed a yajña wanting a son. You are a karma yogī. Know me now. I live in the forests bereft of comforts and my companion is just this bunch of darbha. I am only interested in realizing the ultimate truth. Through such eyes, I see your son Rāma as a perfect mix of valour and humility. You must send your son with me, for this journey will fetch him good repute. Vasiṣṭha will vouch for my opinion, even if he chooses to disagree with me on other subjects. Vasiṣṭha's agreement is not because both of us are bramharṣis, but for the irrefutable truth that lies in what I say. Vasiṣṭha, who is the very son of Sarasvatī and an accomplished yogī, will know that Rāma is the most capable of all rājakumāras.'

Vasiṣṭha murmured in the ears of Vāmadeva, 'Earlier as a rājā, Viśvāmitra asked for the cow in my āśrama and I refused to part with it. Today he is asking Daśaratha for his son.' The latter quipped, 'Will Daśaratha part with his son?'

Vasiṣṭha smiled and said, 'Let us wait and watch.'

The rājā approached Viśvāmitra and sat near his feet. He started pressing the ṛṣi's legs giving every indication of not parting with his son. He bent his head and said, 'O friend to this entire universe! Your fame is undiminishing. You created a svarga for Triśaṅku and stood strong before Vasiṣṭha. I am sure my son will be in safe hands when he comes with you. But my son is not even sixteen years old, the minimum age required of a kṣatriya for fighting in battles. He has neither mastered archery nor its associated skills such as the ability to determine the enemy's might. He doesn't have a moustache, as yet. He is a little boy. A boy who is yet to part with his toys and you call him to a battle? People still confuse my son Rāma with the other Rāma, the one who held the paraśu and beheaded his mother in order to adhere to his father's words. That was Paraśurāma. While my Rāma, the one with lotus-like eyes, wakes up late and goes to bed early. You are calling him to fight the rākṣasas who are active during the nights. How can my son, who adheres to the rules of war, fight the rākṣasas who have never fought by rules? You will know that I have obtained my son through the immense efforts of ṛṣis like you, for which I am indebted. But sending him along with you doesn't seem feasible.'

Viśvāmitra frowned at what Daśaratha said but the rājā was unfazed and continued, 'Śiva once halted the yajña performed by Dakṣa while Gaṅgā whom he carries in his jaṭā, the matted locks, halted the yajña performed by Janhu. Sarasvatī once halted the yajña performed by Bramhā while Bramhā was angry when you created a different abode for Triśaṅku. I shall come with you and guard the yajña all the ten nights.'

Before the rājā could continue any further, Viśvāmitra rose from his seat. With eyes that resembled balls of fire, he walked up to the gates of the sabhā and exclaimed in a voice that caused the pillars to tremble. He said, 'From today onwards, you will be known as the rājā who makes false promises. I hope that you live happily with your family.'

Vasiṣṭha, who witnessed all this, walked up to Daśaratha and said, 'Daśaratha! I take cognizance of your love for Rāma. I know of the curse pronounced upon you when you were young and am aware that you have kept that a secret. Śibi fulfilled his promise to a dove while Raghu, one of your ancestors, fulfilled his promise to a brāmhaṇa. But today you don't seem to be able to keep your promise to Viśvāmitra. You are not just a father, but a rājā to your subjects and a caretaker of the ṛṣis. Viśvāmitra is a bramharṣi. He owns the astras bestowed upon him by Bhrisāśwa and is even capable of creating newer ones. If such a person is asking for your son, without a further question, send Rāma along with the ṛṣi.'

Viewing Viśvāmitra's livid face, Vāmadeva commented to Vasiṣṭha 'The pūrṇāhuti that was to take place in the forests has happened now in the face of Viśvāmitra. His ears are the sacrificial ground, Daśaratha's words of denial have become the fuel, and Viśvāmitra's eyes have become the blazing fire.'

Daśaratha ran to the end of the road and prostrated at the feet of Viśvāmitra. The ṛṣi said, 'Daśaratha, did you not know that the puṇya of constructing wells, ponds, bridges, free canteens will disappear like a bubble if one doesn't keep his promise?'

13

Viśvāmitra's Tutelage

Daśaratha said, 'O Viśvāmitra! I have realized my folly. I shall give you my son Rāma with Lakṣmaṇa who is as inseparable as a shadow from Rāma. I pray that you play the role of a mother, a father and an ācārya. Do what is good for them. I trust you.' He kissed Rāma on his forehead and sent the duo behind the ṛṣi.[1]

People who stood on both sides of the street to bid farewell to Rāma looked like a festoon of eyes. 'To bring welfare to this world this ṛṣi is taking our Rāma,' said one man while the other remarked that the ṛṣi was aptly called Viśvāmitra.

Rāma and Lakṣmaṇa, with their swords, bows

1 19 December, 5104 BCE, Nala saṃvatsara, Phālguṇa, Kṛṣṇapakṣa, Caturthī tithi, Viśākha, Monday.

and quiver of arrows, looked like three-headed serpents that marched behind the ṛṣi. Vāmadeva, who looked at the weapons held by the young men, remembered seeing Garuḍa fly towards their balconies the previous night carrying the same.

While the trio reached the southern banks of Sarayū, Viśvāmitra was worried that the rājakumāras would be tired. He wanted to call Rāma by his name but was hesitant since Vasiṣṭha, who was his sworn enemy, had named the rājakumāra. At the same time, he knew that the name Rāma signified his beauty, sweet speech, lustrous countenance and superior demeanour. In a sweet voice, he said, 'Rāma, go and perform ācamana.'

Both the rājakumāras obeyed the ṛṣi and wrapped up their routine with abhivādana. Viśvāmitra said, 'Two mantras named bālā and atibālā were taught to me by Bramhā. He treated these mantras as his very own daughters. I can't find a better person than you to teach these mantras. Reciting them will ensure that you are protected from fatigue and fever. Your hunger and thirst will also be kept away. Even if these mantras may not be your immediate requirement, keep reciting them as the future remains uncertain.' He muttered the mantra in the right ear of Rāma and later to Lakṣmaṇa.

In the early hours of the next day, Lakṣmaṇa rose from the bed of grass and rushed to Sarayū for a bath. In the meantime, Viśvāmitra went near Rāma and said, 'Rāma! Fortunate is Kausalyā to have begotten such an obedient son as you. You are born into Sūrya vaṃśa and hence you need to rise before Sūrya to perform duties ordained by the smṛtis. Your actions will be the guiding light to the rest of the world. Wake up.'

While Rāma's eyes opened a little, the ṛṣi was captivated by Rāma's eyes like a ṛtvik who gazes at a black bee wandering inside a lotus which is to blossom in the early hours of a day. He continued, 'Rāma, you look adorable while sleeping. I would now like to see your face blossom. Wake up. You are the tiger amongst men! You have the duty of protecting my yajña besides carrying out your routine. I am fortunate that the beneficiary of my yajña will be its protector as well. Every day, I offer arghya looking at Sūrya to whom the supreme

Nārāyaṇa is the aṅtaryāmī. And today, I see an opportunity to offer arghya to you instead. Wake up.'

Rāma woke up to find Lakṣmaṇa ready and waiting. He offered his praṇāmas to the ṛṣi. After a dip in the holy Sarayū, Rāma recited Gāyatrī, the best among mantras. Viśvāmitra, along with the rājakumāras, performed a yajña and entered Kāmāśrama[2], elaborating its history.

2 Balia, a town in the Indian state of Bihar.

14

Kāmāśrama and the End of Lust

The devas wanted a senāpati, an army-chief, to conquer Tāṭakā. This could be achieved only by subduing Śiva, the repository of mantras and a bhakta of Nārāyaṇa. Indra, who realized that Kāma alone could accomplish this task, summoned him to his court and said that he had only two reliable weapons, of which one was Vajra and the other was Kāma himself. However, he added that Vajra was powerless against men of tapasyā while Kāma could accomplish almost everything. Kāma said, 'I shall break down the self-restraint of Śiva,' and left.

Kāma in New York Metropolitan Museum of Art (USA) sculpted in the Kārkoṭa dynasty (8th century CE)

Kāma saw Śiva sporting a jaṭā, a mass of matted hair, tied with a serpent. He noticed a double string of rudrākśa hanging

Pārvatī performs tapasyā in VA Museum (UK) sculpted in the Eastern Cālukya dynasty (8th century CE)

around his neck, and a black antelope's hide knotted at the hip. It was then that Pārvatī approached Śiva, who was on the verge of seeing Nārāyaṇa through his inner eyes. She offered a rosary of lotus seeds at his feet, and Śiva opened his eyes.

At that very moment Kāma placed Sammohanā, his unfailing arrow, in the bow and shot it at Śiva who, like the agitated sea during purṇimā, disturbed by the sudden weakening of his tapasyā, cast his eyes on Pārvatī's lips. Śiva, perturbed by this very thought, wanted to quickly ascertain the reason, and searched in all directions. At once, a blazing fire with flames sprang from his third eye and burnt Kāma to ashes.

~

While just about to complete the narration, Viśvāmitra said, 'Kāma, who was thrown, was reduced to a heap of ashes here. He was left with no body and is still referred to as Anaṅga, the bodiless. This place was called Kāmāśrama from then on and has been blessed with multitude of ṛṣis performing tapasyā here for its long association with Śiva.'

A group of ṛṣis walked towards the trio and said, 'Welcome bramharṣi, the one whose fame knows no bounds. We also welcome the two young men of Ikṣvāku vaṃśa who have blessed our āśrama. Your very presence has driven away our fears of Tāṭakā, who has been tormenting us for a long time. All these years, we have wondered why people refer to this place as Kāmāśrama when it should be Sthānavāśrama. Will anyone commemorate a place for Kāma when he has been won over by Śiva? But today, we have understood their anticipation of your arrival, Rāma, you who look like the father of Kāma personified!'

After having performed their daily rites, the rājakumāras sat before Viśvāmitra, who was stringing flowers for the śālagrāma worship.

Rāma asked, 'Bramharṣi! I hear a massive sound from the river. What is this?' Viśvāmitra narrated that a river which originated from a lake called Mānasa flowed beside Ayodhyā and met with the waters of Gaṅgā not very far from Kāmāśrama. The river that came from a higher level creating a thunderous noise was called Sarayū. Rāma held his palms together and offered prayers to the river.

As the trio walked, they saw the confluence of Sarayū and Gaṅgā and decided to stay close by.[1] Neighbouring them was a dense forest that did not encourage any habitation. Viśvāmitra began narrating the legend of the forests.

1 Chhapra, a city in the Indian state of Bihar.

15
First Lesson in Governance

Indra once killed Vṛtra, a rākṣasa sent by Tvaṣṭṛ, and acquired the bramhahatyā. As a result, Indra had patches of infected skin all over his body and suffered from incessant hunger. A group of ṛṣis along with the other devas wanted to help Indra. They brought him to the forests near the Gaṅgā–Sarayū confluence and bathed him with holy waters stored in golden pots. Over a period of time, the diseased skin healed, and his persistent hunger receded. These forests which once gave shelter to Indra were later blessed with immense wealth in the form of pious inhabitants. They were renamed Malada[1]—the nagara that removed Indra's dirt, and Karuśa[2]—the nagara that satiated his hunger.

~

The meek yakṣas sought shelter in the region headed by Suketu, their intelligent chief. In order to beget a son, Suketu performed

1 Malda, a city in the Indian state of West Bengal.
2 Pandua, a city in the Indian state of West Bengal.

severe tapasyā seeking the grace of Bramhā. Bramhā appeared before Suketu and said that he would have a daughter with the combined strength of many elephants. A girl was born to Suketu, and she was called Tāṭakā, who was given in vivāha to Sunda, the son of Jamba, another yakṣa chief. The daṃpati had two sons called Mārīca and Subāhu.

One day, Sunda, who set forth on a hunting expedition, reached the āśrama of Agastya. He started uprooting the trees that Agastya had once planted. The inmates of the āśrama requested him not to spoil the serenity of the place and asked him to return to his dwelling before the ṛṣi returned. Sunda refused to heed the advice. He spotted a herd of rare deer species in the āśrama which was nurtured by Agastya. In order to taste venison, he ran behind the deer like a hungry lion, pounced and caught it by the neck. As he started eating the flesh, the shriek of the deer was unendurable for the inmates who stood helpless, when Agastya arrived. He instantly took in the situation and looked at Sunda with angry eyes. The latter experienced a burning sensation all over his body and fell dead. A friend of Sunda informed Tāṭakā and their two sons about this misfortune. The furious trio raced to the scene and saw Sunda lying dead on the ground. Without pausing to comprehend Sunda's brutality, Tāṭakā ordered her sons to kill the remaining deer and eat them in front of Agastya's eyes. While the sons rushed towards the animals which trembled in fear, Agastya said, 'A husband's demise and a father's death is an irreparable loss to the family. But you have failed to acknowledge the barbarism of Sunda towards these meek animals and selfless trees. Over and above this, your behaviour is identical to Sunda's inhumanity. Despite having been born in a yakṣa jāti, you seem to have developed the habits of a rākṣasa. I curse you all that you will gradually acquire the remaining characteristics of rākṣasas and shall be members of their jāti. Society will denounce you for your atrocities and you shall find death in the hands of a compassionate rājakumāra in order to remind the world of how barbarism can never prevail forever.'[3]

~

Viśvāmitra continued, 'Rāma! Because of the presence of Tāṭakā, these cities called Malada and Karuśa, which were once prosperous, have now turned into uninhabited forests. Tāṭakā, who is now old, doesn't come out but manages to deploy her sons who eat little children out at play. Her sons are a big impediment to the yajña we perform. Destroy her immediately.'

Rāma put his palms together and said, 'Ṛṣi! Isn't a woman to be respected? How can I kill a woman when she has committed no harm to me and whom I haven't seen committing evil acts? Above all, as a rājakumāra, how can my first battle be against a woman? I see no precedent in my vaṃśa where a rājā has killed a woman and I do not believe in setting a wrong example.'

Viśvāmitra said, 'Do not question like a commoner, Rāma! You belong to the vaṃśa of Ikṣvāku. Protecting your subjects is your foremost duty. She eats little children and causes agony to the travellers. This is a strong enough reason for you to kill her. A rājā should not wait for an opponent to harm him and then decide on the course of action. If she torments your subjects, it is the same as harming you. A rājā doesn't always need to perceive everything visually but also needs to accept the verbal testimony of brāmhaṇas.'

The ṛṣi continued, 'A woman is to be respected, no doubt. But showing physical signs of a woman doesn't amount to femininity. Imbibing basic qualities like mercy and love form an integral part of being a woman. Tāṭakā has failed in this aspect and is not to be regarded as a woman. The question of killing a woman for the

---

3 *Mahodadigaḷin Surrungāda Perumtanmaiyum Suketusudai Sundaratthaiyum Orunngu Munnāl Madivittha Sirumeni Uyartthavatton Madalvezh Poomalayatthu Māmuni*

Talavaipuram copper plate inscription from the Pāndya dynasty (9th century CE) refers to Agastya's curse on Suketu's descendants

first time doesn't arise, thus. Rāma, killing a woman may have not occurred in your vaṃśa, but killing women has occurred in the past. It has been said that the daughter of Virocana, who was called Mantharā, used to trouble her neighbourhood in the night. When the residents complained to Indra, he killed her. I will cite another example. Śukra once went to the woods to perform tapasyā seeking the extermination of the devas. Meanwhile, his mother, Khyāti, wanted to poison the food served to the devas, thereby making her son's work easy. Knowing of this plot of hers, Viṣṇu appeared, and is said to have killed her. Ignoring the pāpas he may have had to accrue, Paraśurāma killed his mother, Reṇukā, just because his father, Jamadagni, had commanded him to do so. To him, obeying his father's words was of utmost importance. Today, I also ask you to follow my command which amounts to obeying your father's words.'

Rāma kills Tāṭakā in Cintalarayasvami Temple (Andhra Pradesh) sculpted in the Vijayanagara dynasty (16th century CE)

Rāma said, 'Ṛṣi, obeying my father's words is my prime duty. I shall kill Tāṭakā in the interests of animals, the inhabitants and Agastya.' Viśvāmitra blessed Rāma to be successful against Tāṭakā. Rāma strung the chord in his bow, upon hearing which, Tāṭakā sent out a frightening noise that made the animals tremble. She threw a volley of fine dust before Rāma and Lakṣmaṇa which created a shroud, behind which she hid herself. Realizing that rākṣasas gain strength as Sūrya sets, Rāma shot the śabdavēdi, an arrow that follows the sonic waves. Hurt by the arrow, Tāṭakā came running towards Rāma at lightning speed with a thunderous noise. Rāma shot another arrow and Tāṭakā fell dead, thus bringing relief to the ṛṣis and the devas.

Viśvāmitra kissed Rāma's forehead and said, 'With your presence, this forest has been rid of its pāpas acquired by housing Tāṭakā and is now on par with Caitraratha, the garden at Kubera's abode. My dear Rāma! The ṛṣis have urged me to bless you with astras gifted to me by Bhṛsāśwa. I will also bless you with mantras that may help you fight the rākṣasas easily.'

16

At Siddāśrama, Vāmana's Abode

The next morning, Viśvāmitra blessed Rāma with astras, including that of Bramhā, Śiva, Nārāyaṇa and other devas. From Tāṭakā vana, the trio reached Siddāśrama, where Kaśyapa attained siddhi. Viśvāmitra began narrating the legend associated with Siddāśrama.

Vāmana in Rani-ki-vav (Gujarat) sculpted in the Caulukya dynasty (11th century CE)

He said, 'An asura called Bali once performed a yajña invoking the blessings of devas. As a result, Indra requested the son of Kaśyapa and Aditi, "O Vāmana! Those who hadn't received what they sought as dakṣiṇā in the past have now queued up at the residence of Bali. You may seek our lost wealth as dakṣiṇā."'

Vālmīki shed tears.

Nārada worriedly asked, 'Why are you wailing?'

Vālmīki remarked, 'How selfish of the devas to dispatch paramātmā to ask dakṣiṇā!'

Nārada smiled and said, 'That is the nature of the devas. They will seek His grace only when in need.'

Unconvinced by this answer, Vālmīki asked Nārada why the yajña to the devas was performed by Bali, an asura.

Nārada said, 'I shall elaborate. Yajña is referred to as yāga when a deva is invoked. Through the mantras, the deva grants the boons sought. Bali, though opposed to the devas, performed the yāga invoking Viṣṇu who is Devarāja, the rājā of devas, in his mind. Vāmana went to the sabhā of Bali seeking land, like a mother who intends to correct her erring child.'[1]

Viśvāmitra continued, 'The events that occurred subsequently with Bali are known to you. This is the place where Vāmana performed tapasyā making it the abode of Nārāyaṇa, the supreme. By being close to Sthānavāśrama, this place is associated with Śiva, the bhakta of Nārāyaṇa. I have thus chosen this place for performing my yāga which is currently being disrupted by the rākṣasas.'

The inhabitants of Siddāśrama, on seeing Viśvāmitra, ran towards him and noticed the two young men standing behind him. Looking at Rāma, they exclaimed, 'Ṛṣi, you look like the Candra flanked by the two bright nakṣatras of Punarvasu.'

Lakṣmaṇa muttered in Rāma's ears, 'Punarvasu! You will have two sons, is it?' Rāma guffawed and said, 'They believe that the two of us are like the pair of Punarvasu nakṣatras, which will help restore lost wealth.'

1 *Tvamekamṛtapadaṃ Māyāvināyena Padatrayārthinā Sadya: Pravṛddhena Punarbalermakhe Vicakrame Trirjagatassvasātkṛto Savostu*
Kasakkudi copper plate inscription from the Pallava dynasty (8th century CE) refers to Bali's yāga

17

The Annihilation of Mārīca and Subāhu

After a siesta, the duo returned for Viśvāmitra's blessings. They requested the ṛṣi to proceed with the yajña as intended and promised to obliterate the rākṣasas. Having received assurance from the rājakumāras, Viśvāmitra vowed to perform the yajña for six nights along with other ṛṣis by duly observing the vow of silence. While an alert Lakṣmaṇa stood at a spot, Rāma went around the āśrama to check on the rākṣasas. On the last of the six nights, Rāma asked Lakṣmaṇa to remain watchful of the rākṣasas.

While the āśrama was protected by a charm called rakśoghna, the rākṣasas called Mārīca and Subāhu came with jars of blood extracted from humans, deer and cows. They rained blood all over the vedikā and around the āśrama. On seeing this, Rāma and Lakṣmaṇa chased the rākṣasas. Rāma reluctantly hurled the mānavāstra, the astra of Manu, on Mārīca, to showcase to the world that humans were not vulnerable and weak. With this astra, Mārīca fell many yojanas away near the oceanic waters but survived because of Rāma's cloaked mercifulness. Rāma wanted to honour Bramhā who had bestowed immunity on Mārīca, by sparing him.

Subāhu, on seeing Mārīca being thrown away, came running to attack Rāma. Rāma wanted to annihilate the vicious and terrible

Subāhu. He deployed the astra of Agni on Subāhu, who was blessed by Śiva. The astra hit his chest. The accompanying rākṣasas were struck by the astra of Vāyu.

Rāma fights Mārīca and Subāhu in Pullamangai Temple (Tamil Nadu) sculpted in the Cola dynasty (10th century CE)

On completion of the yajña, Viśvāmitra performed the avabhṛtha ritual, and with the darbha-grass ring on his finger, he patted the backs of Rāma and Lakṣmaṇa in praise. Viśvāmitra then said, 'Rāma, you have accomplished what your father Daśaratha promised. Your dexterity has given Siddāśrama its true meaning.' Rāma and Lakṣmaṇa who prostrated at the feet of Viśvāmitra on hearing his words of appreciation, now proceeded to perform sandhyāvandanā. Viśvāmitra spent the night wondering what token of appreciation could he give to the rājakumāras.

The next morning, Rāma walked up to Viśvāmitra and expressed his desire to render any kaiṅkarya sought by the ṛṣi. Nārada turned to Vālmīki and said, 'This is the quality of a paramātmā—he is primed to serve his bhaktas at all points in time.'

In the presence of Viśvāmitra, a group of ṛṣis approached Rāma and said, 'A yajña is to be held in Mithilā. The rājā shall be conducting this ritual amidst an assembly of ṛṣis. A colossal bow will be placed for public-viewing. The bow was bequeathed to Sīradhvaja by Devarāta, one of the early rājās of this vaṃśa. Devarāta had performed tapasyā venerating Śiva, in order to secure the bow used by Śiva to destroy the yajña performed by Dakṣa. Śiva, who is known to be merciful to his bhaktas, gave away the bow to Devarāta. This bow of Śiva has been worshipped from then on through such rituals and festivals. Even the uninvited can attend a yajña. Rāma, you may come.'

Rāma instantly agreed to accompany the ṛṣis and Lakṣmaṇa concurred with Rāma's decision. With Viśvāmitra leading the way, the ṛṣis loaded a hundred carts of paraphernalia for the yajña and began their journey. Their journey was to Himālaya on the northern banks of river Gaṅgā. Offering their praṇāmas to Vanadevatā, the ṛṣis halted by the banks of river Sona[1] that night.

1 A tributary of Ganga with a length over 750 kilometres. Flows through the Indian states of Madhya Pradesh, Uttar Pradesh, Jharkhand and Bihar.

18

Viśvāmitra's Origins, Even as Mithilā Beckons

The next morning, Viśvāmitra narrated the legend of Girivraja, on the banks of Sonā where they were stationed, while Rāma and Lakṣmaṇa sat in rapt attention.

He said, 'A righteous rājā called Kuśa had four mighty sons, namely Kuśamba, Kuśanābha, Adhūrtarajasa and Vasu. Upon receiving directions to set up their own rājadhānīs, the sons built Kauśambi[1], Mahodaya[2], Dharmāraṇya[3] and Girivraja[4], respectively. Girivraja is the rājadhānī that is blessed with the flow of Sonā waters.'

He then recounted the story of Kuśanābha, the second of the sons of Kuśa. Through an apsara called Ghṛtācī, he begot a hundred daughters. They were beautiful, well-mannered and obedient. While

1 A district in the Indian state of Uttar Pradesh.

2 Kannauj, a city in the Indian state of Uttar Pradesh.

3 Mirzapur, a city in the Indian state of Uttar Pradesh.

4 Rajgir, a city in the Indian state of Bihar.

Vāyu lusted after them and wanted to violate their chastity, the daughters of Kuśanābha spurned his advances. A frustrated Vāyu struck them with all his might, thereby deforming their bodies. On learning of this incident, their father appreciated the fact that his daughters had desisted from cursing Vāyu for his perversity. Vayu's violence had resulted in the daughters of Kuśanābha developing deformities, hunchbacks. They were given in kanyādāna to Bramhadatta, who ruled Kāmpilya[5]. Kuśanābha knew that Bramhadatta was born to a resplendent ṛṣi called Culee through an apsarā called Somadā. He was also confident that Bramhadatta, of immense splendour, could eventually relieve his daughters of their deformities. And so it eventually happened to the girls. They were cured of their deformities, just as desired by their father.

Kuśanābha, who ruled Mahodaya, renamed his rājadhānī as Kanyākubja—the nagarī of the hunchback virgins—to celebrate his daughters' steadfast adherence to virtue. After the vivāha of his daughters, Kuśanābha performed the putrakāmeṣṭi, seeking male progeny. As a result, Kuśanābha was blessed with a son, who was called Gādhi. Gādhi had a daughter called Satyavatī, who married Ṛcīka, a radiant ṛṣi. Later, Gādhi had a son called Kauśika, who later came to be called Viśvāmitra.

The assembly of ṛṣis, along with Rāma and Lakṣmaṇa, found the narration of Viśvāmitra's ancestry exhilarating. They spent a second night on the banks of river Sonā.

The following morning, the entourage reached the banks of river Gaṅgā. They recited the aghamarśana sūkta, bathed, and the ṛṣis performed tarpaṇa to pitṛs. As Rāma wished to know the legend of river Gaṅgā, Viśvāmitra began narrating it.

Himavān married Manoramā, also known as Menā, the daughter of Meru. The daṃpati had two daughters, Gaṅgā and Umā. The devas, intending to bring purity to the worlds, requested Himavān

5 Kampil, a town in the Indian state of Uttar Pradesh.

Śiva weds Pārvatī (Tamil Nadu) sculpted in the Cola dynasty (11th century CE)

that he permit Gaṅgā, the elder of his daughters, to transform into a river. Acceding to the request, Himavān let Gaṅgā flow towards the abode of devas.

Umā, through immense austerities, married Śiva.
In order to fetch a son of Śiva who could vanquish Tādaka, the devas, with Bramhā in the lead, travelled to Kailāśa. Bramhā requested that the retas of Śiva be preserved for a larger purpose. Śiva, who was in sexual congress with Umā, clandestinely shot his retas, that had the potency to annihilate the earthlings on Bhūmi. This retas was collected by Agni devatā, and carried by Vāyu to a forest infested with śara, the reed plants. Gaṅgā carried the retas, as resplendent as the fire, in her. At an appropriate moment, the foetus slid from her sac. Six women, namely Ambā, Tulā, Nitartini, Apraganti, Mehanti and Vardhayati, who were representative of the Kṛttikā nakṣatra, saw this and protected the child. The boy was suckled by the Kṛttikā women. Nurtured in the śara forests, he was called Śaravaṇabhava and mothered by the Kṛttikā ladies, he was called Kārttikeya. Associated with the waters of Gaṅgā, he was Gāṅgeya. Having slid from the amniotic sac, he was Skanda. And having shone with effulgence, he was Kumāra.[6]

Umā, having realized that a trick was played on her, cursed the devas to remain impotent. Her exasperation turned on Bhūmi, as she said, 'You shall appear bizarre with a heterogeneous landscape and shall be regarded as polyandrous for your association with many

6 Satapatha Brāmhana, 6.1.3.8.

monarchs. You shall never be gratified by your children.' In a fit of pique, Śiva retired to Kailāśa for tapasyā.

Viśvāmitra continued, 'I will need to elaborate on the Aśvamedha conducted by your ancestor. That will eventually answer your question on the descent of Gaṅgā.'

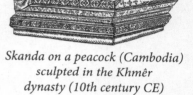

Skanda on a peacock (Cambodia) sculpted in the Khmêr dynasty (10th century CE)

19

Glorious Gaṅgā's Story

Sagara, the valiant rājā of Ayodhyā, had two wives. The first was a rājakumāri of Vidarbha. Her name was Keśinī. The second was the daughter of Kaśyapa and sister to Garuḍa. Her name was Sumati. In order to seek the grace of Bhṛgu, the rājā with his two wives left for Bhṛgu prasravana. The ṛṣi prophesied that the rājā would be blessed with sons. While Sumati gave birth to many sons, Keśinī gave birth to a son who was called Asamañja. Sagara ostracized Asamañja for his sinister activities, but fondly accepted Aṃśumān, Asamañja's son, for his desirable qualities. Sagara, wanting to perform the Aśvamedha, chose the region of Āryavarta between the mighty Himālaya and Vindhya as the venue for the ritual.[1]

Indra, in disguise, stole the sacrificial horse on the day of Ukthya. Ordered by Sagara, the sons of Sumati who could not find the horse, started digging Bhūmi. Equipped with tridents and spears, their

1 *Āsedatrānvavāye Sagara Iti Nṛpastarjitāśeṣabhūpo Yenārādhyopi Kāmaṃ Hayamakhanikarairtrāsito Devaraja: Yatputrāṇām Prabhāvāllavaṇajalanidhou Sāgaratvaṃ Prapanneśeṣaṇām Vāridhināmapi Sakalagurusāgaratvancakāra* |
Sarala copper plate inscription from the Cola dynasty (11th century CE) refers to Sagara's Aśvamedha Yajña

Bhagīratha performs penance for the descent of Gaṅgā (Tamil Nadu) sculpted in the Pallava dynasty (7th century CE)

digging disturbed the fauna around. During this search, they saw the cardinal elephants like Virūpākṣa, Mahāpadma, Saumanasa and Bhadra managed by Indra, Yama, Varuṇa and Kubera, respectively. When they reached the āśrama of Kapila[2], they saw the missing sacrificial horse tied to a post. Infuriated that Kapila had stolen the horse, they rushed towards him with weapons. Very displeased by their wanton destruction of nature, Kapila reduced the attacking sons of Sagara to a mound of ash by just uttering the sound 'hum'. With neither the horse nor the sons returning to Āryavarta, Sagara ordered his grandson Aṃśumān to begin the search. While Aṃśumān brought back the horse for the completion of Aśvamedha, he was indicated by Garuḍa about Kapila's curse pronounced upon his uncles. To the bereaving Aṃśumān, Garuḍa appeared in the samādhi state, and recommended that Gaṅgā waters from devaloka be used for performing tarpaṇa.

Aṃśumān, who wished to bring Gaṅgā waters, didn't have the resolve to carry out this daunting task. His grandson, Bhagīratha, handed over the administration of the rājya to his mantris and retired to Himālaya. With four fires lit around and the rays of Sūrya falling on him, he stood amidst the pañcāgni on one leg with raised hands.

---

2 Sagar Island (Ganga delta) in the Indian state of West Bengal.

He ate once a month and performed severe tapasyā, to propitiate Bramhā.

The latter arrived at the tapasyā spot and said, 'May your vaṃśa prosper. No one else but Śiva can sustain the force of Gaṅgā falling on Bhūmi. He is commissioned by Nārāyaṇa to undertake the task of assisting the bringing of Gaṅgā to Bhūmi.'

Learning of this, Bhagīratha continued his tapasyā towards Śiva, who readied himself to accept the Gaṅgā waters. From the devaloka, the Gaṅgā waters flowed tumultuously with unwarranted fury. Śiva stood with his untamed locks open like a large crater that awaits torrential rain. As the Gaṅgā waters thundered into the cavernous locks of hair, Śiva trapped her totally within his hair by knotting up his locks. Bhagīratha continued his prayers to Śiva, to forgive Gaṅgā.

Śiva graciously let her flow into a lake called Bindu[3] saras. This lake was formed in the past with the interminable flow of Viṣṇu's tears who was gratified and overwhelmed with Kardama's austerities. The lake that swelled due to the sudden entry of Gaṅgā waters branched into three directions. She flowed westward as Sucakṣu, Sītā and Sindhu streams. She flowed eastward as Hlādini, Pāvani and Nalini. She flowed southwards, following Bhagīratha's chariot dutifully. As she flowed, makaras swam along. In some places, she flowed steadily, while she gushed in some places. Gaṅgā inundated the āśrama of

3 Siddhpur, a town in the Indian state of Gujarat.

Janhu[4], who was engaged in a yajña. Looking at the damage that Gaṅgā had caused, the enraged ṛṣi stopped her flow. Bhagīratha requested the ṛṣi to show leniency for a larger cause. The ṛṣi, who was all ears to the rājā's request, let her continue behind Bhagīratha's chariot. Gaṅgā, who wished to be known as the daughter to Janhu, was called Jānhavi from then on. She followed the chariot till she reached the heap of ashes, near Kapila's āśrama. Bhagīratha, with her waters and black sesame seeds, performed tarpaṇa to his ancestors and finally felt contentment. Gaṅgā emptied herself into Sāgara, the sea, once created by the sons of Sagara.

Nārada asked Vālmīki to pause, and said, 'I wish to explain the antecedent of river Gaṅgā. Vāmana who reached the yajña of Bali, obtained three measures of land. He grew as Trivikrama, with his left foot extending till the shell that covered the cosmic egg. The big toe nail tore open the shell, letting the Gaṅgā waters seep in. These waters that washed the kuṅkuma-anointed foot of Nārāyaṇa reached Dhruva maṇḍala. The Saptaṛṣis sprinkled some of these waters on their tufts, while the waters reached the realm of Sūrya and Candra. Further, it reached Meru[5] on which Bramhā sat. He collected the waters in a kamaṇḍalu. Bramhā paid praṇāmas to the lotus-like foot of Trivikrama that bore the marks of Sudarśana, Pāñcajanya, Kaumodakī, Kalpaka, Dhvaja, Aṅkuśa and Vajra, as he further lowered his foot. Śiva's prayers to Saṅkarṣaṇa were fructified when he received those waters of Gaṅgā in his tufts through Bhagīratha's tapasyā. She is Viṣṇupadī for tracing her origin to Viṣṇu's foot while she is Hara-vallabhā for being Śiva's spouse. Her association with Bramhā's kamaṇḍalu, Viṣṇu's foot and Śiva's hair locks, makes her

4 Nabadwip, a city in the Indian state of West Bengal.

5 Pamir mountain range of Tajikistan extending till Afghanistan, Kyrgyzstan and China.

Tripathagā. From Himālaya to Amarāvatī, later to Śiva's matted locks, and finally behind Bhagīratha's chariot, Gaṅgā cruised at three levels.'

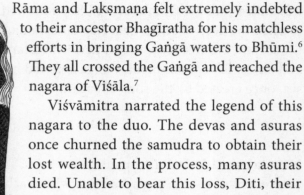

Gaṅgā in the National Museum (Delhi) sculpted in the Gupta dynasty (5th century CE)

Rāma and Lakṣmaṇa felt extremely indebted to their ancestor Bhagīratha for his matchless efforts in bringing Gaṅgā waters to Bhūmi.[6] They all crossed the Gaṅgā and reached the nagara of Viśāla.[7]

Viśvāmitra narrated the legend of this nagara to the duo. The devas and asuras once churned the samudra to obtain their lost wealth. In the process, many asuras died. Unable to bear this loss, Diti, their mother, performed austerities while being pregnant again. She wanted the child to be strong and invincible. Indra noticed that his stepmother Diti was not devout and had erred during the vow. He managed to perform a ritual that could non-invasively damage the foetus. Diti, who realized the mistake, asked Indra to spare the foetus. She asked that the foetus, when born, be called Marut, and in the due course of time become the ruler of ethereal spaces. Indra, who saw Marut in

---

6 *Surasarit Avatārita Iti Matvā Tapasiratena Bhagīrathena Rājñā Narapatiravatāraya Anyashothir Nijabhuvi Tām Sakaverkanyākākhyām | Āsedatra Bhagīratha: Kṣitipatirvaṃśe Svavaṃśodbhavān Uddhartuṃ Kapilaprakopadahana Jvālāvali Bhasmitān Svasindhum Vasudhānnyantripathagācakre Sa Bhāgīrathīṃmaratyāpyamṛtān Vyadhāt Surasarit Vāripravāhasparśam |*

Tiruvālangādu and Sarala copper plate inscription from the Cola dynasty (11th century CE) refers to Bhagīratha bringing Gaṅgā to Bhūmi

7 Vaishali to Hajipur stretch in the Indian state of Bihar.

seven forms, called them āvaha, pravaha, vivaha, parāvaha, udvaha, samvaha and parivaha. Viśāla was the nagara that Diti chose for her tapasyā, concluded Viśvāmitra, just as Sumati, its ruler, offered praṇāmas to the ṛṣi. The rājā arranged for their stay in Viśāla. The next day, as they walked past an abandoned āśrama, Rāma asked Viśvāmitra to detail its history.

20

Rāma's Grace and Ahalyā's Emancipation

Gautama, a ṛṣi of immense power and austerities, was once summoned by Bramhā to Puṣkara. He gave his young daughter to the care of Gautama and asked him to bring her up and return her to him after she attained puberty. Gautama took utmost care of Bramhā's daughter. He brought the bejewelled girl to Bramhā, after nurturing her for a considerable time. Bramhā, who saw his daughter of blemishless beauty, named her Ahalyā. Indra, who was present on the scene, asked Bramhā to give Ahalyā in vivāha to him. Bramhā asked him to go around the Bhūmi to prove how steadfast he was in the relationship. While Indra left the place in glee, Gautama informed Bramhā that the cow in his āśrama had delivered a calf in the early hours of the day. He added that he had been fortunate to perform pradakṣiṇā around the cow while she was giving birth. Bramhā, who was euphoric at this news, quoted the śāstras that deemed the pradakṣiṇā of Bhūmi to be equal to the pradakṣiṇā around a cow when she was calving. As a result, he gave Ahalyā in vivāha to Gautama ṛṣi.

In the month of Kārttika, Gautama left for Puṣkara[1] to attend the purṇimā festival. Indra, still smarting under the disappointment of not having Ahalyā for his wife, wanted to seize the opportunity of Gautama's absence to satiate his carnal desire for her. In the guise of Gautama, Indra entered the āśrama. On the pretext of collecting darbha grass, he gained proximity to Ahalyā. Though it was not the appropriate time for coitus according to the śāstras, he slowly disrobed Ahalyā. The ṛṣi's wife sensed that he was not her husband when he embraced her. She identified Indra in her husband's disguise from the pollen of pārijāta flowers strewn on his jaṭā. She was blown away by Indra's charm, and she surrendered to his carnal advances.

Gautama, who returned from Puṣkara, was shocked to see Indra embracing Ahalyā. Becoming aware of the ṛṣi's arrival, Indra tried to sneak out like a sly cat. Gautama cursed Indra that his testicles would fall off instantly and he would become impotent. He added that Indra would develop multiple vulvas on his body and that his beauty would be ceded to the Aśvinikumāras. A shocked Indra left the āśrama and appealed to Agni devatā for a solution. Agni detached a pair of testicles from the ram meant for a yajña and gave them to Indra. In the ensuing days, Indra saw his body develop various apertures that resembled the vulva, making him Bhagaṅga. He migrated to Nāgadvīpa[2] and meditated on Umā. Appearing as Indrākṣī, the devī turned each of the vulva into an eye-like feature. Indra, from then on, was referred to as Sahasrākṣa—the one with many eyes.

Viśvāmitra continued, 'Gautama saw a petrified Ahalyā and deprecated her for her adultery. To punish her, he cursed that she would remain sensationless, deadened to winds and go unnoticed by the passersby. From that day, Gautama abandoned Mithilopavana, this āśrama.'

---

1 Pushkar, a city in the Indian state of Rajasthan.

2 Nainativu, an island in the norther province of Sri Lanka.

With Viśvāmitra leading them, Rāma and Lakṣmaṇa decided to grace the āśrama.[3]

Ahalyā seeks redemption from Rāma, National Museum (Delhi), sculpted in the Gupta dynasty (5th century CE)

As Rāma strode in majestically, the uninhabited āśrama saw a volley of dust rise. One speck of dust that was stirred up by the pādukās of Rāma incidentally fell on Ahalyā, who was performing tapasyā as an act of remorse. Ahalyā, the woman, emerged as holy and as radiant as the fire in a yajña. The moment she saw Rāma who was mercy incarnate, she hurriedly ran towards river Kauśikī[4] and fetched some water in a jug. She offered pādya and arghya to Rāma, while offering jātiphala as a sign of hospitality.

Viśvāmitra and Lakṣmaṇa were stupefied at the sequence of events. They saw Ahalyā gaze at Rāma's pādukās like a child that looks lovingly at his mother.

---

3 Ahalya Asthana Temple in Darbhanga town in the Indian state of Bihar.

4 Koshi, a transboundary river through Tibet, Nepal and India. Tributary of Ganga with a length of over 700 kilometres.

Gautama ṛṣi, who was earlier propitiating Śiva in the form of Tryambaka in Bramhagiri[5], now entered the āśrama. The ṛṣi's eyes met with the eyes of Ahalyā, and it seemed to the onlookers as if ājya was being poured into fire. Rāma asked Gautama not to look at Ahalyā as a fallen woman, but to accept her as his wife again. Taking leave of the ṛṣi daṃpati, the trio left the āśrama.

Nārada said, 'Rāma's ability to annihilate evil forces was explicit in his handling of Tāṭakā, Subāhu and Mārīca, while his emancipation of Ahalyā demonstrated his divine ability. The ṛṣis don't concur on what gave Ahalyā the relief. Some say it was his mere look while others say that it was his feet. Some say it was Rāma's pādukās, while others say it was the dust that sprang from them. If Gaṅgā waters that rose from Viṣṇu's feet gave relief to Rāma's ancestors, it is Rāma himself who comforted Ahalyā.' Vālmīki, who was choked with emotions, expressed his inability to pen these profoundly moving experiences.

---

5 Trimbakeshwar Siva Temple in Trimbak town in the Indian state of Maharashtra.

21

Meeting Janaka

Lakṣmaṇa erected a tent on the riverbanks while Rāma welcomed Viśvāmitra inside. On learning that Viśvāmitra had arrived in the outskirts of Mithilā[1], Sīradhvaja wanted to honour the bramharṣi. With Śatānanda, the upādhyāya, leading, the rājā arrived with his retinue. Sīradhvaja also held the name Janaka, a title bestowed on all rājās of Videha. Janaka offered arghya and pādya to Viśvāmitra while Rāma and Lakṣmaṇa offered their praṇāmas to Janaka. In return, the rājā offered madhuparka to Rāma and Lakṣmaṇa, like a father-in-law does to his sons-in-law.

As Viśvāmitra seated himself, the rest followed suit. Janaka said, 'The ṛtviks say that the vājapeya, which we are conducting, will

1 Balirajgarh, a town in the Indian state of Bihar.

conclude in twelve days. But your presence here seems to have given me the benefits of the vājapeya, already.'

Pointing to the rājakumāras, Janaka said, 'Each of them carries a sword, a bow and a quiver of arrows. One shines like Sūrya, while the other like Candra that reflects the light of Sūrya falling on it. One walks like a majestic elephant while the other follows him like an awesome lion. One walks like a terrifying tiger while the other follows him like an adamant bull. Their eyes are as broad as the lotus petals, and their eye gestures are alike. These adolescents who ooze vigour are as charming as the Aśvinikumāras. For a moment it seemed to me as if the devas strode in from Amarāvatī and camped on Bhūmi. With the duo rooted in Bhūmi, I am confident they are mortals. But why have they walked on this rugged path? Viśvāmitra, is this expedition on foot a precursor to any of their future ordeals?'

A beaming Viśvāmitra said, 'Janaka, these are the sons of Daśaratha. While Daśaratha ensured that his sons were well-nourished and equipped, Vasiṣṭha took on the reins of their tutelage, the moulding of character and demeanour. The duo helped vanquish Tāṭakā, Subāhu and Mārīca, thereby ensuring my yajña was complete. I brought these archers here to show them that bow of Śiva which has been worshipped in your rājya.'

Turning towards Śatānanda, he said, 'As we entered Mithilopavana, Rāma gave relief to Ahalyā who was in tapasyā for a long time. She is finally united with Gautama, her husband.'

This news of Gautama and Ahalyā's reunion brought immense happiness to Śatānanda, who was the eldest of their sons. Like Jamadagni and Reṇukā who were reunited by their son Paraśurāma after a series of unpleasant happenings, Rāma brought Gautama and Ahalyā, the parents of Śatānanda together. Śatānanda was as much indebted to Viśvāmitra, as much as he was to Rāma. He took Rāma to a cowshed and narrated the life history of Viśvāmitra.

22

From Kauśika to Viśvāmitra

There was a rājā called Gādhi who was succeeded by his son, Kauśika. This newly anointed rājā once arrived at the āśrama of Vasiṣṭha with his retinue.[1] Looking at the āśrama, for a moment Kauśika thought he was in Satyaloka, the abode of Bramhā. The presence of vaikhānasas and vālakhilyas seemed to corroborate his belief. Vaikhānasas, who lived on half-boiled food, were believed to have sprung from the nails of Bramhā while Vālakhilyas, who never stocked food for the future, had sprung from Bramhā's body hair.[2] Vasiṣṭha welcomed Kauśika, offered him a seat and offered a bowl of madhuparka. Vasiṣṭha asked, 'It is said that there are four distinct features of a righteous administration which are, to righteously earn, enhance, safeguard and bequeath wealth. I hope your subjects are content with your administration. I hope you would have vanquished your enemies while keeping your forces equipped. I also hope your family is keeping good health.'

On hearing this, Kauśika replied in the affirmative. Upon repeated requests to accept his hospitality, Kauśika agreed to camp in Vasiṣṭha's āśrama.

---

1 Rishikesh, a town in the Indian state of Uttarakhand.

2 Taittiriya Brāmhana, 3.8.1.

With the grace of Śabalā, the speckled cow of Vasiṣṭha, many varieties of food that were sweet, sour, savoury, caustic, bitter and astringent were cooked. They included food that could be chewed, licked, drunk and have their juice squeezed out. While the food was made ready for consumption, the army was served with vāruṇi, prepared from rice, sugar molasses and dates. All of them enjoyed the food and made merry. Looking at the lavish display of riches by the ṛṣi, Kauśika asked Vasiṣṭha to barter Śabalā in return for innumerable cattle. Vasiṣṭha refused to part with the cow, considering her inseparable from his existence. He required her presence for the completion of rituals like agnihotra, bhūtabali, vaiśvadeva and darśapūrṇamāsa. He added that the words like vaśat and svāhā, which were used for homas, were dependent on Śabalā's blessings.

When Vasiṣṭha refused to part with Śabalā, Kauśika tried to seize the cow. She wailed in pain and sought asylum at the feet of Vasiṣṭha. Vasiṣṭha was reminded of his very own prowess, and of the fact that the wealth accrued by a ṛṣi through homas and tapasyā did not belong to the kṣatriyas.

Things slowly began to fall in place, for Vasiṣṭha remembered a saying that a ṛṣi's wealth, when forcefully appropriated, would cause irreparable damage to the wrongdoer's family. Vasiṣṭha sent clarion calls to pahlavas, yāvanas, sakas, mlecchas, hāritas, kirātas and kambojās, that could fight Kauśika's army. In no time, the army arrived to assist Vasiṣṭha fight the mighty Kauśika. As Kauśika fired astras at the attacking army, more of the armies kept coming from Vasiṣṭha's side. Kauśika's army was completely massacred. With an obliterated army, Kauśika stood as helpless as a fangless snake, a wingless bird, a sea with no tides and a Sūrya whose shine was hidden.

Kauśika asked his son to manage the rājya while he retired to Himālaya to perform tapasyā to gain Śiva's benevolence. When Śiva arrived before him Kauśika said, 'I pray that you bless me with astras, and their associated mantras. You alone can bestow these upon me.' Kauśika was blessed by Śiva and with the astras received, he attacked the āśrama of Vasiṣṭha without any delay. Looking at the residents running helter-skelter, Vasiṣṭha was enraged at Kauśika's homicidal tendencies. Looking like the fearsome Vīrabhadra, Vasiṣṭha held up his Bramhadanḍa, the stick which could be catastrophic. Bramhadanḍa absorbed every astra fired by Kauśika, including the Bramhāstra.

Vasiṣṭha, exercising great restraint, forgave Kauśika for his excesses. Kauśika left the place defeated but still vengeful.

Kauśika, who retired to the forests with his wife and a śiṣya, lived in the neighbourhood of Caṇḍālas. In the famine-afflicted deśa, Kauśika stealthily went inside the hut of a Caṇḍāla to check if there was any food to satiate his hunger. When he spotted a cooked flesh ball and was about to eat it, the gṛhastha prevented Kauśika. He said that it was the meat of a dog and Kauśika shouldn't be consuming such food. This advice further induced Kauśika to perform tapasyā towards Bramhā. He retired to Gokarṇa[3], a place for dhyāna located by the seas.

---

3 A town in the Indian state of Karnataka.

23

Hariścandra, the Superior Prince

In Ayodhyā, there lived a rājā named Tryāruṇi who was righteous in his administration. He had a son called Satyavrata who, in contrast, was harsh and vindictive towards his subjects. Satyavrata was married to the rājakumārī of Kekaya deśa and they had a son called Hariścandra.

Satyavrata once barged into a vivāha. He abducted the bride when the last mantra of saptapadi, which marks the culmination of vivāha, was to be recited. Neither the groom nor the attendees could match the might of Satyavrata and stood helpless. Learning of this alarming behaviour of his son, an abashed Tryāruṇi banished Satyavrata to the forests. Tryāruṇi, who was distressed at this incident, hoped that at least Hariścandra would compensate for his father's misdeeds.

Hariścandra developed into a fine human being with exemplary values. Anointing Hariścandra as his heir, Tryāruṇi left for the forests as a vānaprastha. Ayodhyā was afflicted by severe famine. Upon consulting with Vasiṣṭha, Hariścandra performed a yajña to please Varuṇa. The deva was impressed with Hariścandra's sincerity and showered rains to help the deśa. Eventually, Hariścandra was blessed with a son called Rohitāśva.

While Kauśika was away for tapasyā, his wife and the śiṣya were left to fend for themselves in the forests. Kauśika's wife tied a cord around the śiṣya's neck and held him in the forest path for the passersby to buy him as a slave. Satyavrata, who was loitering in the forests, took pity on them. He freed the śiṣya of Kauśika from the neck cord, and thus the freed śiṣya earned a new name—Gālava. Satyavrata escorted Kauśika's wife and Gālava to the neighbourhood of Caṇḍālas. He promised to serve them the flesh of deer, boar or dog on a daily basis. Due to the shortage of meat, Satyavrata resorted to stealing a cow from the āśrama of Vasiṣṭha. The stolen cow was slaughtered, and the cooked meat was served to Kauśika's wife.

Vasiṣṭha, who learnt of the happenings, said, 'Satyavrata, you have committed three irrevocable pāpas namely, abducting a woman who was married to another man; stealing a cow and consuming its meat; and not offering any food consumed in the past as naivedya to Nārāyaṇa, the supreme. You will be known as Triśaṅku, the one who has committed the "heinous three" from now on.'

Satyavrata, who was already weak, was further plagued with this derogatory name of Triśaṅku. He meditated on Śiva at Vyāghrapuri[1] and stayed in the forests. Hariścandra, who learnt of his father's trauma, sent his mantris to escort Triśaṅku to Ayodhyā. But Triśaṅku refused to return and sent only his blessings to his righteous son.

1 Nataraja Siva Temple in Chidambaram, a town in the Indian state of Tamil Nadu.

24

Triśaṅku

Alone in the forests, brooding on his vidhi, Triśaṅku developed an unholy desire to ascend to Amarāvatī, the rājadhani of svarga, with his mortal body, contrary to the śāstra that rubbished such a possibility. He approached Vasiṣṭha to perform a yajña that would help achieve his purpose. Vasiṣṭha refused to perform a yajña whose objective did not conform to the śāstras. Triśaṅku then sought asylum at the feet of Vasiṣṭha's sons, headed by Śakti.

Upon understanding Triśaṅku's notion, Śakti, who was infuriated said, 'When the tree of wisdom called Vasiṣṭha has himself rejected your forbidden request, what audacity prompted you to come and ask us who are its branches! You have for long been in the habitat of Caṇḍālas. May you turn into a Caṇḍāla from now. Let your yellow silk clothes turn black; your silky-hair turn shaggy; your effervescent garlands turn into funeral wreaths and your priceless ornaments into rugged iron ornaments.'

Triśaṅku was depressed, and to seek solace, he crossed the waters of Mahānadī[1] river and went to Āndhra deśa.

---

1 A river with the length of over 900 kilometres. Flows through the Indian states of Chhattisgarh and Odisha.

Bramhā, who was impressed by the tapasyā of Kauśika, bestowed the title of rājaṛṣi on him. But Kauśika wasn't happy for he aspired to be only a bramhaṛṣi. On his way back from Gokarṇa, he encountered Triśaṅku. He understood from Triśaṅku that Vasiṣṭha and his sons had refused to perform the yajña. He was appreciative of Triśaṅku's benevolence towards his wife and śiṣya during his absence.

Triśaṅku said, 'With no alternate course to achieve my desire, I perform prapatti to you. It is within your ability to counter my vidhi.' Kauśika who undertook this arduous task on himself, officiated a yajña. Gālava went to various regions inviting ṛtviks. During this sojourn, they met the sons of Vasiṣṭha who refused to join the yajña.

Śakti ṛṣi said, 'How will the devas partake the havis in a yajña where Kauśika, a kṣatriya is the yājaka and Triśaṅku, a Caṇḍāla the kartā? And with all this, Triśaṅku ascending to svarga with his mortal body seems impossible.'

Upon learning of these comments, Kauśika developed deep antipathy towards Vasiṣṭha's sons also.

The devas did not come to receive their havis at the end of the yajña. An enraged Kauśika, through his accrued spiritual prowess, asked Triśaṅku to start climbing the hill towards Amarāvatī. As Indra noticed this, he repelled Triśaṅku and hurtled him upside down. Crying to be saved, Triśaṅku tumbled down the hill. A shocked Kauśika, who saw this, exclaimed, 'Wait there, wait there.' To everyone's amazement, Triśaṅku was held midhill.

As a stopgap, Kauśika created another abode that was identical to Amarāvatī, and asked Triśaṅku to enjoy living in his own world. Kauśika was undecided as to whether he would have to create an Indra-like person for the new svarga that he had created or to do away with that position by coronating Triśaṅku as the chief.

Astonished at this act of Kauśika, the devas said, 'Triśaṅku, who will be a deva look-alike, will have the nakṣatras venerate him. But he shall stay upside-down for working against Vasiṣṭha's will.'

Kauśika agreed to the stipulations of the devas, but left with an enhanced hostility towards Vasiṣṭha.

25
Hariścandra, a Man of His Word

Hariścandra, the rājā of Ayodhyā, was hailed as a rājarṣi for his adherence to dharma. Under the direction of Vasiṣṭha, he performed a rājasuya yajña like no other rājā. He gave away whatever the ṛtviks sought as dakṣiṇā. Kauśika despised the rājā for being obedient to Vasiṣṭha who was his sworn enemy. Kauśika, as a ṛtvik, asked the rājā for his rājya and all his riches except the rājā, his wife and son, as dakṣiṇā. Hariścandra, who had committed himself to giving anything that the seeker sought, instantly abandoned the rājya, its riches, his ornaments and clothes. Along with Tārāmatī, who was known as Saivyā, and his son Rohitāśva, he left for the forests. Seeing their beloved rājā leave the nagarī, its prajā wept uncontrollably.

Hariścandra, with his family, reached Kāśī. To his surprise, Kauśika was present at the doorway of the nagarī. He said, 'Hariścandra, I received the rājya from you. But you still owe me the last share of wealth. Give me that share now.' Hariścandra, without doubting the ṛṣi's calculation, bought time and promised to pay that share by the end of the month. On the last day of the month, Kauśika reached the place where Hariścandra stayed. He sprinkled some water on the exhausted face of the erstwhile rājā and said, 'Rise and give me the fee you had promised. Sūrya shines and Bhūmi holds us together because of truth. It is said that truth easily outweighs a hundred Aśvamedha yajñas.'

The rājā, who was incapable of generating further wealth, looked at Tārāmati. She asked that she be sold off as a slave.[1] The rājā remorsefully hoisted her to a platform for the passersby to see. A brāmhaṇa, who lived in Kāśī, decided to gift Tārāmati to his young wife, to assist her in the daily chores. Handing over a pouch of gold coins to Hariścandra, he dragged Tārāmati to his house. Unable to part with his mother, Rohitāśva, the little boy, attached himself to his mother, only to be ridiculed by the brāmhaṇa.

Hariścandra duly handed over the pouch to Kauśika who insisted that a small share of the fee to be paid still remained. A disfigured Caṇḍāla of dark complexion and a pot-belly, with a skull in his hand, was walking by the street. Kauśika asked the Caṇḍāla to buy Hariścandra as an apprentice. Hariścandra, who abhorred this idea, stood unmoved without expressing his thoughts openly. Kauśika, who was adept at construing body language, looked at the Caṇḍāla and said, 'This slave of mine called Hariścandra is being sold to you for gold.' Kauśika collected the pending share of wealth that was promised to him by Hariścandra from the Caṇḍāla and left Kāśī with a smirk.

Hariścandra was employed in a graveyard by the Caṇḍāla.

His job was to disrobe the dead bodies before they were burnt. Months passed and one day, Hariścandra spotted a lady trying to light the funeral pyre without his consent. As he went closer, he noticed that the body of his son Rohitāśva lay on the pyre and the lady was none other than Tārāmati. Learning that his son had been killed by a snake bite, the afflicted man rolled on the ground in sorrow.

---

1 *Asminvaṃśe Bhavadabhibhavan Yojasā Rājavṛndaṃ Labdhānanda Samitishou Hariścandranāmā Narendra: Itisāmekāṃ Dadhadapi Nayan Kauśikīyāndharthanāyāṃ Svaṃ Vyakrīṇātṛnamiva Tathā Yassputraṃ Kalatram*

Sarala copper plate inscription from the Cola dynasty (11th century CE) refers to Hariścandra selling his wife

With folded palms, he said, 'Nārāyaṇa, the supreme, what more do I endure?'

As he wailed, Dharma, the devatā for righteousness, appeared. He hailed Hariścandra's commitment to truth. Confessing to have orchestrated the ordeal undergone by Hariścandra, Dharma added that it was all done to showcase Hariścandra's virtues to the world. Hariścandra was blessed to rule Ayodhyā again and to live with his family. Kauśika, the rājarṣi who reluctantly gave Ayodhyā back to Hariścandra who was also a rājarṣi, felt humiliated at the hands of Vasiṣṭha yet again. He left for Puṣkara along with his sons to perform tapasyā to gain the benevolence of Bramhā.

26

Saving Aṃbarīṣa's Yāga

In Ayodhyā ruled a rājā called Aṃbarīṣa. He performed a yāga under the guidance of Vasiṣṭha. Indra stole the sacrificial animal, as was his usual practice. The yājaka said, 'O rājā, your inattention to the yāga has resulted in this loss. This missing animal from the yāga will itself become a blemish on your rājya. Either the intended animal needs to be brought back or a human is to be sacrificed in its place.'

Aṃbarīṣa, realizing the magnitude of this lapse, went searching for a family that could barter one of its members in return for a thousand healthy cows. As he crossed various regions, he reached Bhṛgu-tunga[1], where Ṛchīka, the descendant of Bhṛgu, lived. He entered the āśrama of Ṛchīka ṛṣi. He asked if the ṛṣi could give away one of his three sons for the yāga. The ṛṣi, citing the need for the eldest son for the performing of the final rites on the ṛṣi's death, refused to part with him. The ṛṣi's wife, on the other hand, refused to give away the youngest of the three sons, whom she adored. Śunaḥśepa, the middle son, understood the situation his parents were in. He knew that his righteous father was not selling him away for the cows, and only sought to assist the rājā in the completion of the yāga. He

1 Mount Abu (1,220 metres), a hill station in the Indian state of Rajasthan.

volunteered to accompany the rājā to Ayodhyā and left the āśrama with the blessings of his parents. The retinue halted by the lakeside of Puṣkara because it was noon time. Śunaḥśepa reached the other side of the lake to offer arghya to Sūrya. He noticed his maternal uncle, Kauśika, in dhyāna. The boy said, 'Ṛṣi, I have no parents now. I have been chosen as the sacrificial animal in Aṃbarīṣa's yāga. I wish the yāga was complete without the sacrifice. Under these circumstances, it is only you who can save me.'

Kauśika, who sensed the pain of his nephew, looked at his sons and said, 'This boy has sought refuge in me. Protecting him has become my foremost duty. As sons, you are all bound to obey your father's words. I wish one of you would go to Ayodhyā with the rājā, in Śunaḥśepa's place.' Kauśika's sons did not accede to their father's command. They felt Kauśika was wronging his sons by agreeing to swap one of them with Śunaḥśepa. They equated this act of exchange to consuming dog's meat. This blatant retort angered Kauśika, who cursed his sons to be Caṇḍālas.

Into Śunaḥśepa's ears, Kauśika whispered the course to be adopted to save himself. The boy who was gladdened by the idea, left for Ayodhyā with the rājā. Upon reaching the nagarī, the officers in-charge gave Śunaḥśepa a customary bath. They draped him in red clothes, applied a red paste all over his body and garlanded him. The yājaka fastened him to the sacrificial post with a rope, muttering these words, 'This post is none but Viṣṇu, the supreme devatā.' This quickly reminded the boy of the esoteric mantras taught by Kauśika.

Śunaḥśepa, in the presence of Agni devatā said, 'This sacrificial post is none but Viṣṇu who is brother to Indra. You walked the land to protect Indra. You measured the worlds with your lotus-like feet. I see no other way to protect my life but by performing prapatti to you. I also perform prapatti to Indra, the bhoktā of this yāga.'

As the boy completed his prayers, the yājaka raised his sword to behead Śunaḥśepa, when Indra arrived on Airāvata, the mighty white elephant. He provided asylum to the boy, while bestowing the fruits of the yāga on Aṃbarīṣa. Śunaḥśepa thanked Kauśika immensely for providing the timely solution.

27

The Temptation of Kauśika

One day, when Kauśika had finished offering the morning arghya to Nārāyaṇa, he sat in dhyāna by the lakeside. He suddenly felt something brush his back, akin to the touch of a gossamer thin cloth. He opened his eyes to ascertain the cause of his distraction. To his amazement, he spotted a beautiful woman who was walking by the steps of the lake. The ethereal beauty of the woman captivated him so much that he willingly abandoned his tapasyā. His lust for her body blinded him to her identity. She was Menakā, the chosen agent of Indra.

The apsarā dived into the waters of the lake and as she swam, her graceful movements put the fish to shame. Every time she rose to the surface, Kauśika felt like he was struck by a flash of lightning. Such was the apsara's effect on him. As she slowly walked out of the waters, Kauśika approached her and said, 'O apsarā, you are drenched. You can visit my āśrama and dry your clothes.' The apsarā, who agreed, followed the ṛṣi to his āśrama. The ṛṣi surrendered to his carnal needs and his tapasyā was sidelined at the altar of lust. The several months that Kauśika spent with Menakā seemed like moments, as he was enthralled by her.

One day, Menakā informed the ṛṣi of her pregnancy. The ṛṣi then realized that his asceticism and the gains he had made had completely faded. He refused to support Menakā any further and left for Himālaya to continue his abandoned tapasyā. Along the valley of Himālaya and by the banks of river Mālinī[1], the apsarā delivered a baby girl. Menakā, who needed asylum, mercilessly abandoned the newborn child and left for Amarāvatī. The child, who was left in the hands of nature, was protected by the birds. Kanva ṛṣi of the Kaśyapa vaṃśa spotted this orphaned child, sheltered by the birds, near his āśrama.[2] He embraced her as his own daughter and called her Śakuntalā.

Kauśika's tapasyā in Himālaya fructified with Bramhā bestowing the title of mahaṛṣi on him. A dissatisfied Kauśika insisted that Bramhā confer the title of bramhaṛṣi on him. But Bramhā maintained that the title sought by Kauśika was reserved only for those who had conquered their senses. A dejected Kauśika retired to Ayodhyā to plan his next move.

1 A tributary of Ganga. Flows through the Indian state of Uttarakhand.

2 Haridwar, a city in the Indian state of Uttarakhand.

28

The Feud Continues

Ayodhyā was at that time ruled by a rājā called Mitrasaha. He had requested Vasiṣṭha to perform a yajña. After the completion of the yajña, Vasiṣṭha retired to his āśrama. He promised the rājā that he would return to the sabhā for lunch.

Kauśika knew of a rākṣasa whose companion was mistakenly hunted by Mitrasaha. He was also aware that the rākṣasa was waiting to avenge the death of his mate. Kauśika, who sensed the opportunity, instigated the rākṣasa to go in the disguise of Vasiṣṭha and request the rājā for human flesh. The rākṣasa did as Kauśika suggested.

The real Vasiṣṭha reached the sabhā and sat down for lunch. With his spiritual prowess, he was able to ascertain the presence of human flesh on his plate. This angered the ṛṣi, who cursed the rājā saying he would be possessed by a rākṣasa for some period of time. The rājā, who was unaware of the rākṣasa's guile, took a palmful of holy waters to curse the ṛṣi. The rājā's wife, Madayantī, stopped him from hastily reciprocating the curse. She reminded Mitrasaha that Vasiṣṭha was a bramharṣi who was to be venerated. The rājā, who realized his folly, poured the holy waters from his palms on his feet. The holy water burnt his feet. From then on, the rājā with spotted feet was called Kalmāśapāda.

The rājā harboured a secret antipathy towards Vasiṣṭha for all that had transpired between the both of them. This was sensed by Kauśika. One day, while Śakti, the eldest of Vasiṣṭha's sons, was walking by the fields, Kalmāśapāda walked down the same path in the opposite direction. The width of the causeway could allow only one person at a time. While the rājā asked Śakti to give way, the ṛṣi insisted that śāstras permitted only the kṣatriya giving way to a learned brāmhaṇa. With the quarrel on, Kauśika smelt an opportunity to take revenge on Śakti, who had refused to participate in the yajña that was conducted to elevate Triśaṅku to svarga. Kauśika deployed the rākṣasa to possess the rājā. Instantly, the rājā, who was speaking, whipped Śakti with the might of a rākṣasa. The ṛṣi, who couldn't bear the pain, died, like a large tree that falls when struck by lightning.

The rājā who came out of the trance, realized his blunder. He ran to the āśrama of Vasiṣṭha and unconditionally apologized to the ṛṣi for the slaying of his son.

Vasiṣṭha, who was shocked at the death of his son, succumbed to an irrevocable sadness. One day, he walked up a mountain cliff with the intention of jumping off its ledge and giving up his life. He tied his body with multiple cords and jumped. He fell into an overflowing river who, with her torrential waters, was able to shred his cords and land him on a sand mound. This river that took Vasiṣṭha's cords off was called Vipāśā[1] from then on. The ṛṣi constructed his āśrama[2] there. His suicidal thoughts were assuaged when he realized that his daughter-in-law, Adriśyantī, Śakti's wife, was pregnant with his son's child.

Meanwhile, Kalmāśapāda summoned Vasiṣṭha to his sabhā. The ṛṣi, who arrived, realized that the rājā of Ayodhyā was cursed by the wife of a brāmhaṇa to never be able to father a child through intercourse. Upon the insistence of the rājā, Vasiṣṭha impregnated Madayantī. Both Adriśyantī and Madayantī, who were pregnant

---

1 Now known as Beas. Tributary of Sutlej with a length of over 450 kilometres. Flows through the Indian states of Himachal Pradesh and Punjab.

2 Manali (2,050 metres), a hill station in the Indian state of Himachal Pradesh.

around the same time, experienced extended gestation periods. While Adriśyantī was patient and let nature take its course, Madayantī broke her amniotic sac using a stone. The son born to the rājā was therefore called Aśmaka. Adriśyantī, on the other hand, patiently delivered her son after an abnormally long pregnancy. This posthumous son of Śakti was called Parāśara.

Kauśika, who was disappointed at his failed efforts to trounce Vasiṣṭha, left for Draviḍa deśa to perform intense tapasyā.

29

Gāyatrī and the Making of the Bramharṣi

Kauśika sat for dhyāna by the banks of river Payasvinī[1] in Kañcī. As he closed his eyes, he heard the chirp of the kokila birds. One of them sat on the branches of the tree under which he was meditating, and crooned a melodious tune. This delighted the surroundings and Kauśika couldn't resist being an audience to it. An arresting apsarā walked out of the river waters. This caught the eye of Kauśika, who did not instantly give way to lust. He studied the situation with his logical acumen. It was neither springtime for the kokila birds to sing nor did the apsarā look native to the Draviḍa deśa. He realized that the apsarā was none but Rambhā, yet another agent deployed by Indra to disrupt his tapasyā. He discerned that Indra was wary of his spiritual progress and wanted to distract him yet again using a beautiful woman as a lure. In retaliation, Kauśika cursed Rambhā to turn into a stone and added that only remorse could undo the curse.

1 Now known as Palar. Length of over 340 kilometres. Flows through the Indian states of Karnataka, Andhra Pradesh and Tamil Nadu.

Kauśika reached a small hamlet[2] in the vicinity of the famed Kañcī. He collected darbha grass for his daily rituals. As he was plucking it, he realized that his earlier efforts were marred either by his wild lust for women, or by his hysterical anger. To tread the spiritual path, he decided that he had to himself get rid of both these evils. He sat at that very place, amidst the field of darbha grass and mumbled, 'Kāma, the desire, and Krodha, the anger, were the performers of the past acts. The jīvātmā in me is not a party to it. Let this havis be offered to Nārāyaṇa, the one who is beyond all distasteful desires and unruly anger.'

These prayerful lines transformed into a japa and brought a never-before experienced bliss to Kauśika. He continued, 'I adore the auspicious divine form of Nārāyaṇa who dwells within Sūrya. I pray that his splendour blesses me with quintessential knowledge.'[3]

The ṛṣis in the territory who were in tapasyā exclaimed, 'The Gāyatrī on Sūrya is finally born.'

Kauśika proceeded to a hillock[4] on the banks of river Bahudhā[5], and repeated the Gāyatrī several thousand times. On completion, he sat to eat the ball of rice that was offered as naivedya. Indra, in the guise of a brāmhaṇa, stood in front of Kauśika and shyly sought the food that the ṛṣi held. Kauśika, who treated this as vaiśvadeva, readily gave away the food to the brāmhaṇa. Soon he noticed Bramhā trek the hill, stand in front of him and say, 'Kauśika, you have conquered lust and anger. Your dhyāna is pristine now. You will live a long life. The "vaśat" sound in a mantra grants the fruit of performing a yajña to the practitioner while the "praṇava" grants the knowledge about Nārāyaṇa. Let the knowledge of these mantras along with Vedas and its ancillaries be vested in you. You are a bramharṣi now. Your pioneering of the Gāyatrī mantra on Sūrya will be remembered in the world. You will be known as Viśvāmitra, the world's best friend.'

---

2 Deepaprakasha Swami Temple in the Indian state of Tamil Nadu.

3 Rig Veda, 3.62.10.

4 Yoga Nrisimha Swami Temple in Sholinghur, a town in the Indian state of Tamil Nadu.

5 Tributary to Palar river. Flows through the Indian states of Andhra Pradesh and Tamil Nadu.

Kauśika, who was now Viśvāmitra, received the blessings with humility. As he walked into Draviḍa deśa, he met Vasiṣṭha[6] on the banks of river Kāverī[7]. Both of them greeted each other and Vasiṣṭha warmly said, 'Bramhaṛṣi, I am pleased to meet you.'

The long-drawn feud of many decades finally came to its end.

Viśvāmitra depicted with tuft and upavīta in the British Museum (UK) on a coin of the Audumbara dynasty (1st century BCE)

---

6 Dhenupureesvara Siva Temple in Patteswaram, a village in the Indian state of Tamil Nadu.

7 Length of over 800 kilometres. Flows through the Indian states of Karnataka and Tamil Nadu.

30

Raghu's Vaṃśa

Śatānanda said, 'Viśvāmitra is the best among munis. He is an embodiment of tapas. His strength is unfathomable. Just his presence alone in Mithilā is akin to receiving many boons.'

As the ṛṣi finished narrating the chronicles from Kauśika's life, the rājakumāras walked from the cowshed to the tent erected by Lakṣmaṇa. The rājā saw Śatānanda approaching and he rose from his seat. Taking leave of the bramharṣi, the rājā and his retinue performed a pradakṣiṇā around him. They offered arghya to Sūrya in the waters of Kauśikī river and departed for their rājya.

Viśvāmitra saw an additional love in the eyes of Rāma and Lakṣmaṇa, when they looked at him. Their actions were more respectful, and their words were more measured than ever before. The ṛṣi realized that his biography had been elucidated to them. He called the rājakumāras and said, 'Rāma, normally a person who adores another fails to acknowledge the contributions of his very own kin. I feel it my duty to elucidate the greatness of your immediate ancestors. Lend me your ears for this inspiring account.'

Dilīpa, a heroic rājā with the stature of a sāla tree, ruled Ayodhyā. His conduct conformed to the rules laid by Manu, the progenitor of the Ikṣvāku vaṃśa. Like the rightful dakṣiṇā that is inseparable from a sincerely performed yajña, so was king Dilīpa from Sudakṣiṇā, his wife from Magadha. After many years of wedded life, they were still not blessed with a child. Along with a retinue, the daṃpati started for the āśrama of Vasiṣṭha.

They noticed Vasiṣṭha, along with Arundhatī, was offering havis in the dakṣiṇāgni. Dilīpa and Sudakṣiṇā sought the blessings of the ṛṣi daṃpati. The omniscient ṛṣi said, 'Rājā, while you visited Indra in Amarāvatī last, you had neglected the presence of Surabhī, the divine cow, and Kalpaka, the wish-yielding tree. Preoccupied in administrative complexities, you forgot to perform a pradakṣiṇā around the wish-yielding duo. Their displeasure has caused you this unhappiness. Surabhī, at present, is in the abode of Varuṇa. You may thus offer your praṇāmas to Nandinī, her daughter who lives in this āśrama. Both of you must gladden the heart of Nandinī. This will be a prāyaścitta for your negligence.' The daṃpati agreed to follow Vasiṣṭha's words and stayed in the āśrama that night.

Next day, the rājā followed Nandinī to the woods. While he fixed his eyes on the cow that was grazing, a lion pounced on the cow. The traumatized rājā ran to its rescue. While releasing it from the lion's clutches, he offered himself in its place to the ferocious beast. The lion was liberated instantly from a curse leaving the rājā in shock. [1]

He brought back Nandinī safely to the āśrama. Vasiṣṭha revealed that the lion was a cursed rakṣaka of Śiva who received mukti at the hands of Dilīpa. He added that the rājā's love for

1 *Iha Samajani Bhūssarvyalokaikadīpa: Kṣapitabhuvanatāpassātrititāripratā pa: Ariyuvativilāpassphāritoddhāmkopa Satatavijayicāpa: Sphītakīrtirdilīpa:* Sarala copper plate inscription from the Cola dynasty (11th century CE) refers to Dilīpa

the cow compensated for his past negligence. Eventually, Sudakṣiṇā was blessed with a son who was called Raghu.

Once when Aśvamedha was conducted in Ayodhyā, Indra, the usual conspirer, stole the sacrificial horse by tying it to the rear end of his chariot. Raghu noticed this clandestine act of Indra and followed him till Amarāvatī. Raghu waged a war with Indra, and destroyed his army completely. Even when struck with the vajra of Indra, Raghu stood unfazed. This unprecedented valour impressed Indra, who wished to grant any boon but the sacrificial horse to Raghu. The intelligent rājā of Ayodhyā asked that the fruits of Aśvamedha be bestowed on him, even without the completion of the yajña. Indra granted the boon gladly. After showing his supremacy over the rājyas in Bhārata deśa, Raghu performed the viśvajit yajña. At the end of it, he decided to donate the accrued wealth among the needy. When all the wealth was distributed, a poor brāmhaṇa, called Kausta, approached Raghu. Kausta sought one crore gold coins that Kausta had promised Varatantu, his ācārya. The rājā, who did not want the brāmhaṇa to return empty handed, planned to attack the abode of Kubera. Knowing of Raghu's intentions, Kubera showered a crore of gold coins, thereby saving his abode from a dastardly attack. Raghu gave all the gold coins to Kausta. Raghu was succeeded by his son, Aja.

Aja was chosen by Indumati, the rājakumāri of Vidarbha, in a swayamvara. The daṃpati had a valorous son called Daśaratha.

One day, as the daṃpati were strolling in the garden, Indumati breathed her last, unexpectedly. Aja, in a melancholic note, left the rājya in the hands of his young son, Daśaratha, and retired to the forests.

Upon the completion of Viśvāmitra's tale, Lakṣmaṇa prodded Rāma in his ribs and spoke in a gratified tone, 'We must be proud to be born into this vaṃśa. Why don't we call the Ikṣvāku vaṃśa as Raghu vaṃśa?' On this note, they retired to bed.

31

Janaka's Bow and Paśupati's Mohaśāstra

Both Rāma and Lakṣmaṇa offered arghya to Sūrya in the early hours of morning and prostrated at the feet of Viśvāmitra. They requested him to elaborate on the history of the colossal bow they were to see in Janaka's assembly. Viśvāmitra obliged and began.

In an earlier epoch, Bramhā created a clone of himself and called him Svāyambhuva. Bramhā also had four other sons called Sanaka, Sananda, Sanātana and Sanatkumāra. The minds of Sanaka and his brothers were fixed on Nārāyaṇa. Their only interest was to understand mokṣa dharma and that sole preoccupation left them disinterested in other activities including sexual dalliances. They expressed to Bramhā their intention of remaining celibate. Bramhā was enraged by their decision. His uncontrollable anger made its way between his brows and fell on his lap in the form of a child. The child cried endlessly, as if to remind Bramhā to give him a name. Bramhā said, 'Do not cry. You are born to make those who propitiate you, suffer. Through their sufferings you will remove their pāpas. You are born to destroy the sorrows of the world. Praṇāmas to you who is angry and fearful.[1] You shall be called Rudra. You will be addressed as Śiva, the form of auspiciousness by your bhaktas.'

---

1 Taittiriya Samhita, 4.5.8.

Bramhā, with his mind fixed on Nārāyaṇa, fathered many sons. They were named Atri, Pulastya, Vasiṣṭha, Angiras, Pulaha, Kratu, Dakṣa, Bhṛgu, Marīchi, Nārada and Kardama. They grew as evolved individuals and diligently followed their father's commands. It almost felt as if Bramhā's eyes gave rise to Atri; his ears to Pulastya; his breathing to Vasiṣṭha; his mouth to Angiras; his navel to Pulaha; his right hand to Kratu; the big toe in his right foot to Dakṣa; his sensory touch to Bhṛgu; his mind to Marīchi; his ability to deliberate to Nārada, and his shadow to Kardama. Bramhā commanded these sons of his to procreate.

Svāyambhuva, the son of Bramhā, had his daughter, Prasūti, married to Dakṣa. The daṃpati had a daughter called Satī who was referred to as Dākṣāyaṇī, the beloved daughter of Dakṣa. She was pining for Śiva and observed a vow to impress Śiva who then agreed to marry her. Dakṣa, the father, too, agreed to give her in kanyādāna to Śiva. Their vivāha was a grand event and the daṃpati lived in Kailāśa.

Once, a yāga was organized by Atri, Vasiṣṭha, Bhṛgu, Marīchi and other ṛṣis at the confluence of the waters of the Gaṅgā and Yamunā. The place was called Prayāga[2], to commemorate the grand ritual. As the dazzling Dakṣa entered the assembly hall, the ṛṣis rose from their seats and so did Indra with the counterparts, as a mark of respect. Śiva, who was engrossed in dhyāna, did not rise. Feeling hurt at this defiance, Dakṣa said, 'I cannot tolerate ignorance and envy. Scholars who say "Śiva is auspicious" don't know that this statement is an oxymoron. Śiva has behaved deplorably. He, whose eyes are like the monkey, has married my fawn-eyed daughter and yet refuses to respect me, his father-in-law. He lives in the abhorrent crematorium with ghosts. He dances and laughs like a lunatic, stark naked. His adornments are skulls and bones. I don't wish to say anymore. He shall never partake havis like the Devas in a yāga, but shall consume only its residue.'

While Śiva sat patiently through the scene, Nandi who stood with red eyes, cursed that Dakṣa would lose his head soon. The brāmhaṇas who did not stand in Śiva's defence were cursed to remain poor.

---

2 Prayagraj is a city in the Indian state of Uttar Pradesh.

Amongst the ṛṣis who had assembled, an infuriated Bhṛgu got up from his seat and said, 'Śiva is unable to stop Nandi from making such disparaging remarks. His followers shall henceforth digress from the path laid down in the śāstras. His followers shall prefer vāruṇi and flesh. They shall become heretics, professing only the wrong doctrines.'

On completion of the yāga, while every attendant completed the avabhṛtha ritual, Dakṣa carried the memory of his insult home.

In Haridvāra[3], Dakṣa commenced a ritual called vājapeya. He appointed Vasiṣṭha as the hotrā, Angiras as the adhvaryu, Bṛhaspati as the udgātā and Nārada as the supervising Bramhā. Dakṣa followed it up with Bṛhaspati-sava, another yajña conforming to the śruti injunction that ordains it.

In Kailāśa, Satī who learnt from her sisters that Dakṣa was conducting a yajña said, 'O Śiva, the one who is adorned with nāgamaṇi. I constitute half your body in the Ardhanāriśvara form.[4] I wish to seek your permission to attend the ritual organized by my father.' Śiva cautioned Satī that her father had spewed venom on him like the rākṣasas who speak ill of Nārāyaṇa. He added that Dakṣa's conduct towards himself, a bhakta of Nārāyaṇa, was condemnable. He finally warned Satī that she would meet an insult at the hands of Dakṣa, a fate akin to death.

Satī, who was unstoppable, sat on Nandi with a lotus in her hand, a canopy over her head, and left Kailāśa. Neither was she welcomed respectfully nor was any havis offered to her consort during the yajña. None in the assembly but Dadhīci questioned Dakṣa's indifference to Śiva and Satī. Dākṣāyaṇī pointed out that Dakṣa was not insulting his son-in-law but one of the greatest yoga practitioners in the universe. She expressed displeasure at being the possessor of a body that had emerged from Dakṣa, who was known for his aversion to Śiva. She sat on the ground facing north in intense yoga. As she controlled her vital air, a burning fire engulfed her body. Those present stood

---

3 Haridwar, a city in the Indian state of Uttarakhand.

4 Ardhanarisvara Siva Temple in Tiruchengode, a town in the Indian state of Tamil Nadu.

in amazement oblivious of the holocaust that was to strike.

Śiva, who sensed Satī's death in Dakṣa's yajña, stood up with unprecedented anger. He threw down a strand of hair from his jaṭā. From it emerged a mighty warrior, Vīrabhadra[5], draped in tiger's skin, with eight hands. With erect ears, he had strong tusks and his mouth extended from ear to ear.

He was equipped with the bow of Śiva that was designed by Viśvakarmā. Impelled by Śiva's anger, the newly created dark-complexioned warrior started for the arena where the yajña was being conducted. As he entered the hall, the attendees ran helter-skelter. Vīrabhadra caught hold of Bhṛgu, and tore off his moustache. He plucked the eyes of Bhaga and broke the teeth of Pūṣa. He charged Dakṣa with his trident, beheaded him and threw the head in the sacrificial fire.

Bramhā arrived on the scene, and asked Vīrabhadra to calm down. The devas, led by Indra, became termites and started eating into the bow string held by the warrior. As the string severed, the bow extended till the skies.[6] Meanwhile, Bramhā ordered that the head of the sacrificial goat be attached to the torso of Dakṣa, while its beard was given to Bhṛgu. He added that Bhaga would be able to see through the eyes of Mitra and that Pūṣa would henceforth chew using the teeth of his śiṣyas. Dakṣa, who was granted another lease of life, apologized to Śiva for his misdemeanours.

---

5 Veerabhadra Siva Temple in Lepakshi, a town in the Indian state of Andhra Pradesh.

6 Aruna Prashnam, Anuvakam 5, Mantra 16.

Viśvāmitra reiterated, 'This celebrated bow of Śiva was handed over to Devarāta, who belonged to the vaṃśa of Nimi. And it is Sītā, Janaka's daughter, who will be given in vivāha to the one who displays his valour by restringing it.'

Vālmīki asked, 'Nārada, did the curse of Bhṛgu come true? And what cult did the followers of Śiva carve?'

Dakṣa venerates Vīrabhadra in Kamalapura Museum (Karnataka) sculpted in the Vijayanagara dynasty (16th century CE)

Nārada said, 'The curse of Bhṛgu was further strengthened by the curse of Gautama. Gautama had constructed an āśrama at Bramhagiri by the banks of Godāvari[7]. Even during famine, the fields close to his āśrama had abundant crops. A group of ṛṣis led by Śāndilya sought asylum in his āśrama. As the famine situation improved, Śāndilya and his disciples left the place without taking leave of their host and mischievously left behind an illusionary cow to tease Gautama. The ṛṣi, who saw the cow, sprinkled some holy water on it thinking it to be real. The cow fell dead, that very instant. Gautama realized that Śāndilya and his group had played a prank on him.

The enraged ṛṣi said, 'You all shall be banished forever from the sphere of vaidika existence and your practices shall be despised by its adherents.' The curse manifested in these ṛṣis who created a system with mystifying and antithetical doctrines. Gradually, practices such as holding skulls, smearing bodies with ashes of burnt corpses and consuming vāruṇi by these transformed ṛṣis were frowned upon by those who adhered to vaidika doctrines. Śiva, also revered as Paśupati,[8] wanted to honour the curses of Bhṛgu and Gautama—two vaidika purists—and created this mohaśāstra as the solution.'

7 Length of over 1,450 kilometres. Flows through the Indian states of Maharashtra, Chhattisgarh, Odisha, Telangana and Andhra Pradesh.

8 Pasupatinath Siva Temple in Kathmandu, the capital city of Nepal.

32

Bewitchment and a Broken Bow

Viśvāmitra, along with Rāma and Lakṣmaṇa, started for Mithilā. As they entered the nagarī, Lakṣmaṇa, in an undertone said, 'Rāma, look at the flag fluttering. Seems to me as if it is welcoming you, like a son-in-law is royally welcomed by his in-laws.'

Rāma stopped and stared at Lakṣmaṇa, while the younger one chuckled. As the ṛṣi walked to the sabhā, Rāma and Lakṣmaṇa were absorbed by an elephant duel taking place in the stadium. The duo later walked through the streets of Mithilā where Lakṣmaṇa noticed a variety of precious stones scattered on the ground. It seemed to him as if they were all collected from the seas when Agastya had once dried up their waters. He was astonished when the passersby paid no heed to the riches strewn around. Seated on platforms and pedestals, the women were chatting in large groups. As these young men walked, the eyes of those women were cast on them. Those who looked at Rāma's long arms couldn't proceed to his chiselled face. Those who eyed his lotus-like eyes refused to blink, unable to move their eyes from his. His feet that looked divine were absorbed in the minds of those who sought mokṣa. Rāma felt abashed as the ladies increasingly saw him with sensual eyes. He silently led Lakṣmaṇa into a byway.

As they entered, a faint sound of the veeṇā was heard. As they moved closer, the melody became louder. They heard a voice that said, 'Sītā, fetch the rolling ball from the balcony', and a jingling sound of anklets accompanied it. As Rāma looked up, a beautiful pair of hands threw open the balcony curtains. He saw a divine beauty in front of his eyes. A fawn-eyed girl, with tender skin, and coral-like lips kept looking at Rāma who was stupefied. Without blinking, they stood like statues. While Sītā's friends shook her, as if to bring her to consciousness, Lakṣmaṇa did the same to Rāma. As they walked away, Rāma and Sītā carried a visual memory of each other.

The rājakumāras slowly reached the sabhā. They were welcomed by the mantris who escorted them to the discussion chamber. As they entered with folded hands, Viśvāmitra gestured at them to be seated. The bramharṣi then said, 'Janaka, I wish the boys to see the bow.'

The rājā, aware that the bow was a nightmare to mighty kings in the past, did not want to scare the young lads with it. But denying any request of Viśvāmitra, he knew, was tantamount to a death wish. Thus, he reluctantly ordered the rakṣaka to fetch the bow.

With a creaking noise that filled the chamber, an eight-wheeled iron casket was dragged in by several musclemen. In it was the bow which had made many a rājā bite the dust. Viśvāmitra looked at Rāma and said, 'Child, you are the prized son of Daśaratha. I had promised to mother you. Instead you have alleviated my worries. I am incapable of reciprocating your kaiṅkarya. For now, I can only give you an opportunity to look at the celebrated bow.'

Rāma, who was adept in grasping nuances of speech and non-verbal communication, noticed the stress on the word 'look'. With measured confidence on his face, he strode majestically towards the bow. He unlocked the casket in style and bowed respectfully to the weapon, once held by Śiva. He delicately ran his fingers over it, just like Sītā used to caress the deer in her gazebo. He said, 'I wish to wield this legendary bow, and shall try taking aim with it.'

Janaka, excited on hearing these words of Rāma, agreed and rose from his seat. He was to be witness to history in the making. He had never before seen masculinity interspersed with humility in a kṣatriya as he was seeing in Rāma. The scion of Sūrya vaṃśa effortlessly lifted the bow with his left hand and clutched its middle. He strung the bow, and bent it towards his ear. The bow broke in the middle with a thunderous noise that sounded like praṇava to some. Mild tremors were felt in the surrounding regions too.

Rāma breaks the bow in Hazāra Rama Temple (Karnataka) sculpted in the Vijayanagara dynasty (15th century CE)

Janaka said, 'A girl desires a good-looking man. Here is Rāma, an embodiment of spotless beauty. A girl's mother desires bountiful wealth. Here is Rāma with priceless qualities, whose rājakumāras are his true wealth. And the kin desire a matrimonial connection with a celebrated vaṃśa. Here is Rāma, who comes from the vaṃśa of Bramhā, Marīchi, Kaśyapa, Vivasvān, Manu, Ikṣvāku, Vikukṣi, Kakutstha, Dhundhumāra, Prasenjit, Māndhātā, Tryāruṇi, Triśaṅku, Hariścandra, Rohitāśva, Sagara, Aṃśumān, Bhagīratha, Ṛtūparṇa, Mitrasaha, Aśmaka, Mūlaka, Dilīpa, Raghu, Aja and Daśaratha. Am I the most fortunate in this Bhūmi?'

33

Sītā and a Prophecy of Separation and Pain

Ūrmilā came running up to Sītā's chamber, panting for breath. Then, she walked silently without letting any of her anklets jingle. She stood behind Sītā and covered Sītā's eyes with her hands, the prank that she always liked to play. To her dismay, she found Sītā's eyes moist. She rushed to face Sītā and asked, 'Sister. When Rāma, the ideal man of our times has sought your hand, what worries you?'

Sītā said, 'I am afraid that the prophecies will turn true.' 'Prophecies?,' Ūrmilā quizzed. Sītā said, 'Yes. Let me tell you what happened last year. Śatānanda and a few other ṛṣis were holding a discussion with our father. They were discussing the divine characteristics of Nārāyaṇa and his auspicious form as discussed in the Vedas. I gatecrashed the discussion and sat on our father's lap. I realized that I was in for his wrath. Instead what happened afterwards amazed me.'

Ūrmilā asked, 'What happened then?'

Sītā continued, 'The ṛṣi said, this daughter of yours is an avatāra of Lakṣmī, the consort of Nārāyaṇa. Lakṣmī is the daughter of Samudra rājā, many say. It was her physique that was the basis for a śāstra called Sāmudrikā. I see your daughter, Sītā, as an exemplar of this śāstra. Look at the bees hovering around her curly tresses instead of circling their usual campaka flowers. The wavy hair on her broad forehead makes her face look like Candra on the night of aśṭami. A mirror can only reflect her blemishless face, not her inner glow. To her mercy-laden eyes, the eyebrows are their boundaries. Her perfect ears are a match to her sesame flower-like nose. It looks as if Kāma is dancing on her eyebrows, holding her nose as the balancing pole. Her pearl-like teeth that emit rays like the Candra are shielded in between her bimba fruit-like lips. Her feet bear the marks of Sudarśana, Pāñcajanya, Kaumodakī, Kalpaka, Dhvaja, Aṅkuśa and Vajra. She will be the rānī to a rājya. But be prepared to see her live in the forests too.'

Ūrmilā asked, 'Did you inform our mother about this?'

Sītā said, 'Yes. She was disturbed by this prediction. She summoned a vagrant fortune-teller. Invoking the name of Guhyāmbā[1], the lady confirmed that I would spend a lifetime in the forests. Adding fuel to the fire, I once forcibly held a male parrot while it was sporting with its mate. I am worried that I will be separated from Rāma, and if I will never see him while I am off to the forests?' Sītā then burst into tears. Ūrmilā promised to stand by her sister, if the prophecies were to turn true.

~

Vālmīki said, 'Nārada, these apprehensions of Sītā have turned accurate, during her exile in the forests with Rāma earlier and her lone exile now! She is in her fourth month of pregnancy. I pray that this is only a passing cloud, and that Rāma is beside her when she delivers.'

Nārada meditated on Janārdana and assured Vālmīki that she would bear valorous sons, and that eventually they would unite the parents. He asked Vālmīki about how the rājakumāras spent

---

1 Guhyeshwari Devi Temple in Kathmandu, the capital city of Nepal.

their time in Mithilā. Vālmīki stated that Viśvāmitra had escorted Rāma and Lakṣmaṇa to his chamber and narrated the life history of Paraśurāma to them. The brothers, without interrupting, listened to the bramharṣi who always acted in their interest.

34

Paraśurāma, the Brāmhaṇa-Kṣatriya

Ṛchīka, the sage, approached Gādhi, the rājā of Kanyākubja, and sought his daughter Satyavatī in kanyādāna. The rājā was wary of the ṛṣi's ripe old age and wanted to dissuade him from vivāha. He sought a thousand horses as white as Candra, with one black ear each, as dowry, from the ṛṣi. With the aid of Varuṇa, the ṛṣi paraded the horses in Gādhi's court. Impressed by Ṛchīka who kept his word and fulfilled such a difficult task, the rājā gave his daughter in vivāha to Ṛchīka. The daṃpati lived in an āśrama in Bhṛgutunga.

Bhṛgu advised Ṛchīka to beget progeny soon. To honour the ṛṣi's words, he planned a putrakāmeṣṭi. The news reached the ears of Gādhi's wife who also desired a valorous son for the rājya. Ṛchīka accepted the proposal of his mother-in-law and performed the yajña for progeny for both daṃpatis. At its culmination, he prepared a charu for the both of them. He advised his wife to embrace the uduṃbara tree, and his mother-in-law, the aśvattha tree after their post-menstrual baths. As he left for the nearby lake to offer arghya, the rājā's wife preferred to swap the charu given to her with her daughter's portion. Satyavatī hesitantly accepted the request. In a few months from then, the ladies were pregnant. The ṛṣi, through his spiritual prowess, realized that the charu vessels had been exchanged.

He divulged to Satyavatī that the charu meant for her, who was a brāmhaṇa's wife, was consumed by her mother, who was a kṣatriya's wife, and vice versa. The ṛṣi cautioned that her mother would deliver a son who would grow into a brāmhaṇa despite being born into a kṣatriya family. Satyavatī wished that her son remained a brāmhaṇa, while her grandson bore the responsibilities of being a kṣatriya. The ṛṣi was filled with misgivings but yet, agreed to the formulae.

Satyavatī delivered a son called Jamadagni, and two other sons eventually. Jamadagni lived a life of piety and rigour. He married Reṇukā, the daughter of Prasenjit, who ruled Ayodhyā. They settled on a hilltop[1], not very far from river Narmadā[2]. The daṃpati had five sons—Rumaṇwat, Susheṇa, Vasu, Viśvāvasu and Rāma. These sons were noble and conformed to the practices of brāmhaṇas. But Rāma became a maverick in due course. He used to pelt stones at mangoes to bring them down, while his brothers were busy reciting the vaidika passages. Rāma, also famous as Bhārgavarāma, sought the blessings of his parents and left for Kailāśa to acquire astras. He performed the pañcāgni tapasyā to invoke the blessings of Śiva.

Riding on Nandi, Śiva arrived at the spot. He blessed Rāma with powerful astras and said, 'Your anger is akin to mine when I destroyed Tripura, the three well-guarded fortresses. I shall give you my paraśu that was bestowed on me by Nārāyaṇa. With this in your hand, you will be dreaded for your unassailable archery. But your pride shall vanish when you come face-to-face with an avatāra extraordinaire.'

Rāma built an āśrama[3] on the banks of river Candrabhāgā[4] at the foothills of Himālaya[5]. His experiments in dhyāna did not yield him the desired results. To seek clarification from Śiva for his perturbed mind, Bhārgavarāma trekked the Kailāśa yet again. The entrance to

---

1 Janapav (880 metres) in the Indian state of Madhya Pradesh.

2 River with a length of over 1,300 kilometres. Flows through the Indian states of Madhya Pradesh and Gujarat.

3 Akhnoor, a town in Indian union territory of Jammu and Kashmir.

4 Chenab, a trans-boundary river across countries like India and Pakistan with a length of over 950 kilometres. Tributary to Indus.

5 Kashmir, a reference to the union territory of Jammu and Kashmir in India.

Śiva's bedchamber was guarded by Gaṇeśa, his elephant-faced son. The entry was blocked for all but Rāma wanted to be exempted and be allowed in. He clashed with Gaṇeśa and hurled the paraśu at him. The paraśu broke Gaṇeśa's left tusk and he became ekadanta, the one with a single tusk. In Kārttikeya's presence, Gaṇeśa and Bhārgavarāma struck a truce.

As Rāma returned from Kailāśa, Jamadagni learned of the happenings. He wanted the world to call his son Paraśurāma, henceforth. Jamadagni blessed Bhārgavarāma with a mighty bow that was once held by Viṣṇu. This bow of antiquity was handed over to Varuṇa, then to Bhṛgu and later to Ṛchīka. To Rāma who searched for his mother, Jamadagni said, 'Your mother has been banished from our āśrama. Let me narrate what transpired.

One day, I noticed that the pot of Narmadā water that she used to fetch everyday hadn't been brought to my yajña chamber. I learnt of her fascination with Citraratha, the rājā of Mrittikāvati[6], who was engaged in water sports with his concubines. Reṇukā developed voluptuary feelings for the man, and that delayed her return. I asked your brothers to behead her and they refused to do as I commanded. I cursed that she be a leper instead. Now that you have come, I command you to search for her, and behead her.'

Paraśurāma found his mother in the protection of a fisher daṃpati. To fulfil his promise, this obedient son beheaded Reṇukā, with a heavy heart. His paraśu was coated with his mother's blood while he was covered with guilt. He was unaware of any remedy for mātruhatyā. He heard an ethereal voice that said, 'Reṇukā devī[7] shall be worshipped by the human communities in this region. Paraśurāma, you must perform tapasyā to get rid of mātruhatyā.' Paraśurāma performed tapasyā on the banks of Lohitā[8], as directed.

---

6 Malwa plateau, spread in the Indian states of Madhya Pradesh and Rajasthan.

7 Renuka Devi Temple in Mahur, a town in the Indian state of Maharashtra.

8 Trans-boundary river across countries like Tibet and India with a length of over 200 kilometres. Tributary of Brahmaputra river.

Mūlamūrti of Reṇukā in Mahur (Maharashtra)

After gaining forgiveness through tapasyā, Paraśurāma returned to his father's āśrama to find it vandalized. As he made his way through the wreckage, he found his father lying wounded grievously. Paraśurāma placed his father's head on his lap and requested him to reveal the name of the culprit. The ṛṣi, in a faint voice, said, 'Rāma, I wanted to honour Kārtavīrya, the rājā of Māhiṣmatī[9] when I heard that he was hunting in our vicinity. He accepted my hospitality but turned greedy to possess our divine cow. He seized the cow and took her away to his rājya. I resisted but his cruel sons attacked me with weapons. Kṣatriyas, who are our guardians from rākṣasas, have now themselves become rākṣasas.'

With these final words, Jamadagni died. Paraśurāma performed the obsequies for his father. Like an erupting volcano, Paraśurāma, with an unabating fury, stormed into Māhiṣmatī, the rājadhānī of Haihayas. He challenged Kārtavīrya, a bhakta of Dattātreya, to a battle that ensued for many days. At its climax, Paraśurāma pounced on the rājā and axed his hands. The sons of Kārtavīrya attacked Paraśurāma, to avenge the death of their father. Sparing a few, Paraśurāma killed the remaining sons. He carried out a massacre on the kṣatriya kings belonging to twenty-one dynasties.

Barring those in his maternal Ikṣvāku vaṃśa, no other rājya could escape his paraśu's butchery. At the end, he performed tarpaṇa to his pitṛs in an area belonging to the kurus. This site of five pits filled with

9 Maheshwar, a town in the Indian state of Madhya Pradesh.

kṣatriya blood was called samanta panchaka[10] from then on.

Paraśurāma performed the avabhṛtha ritual in Sarasvatī[11] waters and summoned Kaśyapa to the spot. He donated the wealth and land accrued from killing the rājās to the ṛṣi. On his return from Kurukṣetra, Paraśurāma chanced upon Dattātreya who recommended prāyaścitta. He bestowed upon Paraśurāma the quintessential knowledge of paramātmā, jīvātmā and their organic relationship. The enlightened warrior retired to the banks[12] of river Vaśiṣṭhī[13] and performed tapasyā. Resolved to reside in a non-kṣatriya land, he crossed the Sahyā mountains to reach the western sea. As he hurled his paraśu, the sea waters receded to a distance. The reclaimed land became the seat of his austerities. He propitiated Śiva[14], his divine supporter, and retired to Mahendra[15] for tapasyā, yet again.

---

10 Kurukshetra, a city in the Indian state of Haryana.

11 (Extinct) trans-boundary river across countries like India and Pakistan.

12 Chiplun, a city in the Indian state of Maharashtra.

13 Flows in the Indian state of Maharashtra.

14 Vadakkumnathan Siva Temple in Thrissur, a city in the Indian state of Kerala.

15 Mahendragiri (1,640 metres), a hill in the Indian state of Tamil Nadu.

35

Janaka Initiates Wedding Plans

The rājadūtas of Janaka reached Ayodhyā in three days. They were duly welcomed by Jayanta and Vijaya. The rājadūtas were escorted to the guest quarters and were treated to a variety of the choicest delights from the royal cuisine. As they were chewing the tāmbula, the rakṣaka informed the rājadūtas that Daśaratha was ready to grant them an audience. The rājadūtas quickly rinsed their mouths and strode to the sabhā. With folded palms, the rājadūtas saw a valiant rājā seated on the throne of Ayodhyā. They offered their praṇāmas to him and sought his permission to read the letter sent by Janaka. Daśaratha assented.

> Greetings to you, Daśaratha. I hope this message is being read at the right time and finds you in good health. I am sure your realm will derive prosperity when you are the rājā.
>
> I pay my praṇāmas to Vasiṣṭha whose mantra we sing, 'ṛtviks sings praises on Sūrya when the morning breaks'.[1]

1 Rig Veda, 7.10.2.

I pay my praṇāmas to Vāmadeva, whose mantra we sing, 'Agni! whosoever sings your praise in the day, you rescue him from distress.'[2]

I am drafting this message in agreement with Viśvāmitra, whose mantra we sing, 'Agni, give us wealth in cattle and in offspring.'[3]

You and I are performers of agnihotra. We are fortunate to be blessed with such luminaries who guide us in sākṣātkāra. You must be aware that I had vowed to give Sītā, my daughter, in vivāha to the one who lifted Śiva's celebrated bow. But I was doubtful about the prowess of the kṣatriyas who attempted the challenge. That worry vanished when Rāma, your cherished son, walked into Mithilā. His unexpected arrival with Viśvāmitra was destined to bring me happiness. He lifted the bow amidst the mighty and won my daughter's heart. I am hopeful of your consent to this vivāha which Rāma wishes the most. I am confident that your blessings will rain happiness on the lives of your children—Rāma and Sītā, your daughter-in-law to be. I hereby solicit your presence with your spouses and sons. With Vasiṣṭha in the lead, I invite your retinue to Videha deśa. Abiding by the words of Śatānanda, our upādhyāya, I am signing off this nimantraṇa patrikā.

Janaka Sīradhvaja

Before the rājadūta took leave of the august gathering, Arthasādhaka presented him with a pouch of gold coins. Daśaratha, with exuberance writ all over his face, looked at Vasiṣṭha and Vāmadeva. He asked if both the ṛṣis favoured the alliance and they nodded in acceptance. He asked the ṛṣis to recount the history of Janaka, and of Sītā's birth.

2 Rig Veda, 4.2.8.
3 Rig Veda, 3.5.11.

36

Janaka and the Loving Daughters of Mithilā

Ikṣvāku had a celebrated son called Nimi. He requested Vasiṣṭha to be the ṛtvik of a yajña that he was to perform. But Vasiṣṭha sought a postponement, as he was committed to officiating in a yajña that Indra was performing. Nimi was conscious of the delay with every passing minute. Cognizant of life's instability, he performed the yajña with the remaining ṛtviks but without Vasiṣṭha. On his return, the bramharṣi was upset to note the yajña's completion in his absence. He cursed that Nimi would die. The ṛṣis assembled there requested Nimi to beseech mercy from the bramharṣi, but the rājā politely declined the proposal. He did not want the jīvātmā to languish in his material body any longer and facilitated its exit by meditating on the supreme Nārāyaṇa. The retas was posthumously extracted from Nimi's body to impregnate his wife. Eventually a child was born and he was called Janaka, the one with an atypical birth. He demarcated a country called Videha with Mithilā as its rājadhānī. He ordered that his successors prefix the word Janaka to their names. Like his father, Janaka, too, yearned for esoteric knowledge.

Once a famed ṛṣi called Māṇḍavya visited Mithilā. He was respectfully received by its rājā and was requested to discourse on sākṣātkāra. The ṛṣi who sat on a pedestal, asked Janaka to state his understanding of the subject. Janaka began, 'The object to which one is attached, becomes the cause of pain in due course. The thirst for wealth grows with its acquisition, like the cow's horn that grows with its body. When wealth is earned, it must be distributed cautiously. "I" is indicative of the jīvātmā. "I" owns nothing in this world. "I" resides in bliss. Even if the entire nagarī of Mithilā were burning, "I" will not ponder, as nothing that belongs to "me" will be burnt. Whatever that burns, is not "mine". A man who has received the knowledge of the jīvātmā and the material body, will start looking at all beings as the body of paramātmā. He becomes free of anxiety, and acquires brilliance like Candra. At the destined moment, the jīvātmā that has acquired sākṣātkāra, sheds the material body and travels to Vaikuṇṭha.' The ṛṣi who was to deliver a lecture received an exemplary explanation instead. He left the sabhā, showering blessings on Janaka and his rājya.

In the vaṃśa of Janaka, came Ḥrasvaroma. He was blessed with two sons. The elder son was called Sīradhvaja who was motivated to conduct the Aśvamedha, after hearing that Daśaratha of the same Ikṣvāku vaṃśa had also performed one. A few years later, he performed the putrakāmeṣṭi. On the next day, he visited the rice fields in his rājya. Upon the request of the farmers, he ploughed the field for a customary distance, creating a furrow. As he was reaching its periphery, the plough's end was caught in a metal string. The string led the rājā to a bamboo casket lying under the shade of a vilva tree. To his surprise, he spotted a beautiful child lying in it.

Her benign eyes resembled the petals of a fresh lotus, while the pink hue of her feet was rosier than the flower itself. The rājā genuflected and picked up the child smiling innocently in his arms. He thanked Bhūmi for gifting him with her most prized possession. Śatānanda hurried to the sabhā, as Janaka carried her in. He called her Sītā, to denote her rise from the plough's tip. She was often referred to as Jānaki, Vaidehī and Maithilī to remind her of her long-lasting relationship with the motherland. In due course Sunayanā, the rājā's wife delivered a girl child who was named Ūrmilā.

Kuśadhvaja, the younger brother of the rājā, showered his love on the girls, as if they were his own. Sudhanva, the rājā of Sānkasya[1], laid siege to the rājadhānī of Videha one day. He ordered that the bow of Śiva and the lovely Sītā be handed over to him. Kuśadhvaja, deputizing for his brother, fought fiercely with the intruder. As Sudhanva was defeated, Sānkasya was annexed to Videha. In the subsequent months, Kuśadhvaja was blessed with two daughters—Māṇḍavī and Śrutakīrti.

1 Sankisa, a village in the Indian state of Uttar Pradesh.

37

Four Brides for Four Sons

Daśaratha was overwhelmed when he understood that Sītā, his daughter-in-law to be, was none other than Lakṣmī herself. He ordered Arthasādhaka to use a portion of the money in the treasury to buy jewellery and clothes for the groom's family and kinsmen. He asked that the rubies of Bramhadeśa[1], the sapphires of Lankā[2] and the pearls from Draviḍa be used for studding the golden śibikā meant for Sītā. Vasiṣṭha hinted to Daśaratha with his fingers that three more such śibikās needed to be readied. Without demur, Daśaratha modified his order. He asked Dṛṣti and Aśoka to send the materials in advance, to avoid any shortages. The horses of Kamboja[3] were ordered to be harnessed to the chariots. Jayanta and Vijaya were asked to stock rations for the groom's entourage as they were to begin their journey. Vāmadeva requested that the utsava mūrti of Nārāyaṇa be taken to Mithilā. After the puṇyāhavācana was performed, the grand procession began.

1 Modern-day Myanmar.
2 Modern-day Sri Lanka.
3 Parts of modern-day Pakistan and Afghanistan.

With the ṛṣis in the lead, and their śiṣyas carrying pots filled with the Sarayū waters, they said, 'In these waters that shine like gold were born Kaśyapa, Indra, Varuṇa and Agni. Let these waters that wet the Bhūmi bring us bliss, strength and power. Let these waters purify us all.'[4]

The śibikā carrying the mūrti was followed by the rājā's chariot and his retinue. After a four-day journey, the procession reached the boundary of Mithilā.

Viśvāmitra, Gautama, Śatānanda and Janaka gathered in a small maṇḍapa that was erected. And they saw Vasiṣṭha, Vāmadeva, Jābāli, Mārkaṇḍeya and Katyāyana arrive. To an onlooker, it seemed as if the galaxy of nakṣatras was on a jaunt.

Holding the pūrṇakumbha, the welcoming ṛṣis said, 'Neither by karma, nor by having children and wealth, but only through prapatti is mokṣa attained. You, the ṛṣis, through an understanding of the upanishads perceive that Vaikuṇṭha is seated in the lotus of one's heart. The jīvātmā attains the paramātmā after the dissolution of the material body, you proclaim.'[5]

The ṛṣis showered lotus petals on the celebrated mūrti whose strong hands were marked by the welts of the Śārṅga. It was he who was seated in their hearts, they concluded.

Janaka, with Kuśadhvaja, advanced towards the chariot from which Daśaratha, the rājā, descended. Janaka garlanded him and said, 'We heartily welcome you to the vivāha of Sītā with Rāma. Your blessings shouldn't be restricted to Ayodhyā, as Mithilā is also yours. You are the foremost in our Ikṣvāku vaṃśa. You must initiate the rituals that are scheduled to begin tomorrow.'

Daśaratha replied, 'While I am just a kṣatriya, you are a rājaṛṣi. You are the knower of dharma. You are going to bestow upon us Sītā, the crowning jewel of Videha. How do I command you? Every ritual will happen under your guidance. And when there are bramhaṛṣis

4 Taittiriya Samhita, 5.6.1.
5 Maha Narayana Upanishad, 9.5–9.

like Vasiṣṭha and Viśvāmitra to guide us, I am sure this vivāha will be etched in our memories.'

Gautama advanced to the rājās and said, 'This momentous occasion has brought joy to all of us. I am reunited with Ahalyā. My sons, Śatānanda and Vāmadeva, are meeting me after a long time. I am indebted to Rāma for all this. I will feel blessed to narrate Lakṣmī Kalyāṇa, the way I have heard it from my ācāryas. Let this vivāha begin with this legendary account.'

Janaka, who agreed to this, summoned Sudāmana, the mantri who was supervising the arrangements. He ordered a grand maṇḍapa for the audience.

Viśvāmitra respectfully signalled to Daśaratha and said, 'You will be aware of Kuśadhvaja's daughters. I suggest Rāmā and Lakṣmaṇa marry the daughters of Janaka, while Bharata and Śatrughna marry the daughters of Kuśadhvaja. I have consulted Vasiṣṭha, who is also in agreement. If you find any merit in this, you may talk to Janaka and Kuśadhvaja.'

Daśaratha received an affirmative reply from both the rājās, and he was overjoyed.

After arghya, the audience gathered in the well-decorated maṇḍapa. On one side sat Daśaratha, flanked by his mantris. Behind him were seated his four sons. The other side had Janaka and Kuśadhvaja seated with their mantris. Behind them were Sītā, Ūrmilā, Māṇḍavī and Śrutakīrti. Vasiṣṭha walked to the centre of the maṇḍapa and said, 'We are in the presence of Viśvāmitra, Gautama, Jābāli, Mārkaṇḍeya, Śatānanda and Vāmadeva. Our blessings to the royal families. To seek the grace of Lakṣmī and Nārāyaṇa, we are going to listen to Lakṣmī Kalyāṇa from the adored Gautama. Let us pay attention and pray for the welfare of this world.'

38

Suras, Asuras and the Loss of Indra's Glory

Svāyambhuva gave his daughters Aditi, Diti, Kadrū, Danu and Vinatā in vivāha to Kaśyapa. The ṛṣi ascended the Meru and performed a yajña. He invoked the grace of Nārāyaṇa, the antaryāmī, to Sūrya. Impressed with his sincerity, Sūrya blessed him with his seven rays, namely aroga, bhrāja, patara, pataṅga, svarṇara, jyotismān and vibhāsa.[1, 2] A visiting ṛṣi called Dīrghaśruta saw this and exclaimed, 'You look like another Sūrya. You are able to see and foresee because of your tapasyās. You are called Kaśyapa, hence.'

The wives of Kaśyapa attended to the guest and they accompanied him to the pūrṇāhuti. Kaśyapa fervently said, 'Agni, please guide us in the right path. You, who can see through everybody's thoughts, kindly bestow auspiciousness on us. Chase away our pāpas. We offer praṇāmas to you.'

He eventually settled with his wives in an āśrama at the foothills of Himālaya.[3] Kaśyapa continued performing tapasyā on the banks of

---

1 Taittiriya Aranyaka, 1.7.1.

2 Multan is a city in Pakistan.

3 Kashmir in union territory of Jammu and Kashmir in India.

river Candrabhāgā. In due course, Aditi and Diti had energetic sons. Aditi's sons were referred to as Suras while Diti's sons, who weren't affable to their half-brothers, were called Asuras. Suras comprised Vivasvān, Pūṣa, Mitra, Aryamā, Bhaga, Indra and more. The Asuras had Hiraṇyākṣa, Hiraṇyakaśipu, among many others, to lead them. Hiraṇyākṣa and Hiraṇyakaśipu suffered ghastly deaths. Bali, the great-grandson of Hiraṇyakaśipu, guided the Asuras in their conquests. Danu, too, gave birth to mighty sons called Dānavas. Vipracitti, Svarbhānu and Vrśhaparva were some of the prominent Dānavas.

Indra performed a hundred Aśvamedha and ruled Amarāvatī. He married Śacī, a descendant of the Dānavas.[4] His opulence was boundless. The wish-yielding Cintāmani was at his doorstep. Kalpaka was at his backdoor and Kāmadhenu in his barn.

One day, he was heading to the forests on Airāvata, his four-tusked elephant. He chanced upon Durvāsa, who was carrying a garland of candana flowers. The ṛṣi said, 'Indra, here is the garland of Lakṣmī, the mother-divine. I was given this by an apsarā, and I thought of you as its fitting recipient.'

Indra, who acknowledged the ṛṣi's presence, prodded the elephant to lift the garland with its trunk. Airāvata, in a sudden spurt of rage, crushed the garland instead. Durvāsa, the ṛṣi known for his mercurial temperament, with reddened eyes said, 'Your arrogance is going to cause the loss of all your riches. Your hauteur will keep you and your province bereft of Lakṣmī's grace.' As the ṛṣi left, Indra was thrown to the ground by Airāvata and it disappeared into the woods.

---

4 *Ya: Pulomatanayāmiva Śakra: Parvatendratanujāmiva Śarrva: Kaitabhāririva Sāgarakanyāṃ Keraleśvarasutāṃ Upayeme*
Udayendram copper plate inscription from the Cola dynasty (10th century CE) refers to Indra marrying Śacī

In his mansion, the Cintāmani was gone while Kalpaka had started drying up. The fire of Bṛhaspati's agnihotra was extinguished, and the river waters started receding. The suras with Indra in the lead, headed to Satyaloka. They sought asylum under Bramhā, who said, 'There is no other recourse but to perform prapatti to Nārāyaṇa, the supreme.'

Bramhā rose from his seat, and said, 'Nārāyaṇa, you are venerated as the Puruṣa with a thousand heads, thousand eyes and thousand feet. You are all-pervading. You are present in the past, present and future. You are eternal. A quarter of this creation that is visible is the grace of Aniruddha, your form. What is unperceived is your prowess as Vāsudeva, Saṅkarṣaṇa and Pradyumna, which is the remaining three-quarters. Like fire that emerges from the arani sticks, so does mercy emerge from you. Show us the right path.'[5]

As he finished his homage, an ethereal voice roared, 'The kṣīrasāgara must be churned with Mandara[6] as the churning stick and Vāsuki as the rope. The suras need to deploy the sāma nīti with asuras and dānavas. Like a snake that knows how to treat a mouse when they are both caught in a niṣāda's net, so should this understanding also be. There shouldn't be any greed for materials that arise out of the waters. The suras will get only what they are destined for.'

5 Taittiriya Aranyaka, 3.12.

6 Mandara Parbat (220 metres) is in Banka District in the Indian state of Bihar.

39

Manthana and the Re-emergence of Lakṣmī

Upon Bramhā's advice, the suras arrived at the shores of kṣīrasāgara. They paid their praṇāmas to Kacchapa[1], the tortoise-king dwelling there. They said, 'To you it is a play-sport but to us, this manthana is our karma. We seek your presence in bringing Lakṣmī back.'

Saying this, they started for the rājya of Bali, a bhakta of Nārāyaṇa. Bali carefully listened to Indra and agreed to the proposal. But his asura and dānava chieftains insisted that they hold the frontal part of the snake, deemed auspicious, during the manthana. Indra instantly agreed and convinced the Suras to agree to holding the tail of Vāsuki. They all proceeded next to the base of Mandara, whose peak was surrounded by clouds.

Mandara was to be moved entirely from its base, an effort which left Kāśyapas, the sons of Kaśyapa, exhausted and unable to shift the mountain. Indra and Bali, anxious about the undertaking, prayed

1 Kurmanatha Swami Temple in SriKurmam, a village in the Indian state of Andhra Pradesh.

to Nārāyaṇa. In a flash, Garuḍa clutched Mandara with his claw and flew to kṣīrasāgara. It was dropped in an inlet of kṣīrasāgara, flanked by dvīpas on both sides. Suras reached one dvīpa, while their half-brothers reached the other. They watched helplessly as the mountain sank. Suddenly, the sinking halted and Mandara started rising from the waters. Bramhā revealed that the mountain was resting on the shell of Kacchapa, the mammoth avatāra of Nārāyaṇa. The multi-hooded Vāsuki swam into the waters, slithered upwards and coiled himself around the mountain.

The manthana began with vigour on both sides. The exertion was unbearable to Vāsuki who started spewing kālakūṭa on the cliffs. Soon kālakūṭa torrents flowed into the waters below. As a result, hālāhala was born. This lethal fluid, with its dark vapours, was suffocating those present. In such times of dire need, who but the benevolent Śiva could rescue them. With Nārāyaṇa as his antaryāmī, Śiva consumed the poison as if it was his share in the manthana.[2] Pārvatī's prayers nullified the potency of hālāhala, but couldn't stop the indelible blue mark that it cast on Śiva's neck, who was called Nīlakaṇṭha from then on. The Kāśyapas offered their praṇāmas to Śiva, who immediately left for Kailāśa.

Samudra manthana in Musée Guimet, Paris (from Cambodia's Prasat Phnom Da Temple) sculpted in the Khmêr dynasty (12th century CE)

A woman holding a pot of vāruṇi was noticed on the dvīpa. Bramhā recognized the woman with intoxicating eyes. The dānavas insisted that she be theirs and laid their hands on her. Bramhā

2 Rig Veda, 10.136.7.

felt reassured that Alakṣmī, the personification of inauspiciousness, had left the manthana. Meanwhile, the clouds showered copious rains to invigorate the Kāśyapas.

As Mandara was pressed from the top by Nārāyaṇa again, the manthana resumed. Many herbs, leaves, fruits and flowers like agniśikha, āmalakī, ashvagandhā, akṣastuśa, brāmhi, grihakanyā, guggulu, harītakī, haridrā, nimba, pippalī, śaṅkhapuṣpī and satāvari fell off the mountain into the waters. Kāmadhenu, the divine cow, returned to the cowshed in Amarāvatī while Kalpaka started sprouting everywhere. The Cintāmani was spotted by Śacī in her gardens, while the Kaustubha on Nārāyaṇa's chest looked resplendent. Bali, who saw Uccaiḥśravas, the white horse with a distinctive neigh, seized it for his use.

A ṛṣi in white dhoti, with leeches all over his body, walked by the shores and noticed a layer of rasāyana floating over the waters. He collected it in his kamaṇḍalu that rasāyana which could ward off diseases and indefinitely delay ageing. Bramhā offered his praṇāmas to Dhanvantari[3], the ṛṣi holding the kamaṇḍalu.

The Kāśyapas stopped the manthana and exclaimed, 'Here is amṛta that can make us all immortal.'

As he was chased, Dhanvantari disappeared into the mangroves.

The pursuing Kāśyapas reached a maṇḍapa where an apsarā was seated. She was totally blemishless. With one hand on the kamaṇḍalu, and the other on her wavy hair, she looked like an enchantress. Bramhā was unsure if she was his creation but looked at her feet which gave her away. Her lotus-like feet were marked with the signs of Pāñcajanya and Sudarśana. She was Mohinī[4], an avatāra of Nārāyaṇa.

She walked with an arresting gait and said, 'Kāśyapas, know me to be Mohinī. I live in these forests, extracting honey. I know you all

---

3 Dhanavantri Swami Temple in Thottuva in Ernakulam district in the Indian state of Kerala.

4 Jaganmohini Keshava Swami Temple in Ryali in the Indian state of Andhra Pradesh.

must be thirsty. Let me quench that, with whatever little I have in this kamaṇḍalu. You can sit in rows to help me distribute.'

It looked as if they were offering their eye-glances to her as they sat in rows. No one other than Vipracitti looked at what was poured into their palms. He knew that it was the same amṛta that was filtered by Dhanvantari in the manthana. He was unsure if any of it would be left for him and his brothers. He secretly shifted rows, while the rest feasted their eyes on the beguiling Mohinī. Nārāyaṇa, in his avatāra of Mohinī with eyes that were akin to Sūrya and Candra, noticed Vipracitti's dirty trick. With sparks flying, Sudarśana emerged at once with the brilliance of many Sūryas. In a wink, Vipracitti's head was floating in the air. A deadly yet inevitable silence ensued in the maṇḍapa.

Mohinī in Chennakesava Temple (Karnataka) sculpted in the Hoysāla dynasty (12th century CE)

Bramhā, who was overseeing this, said, 'Nārāyaṇa has punished Vipracitti for his dastardly act. But Vipracitti shall continue to possess the shadow cast by Bhūmi on Candra, and of Candra on Bhūmi, during grahaṇa. Rāhu and Ketu shall be his claim to fame.'

As he completed his sentence, the manthana sound was heard again. The Kāśyapas ran to the spot and found the manthana process happening without anyone being there.

Bramhā, who gazed at it, said, 'It is Nārāyaṇa who is doing it, in his avatāra as Ajita. We are all blessed to witness what is going to emerge.'

In Kailāśa, Pārvatī noticed that Candra on the locks of Śiva had gained his lost sheen. She asked, 'Candra with cool rays is here, but where is Lakṣmī, his sister?'

The manthana stopped, and from the waters emerged Lakṣmī, the mother divine. She arose as the daughter of kṣīrasāgara. With pushkalāvarta clouds bathing her and Airāvata showering petals, Lakṣmī looked like the personification of everything auspicious. As she walked into the dvīpa, she sighted Nārāyaṇa hidden among the Kāśyapas. She walked into the gathering, and unabashedly embraced him. As Nārāyaṇa held the palm of Lakṣmī, Bramhā performed the pāṇigrahaṇa for the daṃpati.

Indra said, 'You are inseparable from Nārāyaṇa, like the smell in a blossoming flower. Nārāyaṇa's eyes, like the black bees, hover around your lotus-like face, yearning for your madhu-like speech. Both of you, as a daṃpati, are the paramātmā. Praṇāmas.'

Lakṣmī flanked by elephants in the Varāha Cave Temple (Tamil Nadu) sculpted in the Pallava dynasty (7th century CE)

Vālmīki asked, 'Nārada, I am blessed to compile the details of the manthana. But I wish to know how Śiva survived the hālāhala, and how amṛta grants immortality. If Lakṣmī had emerged from the kṣīrasāgara, was Nārāyaṇa unmarried till then?'

Nārada said, 'Hālāhala did no harm to Śiva as he performed ācamana by repeating the names Acyuta, Ananta and Govinda. This manthana saw many avatāras of Nārāyaṇa like Kacchapa, Mohinī, Dhanvantari and Ajita. Lakṣmī's rise from kṣīrasāgara was just another avatāra of hers like how she was born to Bhṛgu as Bhārgavi[5] in olden times. Nārāyaṇa is eternally present with Lakṣmī, his consort.

'Kāśyapas mistook the rasāyana for an immortality-granting fluid. They were ignorant that the jīvātmā is immortal while the material body is perishable. Their greed to survive eternally with their physical bodies continues, and their search for amṛta isn't over. Dhanvantari, on the other hand, taught this skill of brewing the rasāyana to ṛṣis, among others. I was once told by Bramhā jokingly that the manthana relieved Kacchapa of his backache. Later, he confessed to me that manthana was the state of contemplation and Kacchapa who supported it was the paradigm to controlling one's senses.

'Vālmīki, you are immensely blessed by Kacchapa, else how could you have won over your senses?'

---

5 Bhargavi Devi Shrine in Tiruvaheendrapuram in the Indian state of Tamil Nadu.

40

Pāṇigrahaṇa

Reminiscing about the Lakṣmī kalyāṇa narration which had captivated them, the rājakumāras and rājakumārīs retired to their apartments. The next morning, Vasiṣṭha ascended the dais[1], the entrance to which was flanked by banana trees with flowers pointing downwards. Agni, the sacrificial fire, was welcomed into the vedikā. The ceremony began with an ankurārpaṇa ritual where five earthen pots were placed on a bamboo plate. In the centre was the pot for Bramhā, while those in the corners were representatives of Indra, Yama, Varuṇa and Soma. Each of those was filled with an admixture of canaka, grāmajaniśpāvi, godhuma, masura, tandula, tila, vājibhojana and more grains. Waters were sprinkled over them and the excess drained through the pores at their bottoms. They were allowed to sprout for the next couple of days.

Rāmā and his brothers underwent intense learning of Yajur Veda and Dhanur Veda under Vasiṣṭha's supervision. Their sincerity was endorsed by Viśvāmitra, another bramharṣi. The samāvartana ritual was performed to mark their graduation. To the existing set of upavīta hanging over their shoulders, another was added to point to

1 Janakpur, a town in Nepal.

their transition to gṛhasthāśrama. Daśaratha gave away a thousand cows to the needy in the names of all his sons while Janaka and Kuśadhvaja gave away cows, land and gold in the names of their daughters. Daśaratha also performed the nāndi shrāddha to seek the blessings of pitṛs.

On the day of Uttaraphālguni[2], the nakṣatra that is ruled by Aryamā, the rājakumārīs were led to the dais by their fathers holding their hands. They were draped in white silk sarees embroidered in red thread and gold zari all over. They were bedecked in necklaces that had embellished haṃsa and peacock motifs. Their diamond ear-studs and ruby-studded bangles matched their anklets fitted with pearl drops. Their heads were adorned with tiaras, which were gilded in gold and silver. Though beautified with such exquisite ornaments, their eyes darted hither and thither searching for their fiancés.

Just then, to the beating of the drums and blowing of the conches, Rāma and his brothers marched into the maṇḍapa. With long arms, broad chests and chiselled faces, they looked like devas. Janaka and Kuśadhvaja escorted their sons-in-law to the dais.

Janaka walked Sītā to Rāma, and said, 'Many might have paid you this tribute, but hear this from me. Rāma, your valour was visible to us when you lifted the bow of Śiva, effortlessly. The women who have seen you in our rājadhanī, have been suffering from pangs of love. You are a perfect blend of prowess and charm. Here is my daughter, Sītā. Like gold that is mined from Bhūmi, so was she gained by me. That she is my daughter is what most believe. They are unaware that I worship her as the very Lakṣmī. And today, she is the bride who will be given in vivāha to you. The rājās of this deśa are referred to as Janaka. They are expected to be detached individuals, and the words "me", "my" and "mine" are abhorred. Today, *I* say, 'Rāma, here is my daughter, Sītā'. This is not to defy them but to proclaim how much she means to me. Rāma, hold her hand in love. She will be your better

---

2 12 January, 5103 BCE, Piṅgala saṃvatsara, Caitra, Śuklapakṣa, Trayodaśi tithi, Uttaraphalguni, Thursday.

half. She will guide you on the right path, and shall journey with you. Never forsake her. May all that is auspicious happen to both of you.'

As Janaka finished his words, he poured water into Rāma's palm that was crossed over with Sītā's, to mark the pāṇigrahaṇa ritual[3]. Subsequently, Ūrmilā was married to Lakṣmaṇa, Māṇḍavī to Bharata and Śrutakīrti to Śatrughna.

Sītā's vivāha to Rāma with Daśaratha, Janaka and Viśvāmitra by their side in Ramaswamy Temple (Tamil Nadu) sculpted in the Nāyaka dynasty (16th-17th century CE)

Vasiṣṭha asked Rāma to bend over and help Sītā take seven steps while gently holding the big toe of her right foot. As taught by the ṛṣi, Rāma, looking at Sītā, said, 'May Viṣṇu guide us to sustained nourishment, in the first step. May Viṣṇu guide us to robust health, in the second step. May Viṣṇu guide us for uninterrupted prosperity and thereby security. May Viṣṇu bless us for consummate bliss. May Viṣṇu bestow on us worthy progeny. May Viṣṇu show us various enjoyments at

3 Rig Veda, 10.85.36.

different stages. May Viṣṇu make our friendship long-lasting. Let us be united in our thoughts and actions, in these seven steps.'

His brothers repeated this ritual of saptapadī, an oath of inseparable friendship and companionship. Rāma, with his ring finger, applied kuṅkuma on Sītā's forehead, and said, 'I invite the devas to congratulate you, who is auspicious. May they wish us a happy married life.'[4]

And he looked into her eyes and said, 'We must never be hostile to each other. We must be devoted to Nārāyaṇa, the supreme. We must be respectful to our elders and kind to creatures.'[5]

Rāma, with his palms cupped below those of Sītā, offered puffed rice into the vedikā. Vasiṣṭha prayed, 'Aryamā, who is anointed with milk, make the bride and the groom one-minded.'[6]

Sītā said, 'Let my husband live for a hundred autumns. I offer these to you.'[7]

As lāja homa was completed, Vasiṣṭha asked Rāma to hold Sītā's hands and perform pradakṣiṇā around the vedikā thrice.

The ṛṣi said, 'Agni, may you unite the bride with the groom for future progeny.[8] Bless them with long life and energy. May they live for a hundred autumns.'[9]

The ṛṣi led the newly married daṃpatis to an open field and asked them to offer their praṇāmas to Sūrya. He asked Sītā and her sisters to get into their respective śibikās, the ornate bridal palanquins. As they mounted, Vasiṣṭha said, 'May this procession of the bride, who is as radiant as Sūrya, with her husband be blissful.'[10]

With Sītā's departure, Mithilā lost its crest-jewel, while Ayodhyā gained an unsurpassable fortune. Carts with ravishing jewellery in gold, silver, pearls and corals, and more cartloads of embroidered

---

4 Rig Veda, 10.85.33.
5 Rig Veda, 10.85.44.
6 Rig Veda, 5.3.2.
7 Atharva Veda, 14.2.63.
8 Rig Veda, 10.85.38.
9 Rig Veda, 10.85.39.
10 Rig Veda, 10.85.20.

shawls and exquisite sarees followed the śibikās. As the cavalcade left Mithilā, many handmaids sent by Janaka to assist the rājakumārīs followed them.

~

Vālmīki said, 'I will need many births to vividly describe this grandeur. But I would like to know which kind of vivāha would this be classified under. And when Bharata is elder to Lakṣmaṇa, how was pāṇigrahaṇa performed for the latter first?'

Nārada said, 'As Rāma was asked to lift the bow to showcase his valour, this is not a prājāpatya vivāha. But it is a brāmha vivāha as it took place after the samāvartana ritual. Bharata and Lakṣmaṇa were not sons of the same mother and thus the rule of precedence doesn't apply. Chiefly, in a pāṇigrahaṇa ritual, the right is always vested in the bride's father.'

41

Ayodhyā Celebrates Even as Paraśurāma Is Humbled

With his sons beside him, Daśaratha looked like a man who had attained all the four puruṣārthas. As the procession approached the outskirts of Ayodhyā, female jackals howled while a flock of crows screeched. As Daśaratha looked left, he saw a herd of deer dashing away and the opposing winds racing towards them and battering the flagpoles on the chariots. The rājā requested Vasiṣṭha to interpret the nimitta around. The bramharṣi warned Daśaratha of an impending hurdle, but assured him of being able to overcome it with divine intervention.

As he finished, the ṛṣi noticed Paraśurāma standing at the gate, with a rudrākṣa garland around his neck, the upavīta around his shoulder and the mighty bow of Viṣṇu in hand. Daśaratha walked up to him and said, 'I am blessed to have the scion of Bhṛgu vaṃśa in our rājya.'

Paraśurāma did not pay heed to Daśaratha, an indifference which only emphasized his hatred for kṣatriyas. He instead roared, 'Let that Rāma of Sūrya vaṃśa who thought it heroic to break a brittle bow, stand up and face me.'

Daśaratha's pleas to Paraśurāma to show mercy to his sons went unanswered. The latter said, 'One of your ancestors hid behind women to escape my paraśu. He was called Nārīkavaca. Today, I know you are married. You can still follow the tradition, or….'

Rāma quipped, 'Or?'

Paraśurāma showed his bow, and gestured to Rāma to string it. Rāma respectfully took the bow and strung it like it was child's play. He fitted an arrow and asked whom he should take aim at. Paraśurāma couldn't believe his eyes and hung his head in shame. Though impressed with his śiṣya, Vasiṣṭha's face remained impassive.

Looking at Paraśurāma, Rāmā said, 'You are the son of Jamadagni, an eminent ṛṣi. Your mother is Reṇukā, the devatā of the poor. You are a bhakta of Śiva, the best among vaiṣṇavas. Yet, your uncontrollable anger and hatred for kṣatriyas has lowered your stature. Despite my father's prapatti, you remain unmoved. For the massacre that you carried out on kṣatriyas, I will not mind killing you and even incurring the bramhahatyā. But, I will desist from killing you since you are related to Viśvāmitra who showered love on us. I only now comprehend why he retired to Himālaya after my vivāha. He probably did not want to be embarrassed by meeting you. And I am surprised that you, of all people, should talk about heroism.

'Well, what should I aim at?'

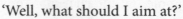

Paraśurāma said, 'You are holding this bow like Viṣṇu held it in the past. Kindly aim at my prowess accrued by tapasyā. And destroy Atula, the asura who has possessed me for long.'

Rāma, the one with the calm demeanour, did all that Paraśurāma asked, in an instant. Returning the bow to Varuṇa, Paraśurāma retired southwards of Mahendra for tapasyā.

Daśaratha was delighted with the departure of Paraśurāma. He embraced Rāma and planted a kiss on his forehead. He looked at Rāma just as a mother would look at her children's saviour.

Sumantra welcomed the rājā and congratulated him on the vivāha of his sons. The streets of Ayodhyā were strewn with flowers and the sounds of drums were reverberating in all directions. Kausalyā, Kaikeyī and Sumitrā stood with the hārati plates to welcome their daughters-in-law, who all resembled Lakṣmī, with their beautiful smiles and golden hue.[1] As the gṛhapravēśa ritual ended, Sītā and her sisters reached the maṇḍapa, where abhiṣeka was being performed to Nārāyaṇa. They noticed their husbands reciting vaidika passages alongside. In the end, turmeric waters were poured on the mūrti, covered in tulasī.

Mārkaṇḍeya ṛṣi stood near the mūrti with hands folded in prayer. He said, 'Nārāyaṇa, you once asked me, "Who are you? Whom do you belong to?" and I said, "I am the jīvātmā, and I am its sole owner." In turn you swore on the vedas that the jīvātmā belonged to you. To reaffirm your claim, you stood in clothes soaked in turmeric waters with a tulasī garland, just like today. I beseech you to bless these newly married daṃpatis.'

As he finished, the curtain was drawn around the mūrti so that he could be decorated with flowers and adorned with ornaments. Vasiṣṭha requested Mārkaṇḍeya to utilize the interval to narrate the avatāra of Nṛsiṃha. The ṛṣi acquiesced at once since it was the nakṣatra of Svāti on that very day, and took his seat to begin his discourse.

---

1 Rig Veda Khila, verse 4.

42

Hiraṇyakaśipu

Kaśyapa once performed an Aśvamedha at Puṣkara. Five seats plated in gold were kept ready. The eldest son born to Kaśyapa and Diti crawled up to the vedikā and sat on the fifth seat meant for the hotrā. He was called Hiraṇyakaśipu from then on. He had a brother, younger than him, who was called Hiraṇyākṣa. They were fond of each other and learnt the vedas under Kaśyapa's tutelage. After the samāvartana ritual, Hiraṇyakaśipu was married to Kayādhu and Hiraṇyākṣa to Ruṣābhānu. They established their rājadhānī on the banks of Candrabhāgā.

One day, the mutilated body of Hiraṇyākṣa was brought to the sabhā. Hiraṇyakaśipu was deeply saddened by the demise of his brother and performed the obsequies. He walked to Ruṣābhānu and said, 'My brother was a personification of valour. Do not lament over his death. What has left his material body is the eternal and imperishable jīvātmā.'

After these consoling words, he left the ladies' apartments only to learn that Varāha, an avatāra of Nārāyaṇa, had killed his brother. Hiraṇyakaśipu gradually developed a repugnance towards Nārāyaṇa. He stopped patronizing rituals and started detesting brāmhaṇas. He left for Himālaya for tapasyā, only to return in a couple of days.

That night, while he was making love to Kayādhu, she hesitantly asked the reason for his speedy return from the mountains. The asura said, 'A brāmhaṇa sat under the same tree, where I was performing tapasyā. He repeated the aṣṭākṣara of Nārāyaṇa. Feeling irritated, I returned.' As he was speaking, he discharged his retas in Kayādhu.

In the subsequent month, the asura set out for Mandara for tapasyā, bidding farewell to his pregnant wife.

Realizing Hiraṇyakaśipu's absence, Indra seized the opportunity to wreak havoc on his rājya. He invaded the quarters of Kayādhu and forcibly held her. As she swooned, he carried her off into the woods. Nārada stopped Indra and said, 'Kayādhu has committed no crime. You will incur an irrevocable pāpa by abducting the pregnant wife of another person. Make haste, and release her.' Indra agreed with Nārada and escorted her to Nārada's āśrama.

Nārada provided all comforts to Kayādhu. He asked her to consume the prasāda that was offered as naivedya to Nārāyaṇa. He conducted the puṃsavana ritual for Kayādhu, just like a doting father. As he played the veeṇa, he said, 'Sarasvatī, the inhabitants of Sālva rājya living on your banks, praise the son of Yugandhara as their rājā.[1] Bless this child of Hiraṇyakaśipu as well.'

He called the inmates of his āśrama and said, 'Now is a good muhūrta to explain the gist of aṣṭākṣara. Sit and listen. The mantra comprises praṇava with one akṣara, followed by namaḥ and Nārāyaṇa words with two and five akṣaras. Praṇava in turn comprises three sounds, "a", "u" and "m". The "a" sound is indicative of paramātmā who is endowed with attributes such as jagatkāraṇatva that denotes his power to create the universe, jagatrakṣakatva that denotes his power to protect the universe, sarvajñatva that denotes his omniscience and sarvaśaktitva that denotes his prowess. The "m" sound is indicative of jīvātmā that is personified knowledge, endowed

1 Somaraja Stuti.

with attributive knowledge too. The jīvātmā is the body to paramātmā and this inseparability is indicated by the "u" sound.' As he paused, he noticed a glow in Kayādhu's face. He was gladdened by the realization that the unborn child must have also enjoyed the elucidation just as his mother had. Subsequently, Kayādhu delivered a boy who was named Prahlāda by the ṛṣi.

43

The Devout Son of an Invincible Asura

Hiraṇyakaśipu stood on one foot with arms upwards. His tapasyā became more intense by the day, and gave Indra the jitters. Bramhā took notice of the fierce tapasyā undertaken by the asura and appeared in his presence. He sprinkled water from his kamaṇḍalu on the frail asura who looked dehydrated. Bramhā said, 'Hiraṇyakaśipu, you have invoked my appearance. What wish of yours needs to be fulfilled? Spell it out.'

The asura, strengthened by the holy waters, offered his praṇāmas to Bramhā, his great-grandfather. He said, 'You are venerated as Prajāpati for creating us all. The ṛṣis have wronged by crediting Pradyumna for all that is seen. The "ka" letter points to you. Himālaya exists because of you, and so does the Samudra.[1] You are venerated as Hiraṇyagarbha, the one who permeated the golden egg-like creation. Kindly grant me the boon of not dying during the day or night; within or outside the sabhā; in space or on Bhūmi; at the hands of any human, animal, snake or deva.'

In a flash, Hiraṇyakaśipu was reminded of Vasiṣṭha's curse on him, that he must be killed by a non-existing creation. This disturbed the

1 Rig Veda, 10.121.4.

asura who mulled over it and continued, 'I must not die in the hands of anything that is animate or inanimate. It must neither be wet nor dry. I must not die in the hands of anything created by you.'

Bramhā granted Hiraṇyakaśipu his boons, as desired.

The asura was welcomed on his return by his mantris with great pomp and splendour. He was delighted to see Prahlāda crawling towards the toys in his mother's apartments. He cuddled and kissed his son on the forehead. In due course, Hiraṇyakaśipu had three sons—Hlāda, Anuhlāda and Samhlāda. The asura wished that his sons also carried his hatred for Nārāyaṇa. He commanded Śaṇḍa and Amarka, the sons of Śukra, to tutor his sons. While the little boys left for their education, Hiraṇyakaśipu became the rājā of his neighbouring regions by subduing them using force.

Prahlāda, at a young age, developed bhakti towards Nārāyaṇa. He woke up before his playmates and meditated on the divine mūrti of Nārāyaṇa. A halo surrounded him and that attracted his classmates, who sat close to him. Prahlāda opened his eyes and said, 'Human life is a hundred years. Half of it is exhausted in sleep, and in the remaining years, we remain irreproachable infants, vexatious boys, flirtatious adolescents, helpless gṛhasthas and decrepit elders. When will we experience sākṣātkāra? Only if we control our senses will the desire to acquire knowledge arise. This will lead us in the path of bhakti.'

Prahlāda, in his dulcet voice, continued, 'Bhakti is like a garden that needs to be watered and nurtured. Passionate listening to Nārāyaṇa's glory, fervent chanting of his names and continuous remembrance of our antaryāmī is the doorway to bhakti. Kaiṅkarya to his bhaktas with folded palms is mandatory. Servitude to Nārāyaṇa should gradually blossom into friendship. And performing prapatti is the zenith.'

The audience was spellbound while the overhearing ācāryas were appalled. Śaṇḍa and Amarka took Prahlāda to Hiraṇyakaśipu who was excited to see his returning son. He seated him on the lap and asked, 'What did you learn in the āśrama, my dear?'

Prahlāda, with folded hands, said, 'I pray to Nārāyaṇa, the cause of everything that exists, but is without a cause himself.' With eyes positioned at his father, he continued, 'The one who is antaryāmī to you and me is our foremost ācārya. He is subtler than the jīvātmā and permeates him. He is free of karma and dhyāna leads to sākṣātkāra. Then, the jīvātmā that is unshackled from karma attains mokṣa.'[2]

The asura, with eyes blazing like fire, looked at Śukra's sons, who trembled. They promised that nothing of what Prahlāda spoke was ever taught to him by them.

2 Svetasvatara Upanishad, 3-20.

44

Nṛsiṃha and His Mantra

Hiraṇyakaśipu thought to himself, 'This son of mine, is an enemy in the making. To the one who undergoes tapasyā, his uncontrolled senses are his biggest enemies. Like the infected limb that needs to be amputated for the welfare of the body, so should this boy also be killed.' He ordered that the rākṣasas take away Prahlāda and kill him in some way or the other.

The rākṣasas, with frightful faces, coppery beards and sharp teeth, reached Prahlāda's cottage. They dragged the little boy, who was just over five years of age, to a precipice. They hurled him from its top and went away guffawing. As they descended the rock face, a sweet voice reciting the name of Nārāyaṇa was heard. And lo, it was Prahlāda.

They asked him, 'You fiend, how did you survive?'

Prahlāda said, 'What harm will I incur when Bhūmi carries me in her arms that are like pastures.'

The rākṣasas held the boy hostage again. They extracted the poisonous juice from the leaves and roots of the karavīra plant. The rākṣasas fed the boy with this extract, with no guilt on their faces. They threw him onto a path regularly used by wild elephants and returned to the sabhā. They vividly described Prahlāda's last moments for the pleasure of the stony-hearted asura.

The next day, as Hiraṇyakaśipu was taking stock of the treasury, into the sabhā walked Prahlāda, yet again. Every tender step of this lad stirred a tremor in the asura's heart. He enquired how his son had found his way back. The boy said, 'I felt dizzy after consuming the juice given by the rākṣasas. Soon after I had drunk it I also noticed a herd of elephants trampling on everything they saw on their way. I invoked the grace of Sudarśana, the rounded wheel that protects even a child like me, who seeks his presence.[1] I fell unconscious, and woke up only with the rise of Sūrya.'

Hiraṇyakaśipu concluded that it was Nārāyaṇa who was protecting his son. He asked, 'Dear Prahlāda, tell me the whereabouts of Nārāyaṇa?'

The boy said, 'There is no place in this universe where he is not present. There is no period of time which hasn't seen him. He, who pervades in you and in me, is beyond space and time.'

Rays of the evening Sūrya started creeping into the sabhā. Hiraṇyakaśipu was enraged that he was facing defeat at the hands of his very own son. Prahlāda's unshakable bhakti towards Nārāyaṇa fueled the asura's anger. He picked up his mace and ran towards one of the sabhā's pillars. As he struck it, a tumultuous sound was heard in all quarters. While Bramhā knew the end of Hiraṇyakaśipu was near, he couldn't determine what would bring that about.

The asura saw a unique creation in front of his eyes. With the head of a lion and the body of a human emerged Nṛsiṃha, an avatāra of Nārāyaṇa. His eyes looked like molten gold; his mane shone like Sūrya; his tongue swirled like a sword; his ears stood erect like pillars; and his nostrils blew hot air like a vedikā during the pūrṇāhuti. The roar was terrifying and unbearable.

Hiraṇyakaśipu hurled his mace at Nṛsiṃha, who effortlessly crushed it. Nṛsiṃha dragged the asura to the doorway of the sabhā. He sat on its step, with the asura on his lap. A deafening roar by this avatāra was enough to make the rākṣasas flee. He pierced the abdomen of Hiraṇyakaśipu with his nails, which were as pointed

1 Rig Veda 1.155.6.

as the vajra. The asura's blood gushed like a fountain, leaving some drops on Nṛsiṃha's mane. The intestines that were pulled out hung as garlands around his neck. He threw the remains of the asura on the floor and walked with a petrifying anger.

Nṛsiṃha fights Hiraṇyakaśipu in Dilwara Jain Temple (Rajasthan) sculpted in the Caulukya dynasty (11th century CE)

Śiva appeared in the scene and said, 'Nṛsiṃha, I perform prapatti to your extraordinary avatāra. Your one eye represents Sūrya, that shines, while the other represents Candra, that cools. Your third eye blazes like the fire that consumes everything. Your nails are possessed of Sudarśana's prowess. I wish to see your tranquil countenance.'[2]

Noticing no change, Śiva took Prahlāda on his lap, and whispered the Nṛsiṃha mantra in his ears. He said, 'Prahlāda, this is the rājā of all mantras. The words ugra[3] and vīra[4] indicate his unabated anger and his supreme creating prowess. Mahāviṣṇu[5] denotes his universal permeability, while jvalanta[6] points to his self-brilliance. His perception of everything makes him sarvatomukha[7] and his fierce looks make him bhīṣaṇa[8]. The word bhadra[9] personifies all

---

2 *Danujaṃ Ya: Sa Vīvyānṛsimah: Vahhativarucā Śāngkhyā Daṃśtram* Sirpur stone inscription of Mahāśiva Gupta from the Pānduvamśi dynasty (8th century CE) refers to Nṛsiṃha avatāra

3 Rig Veda, 2.33.11.

4 Taittiriya Samhita, 1.2.27.

5 Taittiriya Upanishad, 2.6.3

6 Brihadaranyaka Upanishad, 4.4.16.

7 Taittiriya Aranyaka, 3.12.1.

8 Taittiriya Upanishad, 2.4.

9 Rig Veda, 1.89.8.

auspiciousness in him. He eliminates untimely death and grants mokṣa, as he is mrityu[10]. To this Nṛsiṃha, I offer my praṇāmas.'

As directed by Śiva, Prahlāda repeated the mantra. Nṛsiṃha looked at Prahlāda with his lotus-like eyes. He placed his hand on the boy's head and asked him to seek boons. The boy asked that Hiraṇyakaśipu's past deeds be forgiven and added that his bhakti to Nārāyaṇa grow exponentially. Nṛsiṃha granted Prahlāda the boons and asked him to perform the obsequies for his father.

---

10 Rig Veda, 10.8.121.2.

45

A Divine Union Blossoms

As the curtains were thrown open, the festoon of eyes in Daśaratha's family glanced upon the lotus-like feet of Nārāyaṇa. Like intoxicated bees, they gazed at the two thighs that looked like banana plants grown in the garden of Kāma. Further up, those eyes were sucked in by the swirls of beauty-waves in the navel region of Nārāyaṇa. The chest region was a fulcrum of the most precious and matchless possessions of the paramātmā like the Kaustubha gem and Śrīvatsa mark. His smile was so infectious that it made the new brides simper for a moment. Rāma smiled at this. He gestured to Sītā using his eyes and both of them were led to their bhavana by the rakṣaka..

As they entered their apartment, the maids who had travelled from Mithilā smiled at the rājakumārī and welcomed the daṃpati with utmost respect. Sītā, that girl who had held her mother's hands while sleeping, was now sitting in the chamber of Rāma, who indeed was her week-old acquaintance. As she was fiddling with the tip of her upper garment worn like an upavīta, she was thinking to herself—'What should I talk to him about? Should I call him by his name? How should I make friends with my brothers-in-law?'

Rāma walked up to Sītā and held her hand. At that moment she felt as if all the previous lotus flowers she had held earlier couldn't match the softness of his palm. As he brought his other hand as a reassuring gesture towards her, she noticed the ring on his finger. She teared up while gazing at it. Rāma immediately sat next to her and said, 'Sītā, this ring is very precious to me. It was presented to me by your learned father at our vivāha maṇḍapa. I was told that he had this ring made long ago for his future son-in-law. On the previous night, he had my name inscribed on it. Look for yourself.'

Sītā, while running her fingers on this ring, kept looking at Rāma's face. He too remained frozen for some time until he heard the musical instruments played while Nārāyaṇa was carried on a procession across the streets of Ayodhyā. As he arose from his seat, he said, 'Sītā, you have not known me long. But we have vowed to be friends at the saptapadi. Feel free to share your joy. And more importantly, your sorrow. If something troubles you, inform me immediately. Like Sūrya and his rays that remain inseparable, so should we be. Sītā, are you agreeable to this?'

As she nodded her head positively, Rāma looked in the direction where her eyes were fixed now. She was seeing his step-mothers walk into their respective apartments after taking part in the procession. Her eyes were indicative of a profound worry. Rāma, adept at understanding human instincts continued, 'Sītā, my brothers and I were fortunate to be under the tutelage of Vasiṣṭha. He was a receptacle of quintessential knowledge. We were also amazed at his relationship with Arundhatī. The daṃpati inspired us to be understanding to our consorts and to be monogamous, above all.'

Rāma took a pause and said, 'Sītā, I promise to you now. I won't entertain lecherous glances of any lady falling on me, let alone entertain such acts.'

Sītā was overwhelmed by Rāma's vow and couldn't control her tears. Rāma embraced Sītā from behind and noticed her pearl necklace which had come unstrung causing the pearls to scatter everywhere. While Rāma sat down to pick up the fallen pearls, Sītā muttered in a sweet tone, 'Ārya, why pick these old ones when new pearls will be born in the seas today.'

Rāma enquired, 'Why, today?'

She said, 'It is Svāti.'

Rāma said, 'Sītā, you may call me Rāghava, or Rāma if you please.'

She quipped, 'Yes, ārya.'

The joyous laughter of the daṃpati engulfed the apartment.

46

Sāvitrī Wins Back Satyavān

'May you live for another hundred years! Rānī Kausalyā desires your presence at the Nārāyaṇa temple,' said the rakṣaka to Sītā. As Sītā quickly rushed to the temple, her sisters were already seated opposite a smaller sanctum. Kausalyā looked at Sītā with a smile and motioned to her to sit. The purohita was offering flowers at the devī vigraha while reciting lines extolling her: 'Let me press out the libation of soma and offer to the omniscient agni. May that agni destroy the wealth of my enemies. He must guide this boat of my existence in the sea of samsāra. Through agni, I now seek refuge in the brilliantly shining Durgā, the one who is of the colour of agni and resplendent on account of austerities. Durgā, I meditate on your form as Katyāyani that vanquished Mahiṣāsura.'

As he was completing the recital, he directed Kausalyā to guide the new brides into the last kriyā. The rānī said, 'My dear children, each of you will be given a thread smeared in turmeric. As you look in the eastern direction, you may tie this sacred thread around your neck.' As Sītā, Māṇḍavī, Ūrmilā and Śrutakīrti followed her instructions, Kausalyā blessed the young daughters-in-law and left the temple.

Sītā signalled her sisters to follow her, while she went to the purohita. She prostrated at his feet and said, 'Svāmi, we would like to know the significance of this kriyā. Could you delineate its significance to us?' The purohita was impressed with the girls who were all agog.

The purohita said, 'By the banks of Candrabhāgā[1], in the Madra province[2], ruled a rājā called Aśvapati. He offered havis to Sūrya many thousand times. In the eighteenth year of his continuous propitiation of Sūrya, he was blessed with a daughter as radiant as Sūrya. She was called Sāvitrī, thus. When she attained puberty, her father solicited the permission of the brāmhaṇas to find her a suitable match. Sāvitrī, who had returned from an odyssey, revealed her love interest to Aśvapati.'

Ūrmilā mumbled, 'Wish our father had also given us this privilege.'

The girls giggled while the purohita continued, 'Satyavān was the chosen one. He was the son of Dyumatsena, a blind rājā who had lost his rājya to avaricious neighbours. Satyavān used to make clay horses to fulfil his fancy for horse-riding. He was called Citraśva for a reason. Though Dyumatsena was a bit hesitant to formalize the relationship, he relented when Sāvitrī agreed to relinquish her riches. The vivāha was unpretentious, as a result. Sāvitrī impressed her aged in-laws by ministering to them and Satyavān through her warmth.

But she fretted about a prophecy that she had heard of Satyavān's death. In the Māgha month, Sāvitrī observed the vrata to Kātyāyani, the one who loves being worshipped by married women. After conducting the vrata for three continuous days to ward off any evil that could occur to her husband, she accompanied him to the forests. She couldn't stop him from going as he was to collect wood for agnihotra, the decree for a gṛhastha. After gathering the required fuel, Satyavān complained of a splitting headache and laid his head on Sāvitrī's lap to rest.'

---

1 Chenab, a trans-boundary river across countries like India and Pakistan with a length of over 950 kilometres. Tributary to Indus.

2 In and around Sialkot, a city in Pakistan.

The purohita noticed the rakṣaka gesturing him to come over to the garbhagṛiha as Sumitra, the other rānī had arrived for darshana of Nārāyaṇa. So, the narrator excused himself.

Yama rides a buffalo, in Odisha State Museum sculpted in the Eastern Gaṅgā dynasty (13th century CE)

Ūrmilā was curious like her sisters to know if Sāvitrī's worries turned true. Sensing the situation, Sītā said, 'Don't worry. I vaguely remember our mother narrating this.' And continued, 'Sāvitrī dozed leaning on the tree trunk. In her dream, she saw a dark-complexioned giant with reddened eyes. As he tightened the noose around Satyavān's neck, Sāvitrī quickly recognized that it was Yama, who was Dharmarājā to the masses who had arrived on the scene. She followed Satyavān's body that was dragged by Yama while she trembled with fear. Yama insisted that Sāvitrī should not follow him while he was discharging his duty. Yet, Sāvitrī refused to retreat.'

Māṇḍavī asked Sītā to explain if Satyavān survived Yama's strike and if it was Sāvitrī who aided Satyavān in this fight.

Sītā said, 'Sāvitrī, through her speech impregnated with wisdom, impressed upon Yama to grant boons that she desired. She sought both vision and rājya for Dyumatsena, both of which he had lost in the past. She desired that her parents had sons capable enough to guard the rājya. In that long list, she cleverly asked that she had strong sons from Satyavān. Yama granted these boons by oversight. Realizing that Satyavān had to be alive for the last boon to fructify, Yama granted him a long life. Sāvitrī's intelligence that conformed to śāstra helped her win over Yama, the one who governs all the cetana through his niyama. It was Sāvitrī's sheer brilliance that helped Yama to counter any accusation of partiality thrown at him.'

As Sāvitrī woke, she found no one nearby but spotted some cloven hoof marks of a buffalo. It had not been a dream. Meanwhile, she noticed Satyavān stirring from sleep. Sensing a sombre atmosphere around, he wanted to know if anything had transpired while he was asleep. Sāvitrī said that a withered tree had caught fire and its smoke had engulfed everything. As Satyavān gathered strength to stand, Sāvitrī embraced his hip. He placed his left hand on her shoulder and as both of them walked back to their āśrama, Sāvitrī noticed the noose mark around his neck. She smiled to herself, not in victory but in humility.

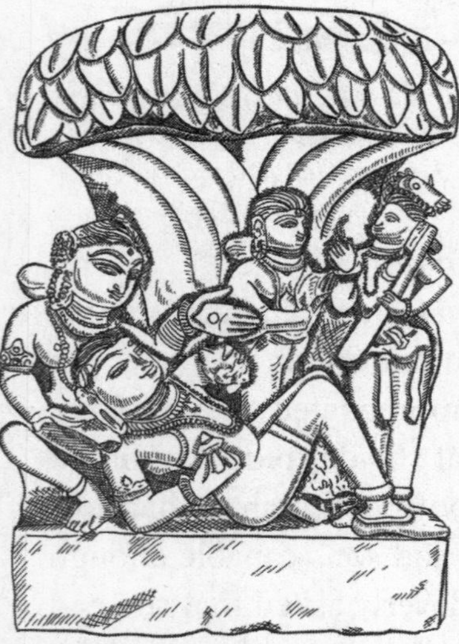

Satyavān on Sāvitrī's lap converses with Yama in Art Institute Chicago (US) sculpted in the Candela dynasty (11th century CE)

As Sītā finished narration, she walked out of the temple premises with her sisters, smiling widely.

47

The Love of Brothers

'Bring that umbrella for me, Śatrughna,' shouted Bharata. As Lakṣmaṇa was carrying a pair of chāmaras to the attic, he pulled Nandana, the rakṣaka, along with him. Nandana was clueless about where he was being taken but did not dare to ask the irascible Lakṣmaṇa anything. A pat on Nandana's shoulder made him turn around to see Śatrughna holding the umbrella. Flanked by the sons of Sumitrā on either side, a shaky Nandana entered the attic. He saw two wooden planks laid like a seat on a stone base with a golden panel as its backrest, in one corner. Bharata placed a tiara on Nandana's head while Lakṣmaṇa covered his left shoulder with a silk shawl. Śatrughna held Nandana from the back by his arms and carried him to the entrance of the attic and said, 'While Lakṣmaṇa and I are fanning you, walk like a rājā.'

'But which rāja?' quipped Nandana.

'Haven't you seen Rāma walk? Walk like him, and sit on the throne,' said Śatrughna.

'Which throne, ārya?' asked the rakṣaka humbly.

The rājakumāras, in unison, pointed to the ad-hoc arrangement placed at the corner. As Nandana stood in the middle, with the sons of Sumitrā fanning him, and Bharata holding the umbrella, the entourage walked towards the throne.

'May Rāma, the scion in the vaṃśa of Ikṣvāku, Bhagīratha, Hariścandra, Aja, now ascend the throne,' announced Bharata.

Nandana felt so royal at that moment. They heard someone approaching the attic, and as they turned together to see the entrance, they froze. It was Rāma. 'What is all this?' he wondered.

The petrified Nandana prostrated on the floor, like a stick that would fall to gravity. He excused himself from the scene.

Bharata said, 'Rāghava, this is our rehearsal for the day when we will see you seated on the throne of Ayodhyā. Every prajā of this city wants your regime. They are waiting for…'

Rāma raised his hand to ask Bharata to stop, and said, 'Bharata, I am fully aware of the love that you have for me and these sons of Sumitrā shower nothing less. That doesn't provide you the licence to speculate about administrative decisions. This day, we are blessed to have Daśaratha, who governs us. Remember that such naïve behaviour doesn't do credit to our upbringing at all.'

Lakṣmaṇa said, 'Rāma, I don't see any harm in what Bharata just uttered. Daśaratha is father to you. But you are father to us. Don't you remember the śruti injunction that treats the eldest brother akin to one's father?'

There was silence in the attic.

'Now that father commands you,' said Rāma while his brothers burst into thunderous laughter. He was unfazed, yet gave his characteristic smile and said, 'Vasiṣṭha wishes to narrate the life-history of Bharata and we must be his audience. Hasten to his āśrama.'

'Bharata, we know you well. Why your life-history to us?' asked Lakṣmaṇa with a straight face.

'You do not know Bharata as well as I do. May be Vasiṣṭha wants you to know him better?' quipped Śatrughna.

As they went to the āśrama, Vasiṣṭha was set for the narration. They prostrated at Vasiṣṭha's holy feet twice and sat in piety to listen to Bharata's life history.

48

Another Bharata

Manu, who was the son of Bramhā, married Śatarūpā. The daṃpati had two sons called Priyavrata and Uttānapāda. The former married Barhiṣmatī, the daughter of Viśvakarmā. His demarcation of the land mass into dvīpas and creation of forest territories was a feat which impressed even Bramhā. A son called Agnīdhra was first born to them. In due course of time, Agnīdhra fell in love with an apsarā called Pūrvacitti. A boy born to them was called Nābhi. He was given in vivāha to Merudevī. Desiring a valorous child, the daṃpati performed pravargya, believed to be the chief among yajñas.[1] The brāmhaṇas who helped perform the yajña predicted that Nārāyaṇa would partially manifest himself as a child to the daṃpati. They also conveyed that paramātmā wished to exemplify the importance of Śramaṇas who saw the air as their clothes and who had controlled their sexual feelings.[2]

Subsequently, Merudevī, who was pregnant, had dreams of a trumpeting white elephant, a gigantic bull, a ferocious lion, a Candra surrounded by nakṣatras, a well-decked Lakṣmī with garlands of

1 Taittiriya Aranyaka, 8.1.7.

2 Taittiriya Aranyaka, 2 Prashna (*vātarashanā ha vā rishaya: Śramaṇa urdhvamanthino babuvu:*).

fragrant flowers and much more. While she wanted to decipher the sequence of her dreams, she realized that the foetus was no ordinary one. Eventually, she delivered a son. The child's palms had little designs of a conch and lotus. He was called Ṛṣabha by his parents, and Aja by the brāmhaṇas. He started assisting his father in the rājya administration. Aja's fame reached different quarters which made an envious Indra think, 'I should stop the rain-bearing clouds from moving atop Ajanābhivarṣa.'

Ṛṣabha, realizing Indra's ploy, sat in dhyana facing the east. The rain-bearing clouds started moving towards Ajanābhivarṣa to bless the land with copious rains. Indra gave his daughter, Jayanti, in vivāha to Ṛṣabha in order to mask his folly. Nābhi and Merudevī knew the rājya was in safe hands and retired to Badarikāśrama to focus on bhakti yoga towards Nara-Nārāyaṇa.

Ṛṣabha and Jayanti were blessed with many sons of whom Bharata was the eldest. The boy grew up with an equable temperament that attracted his subjects. Ṛṣabha married another woman called Sunandā, who gave birth to a heroic son called Bāhubali. Ṛṣabha summoned his children and said, 'It is because of karma that the jīvātmā comes in association with the body. Due to an indiscernible timeless association, we assume the jīvātmā is the body itself. This gives rise to false ego which is detrimental to sākṣātkāra. To get rid of this false perception, it is important to seek refuge at the feet of an ācārya. Through his preaching, the śiṣya understands that the entire creation is the body to paramātmā. Alongside, this spiritual aspirant needs to associate with brāmhaṇas who have controlled their minds and senses, who adhere to patience, truth, mercy sans any discrimination; and who are inclined to only mokṣa. Know that Bharata who is respectful to bhaktas of Nārāyaṇa should be revered by all of you.'

Subsuming the āhavaniya fire within himself, Ṛṣabha exited the rājya in a naked state with dishevelled hair. He was called Ṛṣabhanātha from then on. To some of the passersby, he seemed like a dumb and a deaf person, while to the others, he was either possessed or a ghost. Only the learned knew that he was an avadhūta, a person who was

Ṛṣabhanātha in Museum of Fine Arts Boston (US) sculpted in the Candela dynasty (11th century CE)

indifferent to the physical world. Ṛṣabhanātha wholeheartedly accepted the abuses hurled at him, well aware that his pāpas would get obliterated thus.[3] He lived like a python that did not loiter around aimlessly, and like the deer, that ate only when he was hungry. While resting, he internalized his learnings about the paramātmā like a cow that quietly regurgitates the grass that it has consumed. During his wandering, Ṛṣabhanātha reached Kuṭakācala[4] and perished in the vanāgni whilst there.

The half-brothers—Bharata and Bāhubali—who were at loggerheads over the sharing of the rājya, were utterly shocked to hear about Ṛṣabhanātha's tragic end. Bāhubali left the rājya in a resolve to attain sākṣātkāra. He stood in kayotsarga, a unique posture, for over a year. The vines that entwined him and the termites that swarmed all over made no difference to him. He is said to have later attained mokṣa on his journey to Kailāśa. Meanwhile, Bharata married Pañcajanī, the daughter of Viśvarūpa. Together they performed both types of vaidika kriyās: those which were called kratu kriyās and which did not use the yupa stambha and also those rituals that used a yupa stambha. Bharata saw paramātmā in every kriyā that he conducted. He relinquished the throne to his son, Sumati, and retired to śālagrāma kṣetra[5] by the banks of river Nārāyaṇi.[6] He meditated upon Nārāyaṇa who resides in the realm

---

3 Taittiriya Sruti 2, Ash.3, Pra.42 (veeva nrityeta, preva chalet, vyasyevākshyou bhāsheta, mantayediva, krathayediva, sringāyeteva).

4 Coorg, a district in the Indian state of Karnataka.

5 Muktinath, a town in Nepal.

6 Narayani or Gandaki, a transboundary river through Tibet, Nepal and India. Tributary of Ganga with a length of over 800 kilometres.

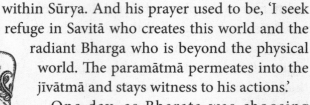

Bāhubali in Śravanabelagolā (Karnataka) sculpted in the Western Gaṅgā dynasty (10th century CE)

within Sūrya. And his prayer used to be, 'I seek refuge in Savitā who creates this world and the radiant Bharga who is beyond the physical world. The paramātmā permeates into the jīvātmā and stays witness to his actions.'

One day, as Bharata was choosing śālagrāma stones from the bed of river Nārāyaṇī, he was chanting, 'Praṇāmas to Acyuta who doesn't betray his bhaktas; Ananta who is beyond the limitations of time and space; and Mādhava who is the consort of Lakṣmī.' As he sat in dhyāna, he noticed a pregnant doe quenching its thirst in the river waters. Its lovely eyes brought a smile to Bharata. This atmosphere of sublime beauty changed in no time when a lion started chasing the doe. The doe took to its heels and when jumping between boulders, the doe's belly hit against a protruding rock. A little deer fell off the mother's sac onto a floating leaf in the Nārāyaṇī. Bharata couldn't help but jump into the flowing waters and rescue the little one that had not even seen its mother. While the lion chased the doe, Bharata brought the little deer to his āśrama. His time was now spent equally in nourishing the fawn and practising bhakti yoga.

As time passed by, Bharata's attachment to the fawn only increased. One day, Bharata was contemplating, 'You would have been sleeping on my chest had you been here. I can only wish that no wild animal has attacked or eaten you up. Has my dear one climbed up to Candra as I can see a deer mark on him? Even while I bade farewell to Sumati, it wasn't as melancholic as what it is now.' In his last moments, he imagined the deer sitting by his side and sobbing. As Bharata's mind was absorbed in the deer, the jīvātmā left his material body and transmigrated to the body of a little deer who was delivered in the mountain of Kālañjara[7] many miles away. In his growing years, the fawn was unlike his other ruminant fellows. It was as if he was perpetually in a pensive mood. The deer left his mother and marched towards śālagrāma. He sat in the same āśrama where Bharata spent his lifetime. Feeding on dry leaves and bathing in the cool waters of Nārāyaṇī, the deer lived in quietude. In due course, the jīvātmā left the material body of the deer too.

In the vaṃśa of Angiras, the jīvātmā now permeated the body of a boy who was born with his twin sister to a learned brāmhaṇa. From a young age, the boy remained aloof to most teachings from the vedas. His indifference was mistaken for irreverence. Samāvartana ritual was performed to this boy upon completion of vaidika studies. The father, understanding the state of his son, did not coax him for vivāha. The boy remained a snātaka to the world, and no one knew that he was an assemblage of esoteric knowledge. Attired in a loincloth, and a greasy upavīta, he was treated as an outcast by the brāmhaṇas. The villagers used to take advantage of his innocence by assigning him strenuous work. He was referred to as 'Jaḍa', the dull one, by people around him.

Kālī in LACMA (US) sculpted in Kerala (17th century CE)

One day, he was caught by dacoits and dragged to a cave where they laid him down to be sacrificed to the mūrti of Kālī, the fierce form of devī. There were indications that Kālī was not ready to accept the sacrifice of Jaḍa. When the dacoits refused to see through those indications, Kālī herself rushed

7 Kalinjar, a mountain in the Vindhya Mountain range bordering Madhya Pradesh and Uttar Pradesh.

into the cave. Using the very sword the dacoits had intended to kill Jada with, Kālī beheaded them. She smeared her body in the oozing blood, and danced like an inebriate. Jaḍa was just a witness to the scene, nothing more.

As Jaḍa continued walking in the forests, some soldiers dragged him to a śibikā and said, 'Help us carry this.' Complying with what was told to him, Jaḍa carried the śibikā. The carrying was haphazard because Jaḍa wanted to protect the colony of ants below his feet. This gave jerks to the śibikā, and the person who was seated inside alighted. He said, 'Tired āstika, you don't look very strong. You don't know how to serve the rājā. It seems as if you are already dead.'

Jaḍa gave a sarcastic smile and said, 'I am neither strong nor weak. I did not carry the śibikā. Your position as rāja, and that of me, as carrier of your śibikā, is temporary in nature. The imperishable jīvātmā inside my material body is referred to as "I". This "I" is subservient only to paramāṭmā and no one else. In case you still feel "I" need to serve you, please command what this "I" can do for you.'

The speechless rājā prostrated at the feet of Jaḍa and said, 'I am Rahūgaṇa, the rājā of Sindhu-Sauvīra[8] rājya. For quite some time, I had doubts on the relationship between the material body, jīvātmā and paramātmā. In order to get enlightened, I was on my journey to the āśrama of Kapila. But I have found my ācārya here by the banks of river Ikṣumatī[9] itself. Kindly accept my praṇāmas at your lotus-like feet.'

8 Covers the states of Punjab and Sindh in Pakistan.

9 A tributary of river Yamuna that used to flow near Kurukshetra in the Indian state of Haryana. The river is non-existent now.

49

'Jaḍa' Bharata and Jātismara

'Ācārya, it is our fortune to listen to this splendid narration from you. I have once heard Vāmadeva refer to the conversation between Jaḍa and Rahūgaṇa as being the very essence of vedānta. Could you summarize those priceless exchanges for us?' asked Rāma.

Vasiṣṭha, who never hesitated to show his admiration for Rāma's eloquence which was laced with humility, smiled and said in an uncertain tone, 'Rāma, for sure I shall narrate their conversation. But I see Lakṣmaṇa and Śatrughna carrying a jug of water each and walking towards us.' Lakṣmaṇa offered his praṇāmas to Rāma, presented the water jug and sat behind him. Śatrughna did the same to Bharata. Vasiṣṭha was teary-eyed not because he wasn't given the water jug by the sons of Sumitra, but he was seeing saubhrātrutva, an enticing brotherhood in front of his eyes.

Vasiṣṭha continued, 'The material body that is a product of karma, is an amalgamation of pañcabhūtas. In it is housed the jīvātmā, which is neither a deva, a human, an animal nor a tree. And paramātmā is witness to its activities. While the jīvātmā is housed in the material body, realizing the ultimate truth should be its objective. This realization is achieved through continuous deliberations about paramātmā's qualities with bhaktas. These were the words of Jaḍa to Rahūgaṇa.'

'This is so inspiring. How did Rahūgaṇa express his gratitude to Jaḍa? How did Jaḍa remember the events of his past births?' implored Lakṣmaṇa.

The ācārya beamed and looked at Rāma.

The latter, with folded palms, said, 'Rahūgaṇa was thankful to Jaḍa for explaining matters that had left him confused in the past. He offered his praṇāmas to bhaktas who were wandering Bhūmi in different forms including that of children and juveniles. One in a thousand jīvātmās manages to carry forward remembrances of past births. Such a person is referred to as a jātismara. In such cases, noted incidents stir up memory. Jaḍa could remember his past birth as deer, and could even pursue sādhanā that he had commenced as Bharata. This bond that had travelled births gave him an eternal name which is Jaḍa Bharata.'

'Where did Rāma learn this history of Jaḍa Bharata?' Lakṣmaṇa wondered.

The rakṣaka sought Vasiṣṭha's permission and entered the āśrama. He informed Vasiṣṭha of Yudhājit's arrival. Vasiṣṭha asked the rājakumāras to leave and welcome the rājā of Kekaya. The rājakumāras duly obeyed the words of their ācārya and left the āśrama.

50

The Princes Leave for Kekaya

'You have grown into such a good-looking rājakumāra. I have heard of your inclination to vedānta. In you and in your demeanour, I see your grandfather.' Yudhājit swelled up while saying these words to Bharata. He looked at the other brothers of Bharata and said, 'Come here sons, embrace me.'

Yudhājit continued, 'I have brought each of you four hundred horses from the Kekaya kingdom. I have also brought a few elephants of the Airāvata vaṃśa for your training. These elephants have travelled a long distance from the Indraśira mountain. I have brought antelope hides for your sādhanā purposes. I have brought some giant dogs with large fangs, and tiger's energy to guard the apartment of your wives. A cart full of woollen clothes in a medley of colours has arrived for your wives with some gold jewellery too.'

'We are indebted for your love,' said Bharata to Yudhājit as he inquired of his uncle about the latest academic discussion his grandfather had had. Yudhājit recounted the session where the sons of Upamanyu, Pulusha, Ballavi, Śarkarākṣa and Aśvataraśvi had arrived at Rājagriha, the rājaśānī of Kekaya. They had wanted to understand Vaiśvānara, and whom the word referred to. Aśvapati of Kekaya laid on the discussion table the various connotations of the word

'Vaiśvānara' such as the digestive fire, the elemental fire, the fire mūrti who is the agni devatā, the jīvātmā and the paramātmā. Depending on the context, the meaning of 'Vaiśvānara' could be deciphered. But Aśvapati was of the opinion that the word 'Vaiśvānara' itself could mean the one who was the ruler of all jīvātmās.

As Yudhājit was describing this week-old discussion of his father Aśvapati with the sons of illustrious ṛṣis, he said, 'Bharata, your grandfather who has handed over administrative responsibilities to me wishes to spend his old age in similar academic exchanges with you. I hope you and dear Māṇḍavī shall come to Rājagriha and spend a few years there. This will bring joy to all of us. I have even obtained your father's permission to this effect.'

Bharata was confused. He was torn between Rāma, his loving brother and Aśvapati , his learned grandfather. He looked to Rāma for guidance. With his mercy-laden eyes, Rāma signalled Bharata to leave for Rājagriha happily. Bharata understood that Rāma wanted him to learn vedānta from Aśvapati , the only rājā of his times who was as learned as Janaka Sīradhvaja. As Bharata decided to leave Ayodhyā, he obtained the blessings of all the elders in his house. Bharata and Śatrughna, seated in a chariot, followed the śibikās of Māṇḍavī and Śrutakīrti. Yudhājit too started for Rājagriha with his nephew, fully convinced that Bharata was not like his mother.

51

Bharata Learns of Śiva's Strengths

'Aren't you aware that the purohita had asked for one hundred and eight vilva fruits for the yajña? But you seem to have lost count of them,' chided one of the śiṣyas. The other asked, 'I will keep them right. But what are these fruits meant for?' 'It is for the yajña arranged by our very own Suyajña,' replied the śiṣya.

The śiṣyas turned their heads towards the entrance of the āśrama as the kettledrums were blown to welcome the retinue from Ayodhyā. Yudhājit, along with Bharata, Śatrughna and their wives, sought the blessings of Suyajña.

'Is he Rāma, who is always referred to by our purohita with the deepest of love?' asked one śiṣya.

'No, I was told he is Bharata, Rāma's immediate brother,' replied the other.

'He looks so divine and calm,' the śiṣya said to himself.

'Yudhājit, I am extremely delighted to welcome you to this āśrama by the banks of the Yamunā. Today is Puṣya nakṣatra, which is blessed by Bṛhaspati. I am happy that Bharata has also joined you. I request that all of you are seated to witness the vilva ārādhanā to Śiva,' said Suyajña.

Those present nodded their heads positively and sat under the shade of the vilva tree. The śiṣyas started placing the vilva leaves atop the small lingam of Śiva placed on a wooden pedestal as Suyajña was chanting the various names and attributes of Śiva. The entire atmosphere wore a festive look with such names filling the ears of those present. This prayer concluded with a hārati for Śiva.

Bharata went forward and prostrated to Suyajña. He reverentially said, 'It was our fortune to witness such a grand ārādhanā of Śiva, the three-eyed one who has the crescent on his jaṭā, the trident in his hand, ashes smeared over his body, snakes running over his body as if they were his ornaments, and always attended to by his gaṇas. But I have always wanted to know the greatness of Śiva. He is referred to as the one who has Pārvatī in his body, the one who removed the ignorance of the ṛṣis in Dārukāvana, the one who destroyed the three cities, the one who brought about the end of Gajāsura, Jalandhara and Andhakāsura. If you could delineate these achievements of Śiva, I will be, rather we shall be, indebted.'

Suyajña smilingly said, 'Bharata, you remind me so much of Rāma. Your demeanour is just like that of him. May you stay blessed.'

'There used to be a bhakta of Śiva called Bhṛṅgī. He was extremely attached to Śiva, so much so that he was often named by Śiva himself as the foremost of his bhaktas. After having performed tapasyā to Śiva, Bhṛṅgī footslogged to the Kailāśa mountain. As he reached a cluster of devadāru trees, he saw Śiva and Pārvatī on Naṅdi approaching him. He felt ecstatic. He exclaimed, "I am blessed to see the supreme teacher appearing to bless me."

'There was a buzzing sound of the bees. Bhṛṅgī noticed alternating yellow and pink karavīra flowers adorning Śiva's jaṭā and bees hovering around them. He sniggeringly said, "Fortunate are those bees that can choose to go around the one whom I too wish to worship alone."

'A pained Pārvatī, who noticed the ṛṣi's disparaging remarks and misogynistic behaviour, said, "Your bhakti is useless tinsel that looks down upon women. Don't you know that Śiva and I are inseparable? The brāmhaṇas worship our unique form of both occupying each other's bodies as Ardhanārīśvara. But you seem to be proud of your half-baked knowledge. Your body shall lose the energy to walk further. Let this punishment bestow wisdom in you."

'Bhṛṅgī slowly started faltering and stooping.

'Śiva said, "Pārvatī, not one bhakta of mine resembles the other. Each of their methods to reach me is different. We must stay patient and rectify our bhaktas. Your curse has only weakened him. I now grant Bhṛṅgī a stick made from this devadāru branch. It will be attached to his back and give him the required support."

'This anecdote, I have heard, exemplifies Śiva's mercy towards his bhaktas and also his unique Ardhanārīśvara form.'

Ardhanārīśvara in Chennai Government Museum (Tamil Nadu) sculpted in the Cola dynasty (11th century CE)

Suyajña turned to his śiṣya and commanded, 'Let Bharata, the rājakumāra of Ayodhyā, receive the prasāda on this day.' He then turned towards Bharata and said, 'Bharata, you have travelled a long distance from Ayodhyā crossing the provinces of Hastināpura, Pañcāla and Kurujāṅgala. You have sanctified this Kuliṅga region with your presence. I will suggest that Māṇḍavī and you do pradakṣiṇā around Aśvattha, the wish-yielding tree. You may then be seated in the āśrama so that I may describe Śiva's exploits.'

While Māṇḍavī started walking towards the tree, Bharata asked, 'Will I be gratified to pray to Rāma's divine feet and his pādukas some day?'

Suyajña smiled and looked to the skies.

Bhṛṅgī in Lepakshi Veerabhadra Temple (Andhra Pradesh) sculpted in the Vijayanagara dynasty (16th century CE)

52

Śiva Destroys a Blind Tyrant

It was evening time. The breeze was intoxicating with the smell of kuṅkuma flowers. The grazing cows were returning home. The fine dust from their hooves covered the air around the āśrama. Kaśyapa was pouring havis in the dakṣiṇāgni. He felt the dhoti sliding down his hip. He noticed Diti, his wife pulling it with a perspiring face and lustful eyes fixed at him. He took note of her sexual advances and said, 'My dear, I am aware of the times we have lost being a daṃpati. I am also very cognizant of your desire for bearing children. But we may need to wait for a short duration.'

Diti, who had cuddled up in the arms of Kaśyapa asked, 'But why?'

'Śiva, covered in ashes, moves from his abode to the crematory accompanied by the gaṇas at this time. This is not a favourable time for us to make love,' he said.

But Diti was reluctant to buy this advice and had begun to caress him.

As a year passed by, she gave birth to Hiraṇyakaśipu and Hiraṇyākṣa. These children grew up with repugnant behaviour. Diti felt repentant for having caused insult to Śiva and thereby suffering with boys who were leading ruffian lives.

With the sincere hope of producing another child who could be invincible against all devas but Śiva, Diti approached Kaśyapa. In the fullness of time, a baby boy was born to the daṃpati. With fine hair all over his body, this little lad was blind since birth. He used to uproot the plants in the vicinity of the āśrama and kept throwing dirt in the yajñas performed by the inmates. Blind not just by birth, but with rage, he was called Andhaka, for a reason.

The concerned Diti once asked, 'Why is our son callous towards everyone?' Kaśyapa in a pensive mood replied, 'Pārvatī once approached Śiva from the behind, and playfully closed his eyes. This unexpected act of Pārvatī has yielded this undesirable effect. Occasionally the repercussions of devas' deeds will be borne by us, the ṛṣis.'

Andhaka's presence was getting menacing by the day. Drunk with power and vāruṇi, he once came across Nārada holding a garland of mandāra flowers. The smell of the flowers was so intoxicating that Andhaka enquired about its source. Nārada said, 'Presented by Pārvatī in Kailāśa.' Andhaka, who was fascinated by the name of Pārvatī, gathered his army of attendants and marched towards the snow-peaked abode of Śiva.

Flanked by two of his mantris, Vaidhasa and Hasti, who kept describing the surroundings to Andhaka, the retinue reached Kailāśa. Vaidhasa noticed a beautiful lady leaving a cave and walking up the rocks. He stood amazed and Hasti also fixed his eyes on her. Andhaka, who sensed this sudden silence, asked, 'Are you there? What has drawn both your attention and made you speechless?'

'The raised toes in her tender feet emit red rays making it appear as if Bhūmi had given rise to lotuses. I see her carefully trudging with heavy bosoms while the haṃsa birds wait to learn music lessons from her rhythmic anklet sound,' said Vaidhasa.

'Who is this?' asked Andhaka.

'Her thighs are rounded yet neither comparable to the thick-skinned trunks of elephants nor with the cold plantain stems. Do I see three folds of skin on her abdomen? No, they are indeed the flight of stairs for Kama to ascend to her upper torso,' remarked Hasti.

Śiva kills Andhaka, Chhatrapati Shivaji Maharaj Museum (Mumbai), sculpted in the Cālukya dynasty (8th century CE)

'I am eager to know her name, tell me,' asked the impatient Andhaka.

'I don't think it is possible for even the lotus thread to pass through the gap between her well-rounded breasts. The pearl necklace is indeed embellished by its mere presence around her neck. Her guileless smile looks as if a row of freshly born pearls were placed over the red-hued corals. Her long arched eyebrows are so controlling that the most valourous of warriors could drop his bow to the ground,' concluded Vaidhasa.

A visibly vexed Andhaka shouted, 'Who is she?'

At the same time, a lady attendant emerged from the cave with a little casket in her hands and called out 'Pārvatī' in a melodious tone.

Andhaka, blind at birth and now in lust, started running towards Pārvatī like a firefly that hurries towards a lit lamp. Upon sighting the asura run towards Pārvatī, an enraged Śiva jumped between the rocks of the tall mountain and rushed towards Andhaka. While Andhaka was about to seize Pārvatī with his hands, Śiva flung him high in the air and pierced his abdomen with the trident.

Andhaka's retinue that was visibly shaken on seeing their leader's gruesome death at the hands of Śiva fled in no time.

53

Śiva's Exploits

There was silence in the assemblage.

'You just heard about the tempestuous Śiva killing the cruel Andhaka. I will continue about an event that occurred on this very day aspected by the Puṣya nakṣatra,' said Suyajña. Taking note of the raised eyebrows, he beamed with excitement and said, 'The burning of Tripura.'

'After the death of Tāraka at the hands of Kārttikeya, the warrior son of Śiva, Tāraka's sons were very agitated. They were called Tārakākṣa, Kamalākṣa and Vidyunmālī. They performed tapasyā to please Bramhā and obtained a boon that a single arrow that pierces through the three of them could alone destroy them. Maya, the architect of asuras, chose a dvīpa with dormant volcanoes to construct mansions for the sons of Tāraka. They obtained mansions made of hard metals that looked like vertices of a triangle. The mansion-trio was called Tripura. Maya also spotted a lake[1] in the valley formed by the mountains whose waters were magical enough to rejuvenate the wounded asuras. Tāraka's sons took undue advantage of the boon bestowed on them, and went in different directions to assert their

---

1 Lake Toba in North Sumatra of Indonesia.

Śiva destroys Tripura in Badami ASI Museum (Karnataka) sculpted in the Cālukya dynasty (8th century CE)

power. Taking cognizance of the atrocities meted by the asuras on animals and humans, the Devas and Bramhā sought refuge in Śiva. Śiva instructed Viśvakarmā to construct a chariot as sturdy as Bhūmi with wheels as resplendent as Sūrya and Candra. Bramhā volunteered to serve as the charioteer of the chariot drawn by the bull revered by Nārāyaṇa. The chariot with a heroic Śiva, and led by a composed Bramhā, reached the shores of the eastern seas in Bhārata.[2] Śiva bent his bow called the Pinākī whose riser was made from the rocks of the Meru mountain, and whose string was formed with the skin moulted by Vāsuki. The arrow was fixed, but Śiva noticed none of the asuras coming in a straight line. To comply with Bramhā's boon, he had to wait for the moment.

Nārāyaṇa, on the other hand, induced the cattle in Tripura to quench their thirst in the central lake filled with healing waters. The caretaker of the lake, whose efforts in chasing the cattle were futile, informed the asuras of the depleting waters in the lake. Tārakākṣa came out of his mansion and started walking down to the lake area. Kamalākṣa and Vidyunmālī, too, followed their brother. As they converged at one point and walked in a line, Śiva in a different land knew about this. He meditated on Nārāyaṇa, whose grace he sought in the arrow. That instant, he could see the presence of Sudarśana, the unfailing discus of Nārāyaṇa on the arrow tip, emitting sparks of fire. Ṛṣis of unfathomable powers gathered around Śiva's chariot and said, 'The time is aspected by Puṣya nakṣatra, and these asuras

2 Tiruvathigai Temple in the state of Tamil Nadu.

shall disintegrate in a few moments from now. Shoot this arrow, Mahādeva. Hasten!'

As Śiva smiled, and discharged the arrow, it travelled like the streak of a lightning, piercing the asuras. It threw them into the lake waters, causing multiple tremors. The volcanoes erupted, and the mansions caught fire. Tripura was burning, and its reflections in the lake seemed as if the waters had merged into the fire. Śiva, from then on, is hailed as Tripurāntaka, the one who brought an end to the asuras of Tripura.'

'We are honoured by your arrival, Dīrghāyu,' said Suyajña as he rose reverentially from his seat. And he continued, 'It is a happenstance that you are here when the sons of Daśaratha are here.'

Dīrghāyu smiled and said, 'Bharata, I am seeing you after a long time. How are Daśaratha and others in Ayodhyā? I will hopefully visit them soon.'

Bharata prostrated at the feet of Dīrghāyu and described everybody's welfare in Ayodhyā.

'Bharata, you just heard about Śiva's exploits in the killing of Andhaka and the burning of Tripura. I wish you would listen to Dīrghāyu describing how Śiva brought about the end of Jalandhara.'

As Suyajña took leave of the company, Dīrghāyu immediately put his palms together as a mark of respect and closed his eyes. A few minutes later, he opened them slowly and said, 'Once, Indra, seated on Airāvata, set out for Kailāśa. At its foothill, he noticed a yogī seated. Despite the elephant trumpeting, the yogī remained unshaken. Indra, with his vajra, thrashed the yogī and marched towards Kailāśa. To his surprise, in Kailāśa, he was not accorded the usual honours. He saw Śiva at a distance and approached him only to find him in an enraged state. In no mood to tolerate Indra, Śiva hurriedly left Kailāśa on Nandi. It was a mark of his disapproval of Indra's behaviour towards his bhaktas. At the other end, Varuṇa, who was walking by the confluence of Gaṅgā and the ocean, noticed an abandoned little boy by its shores. He realized that the boy carried the effect of Śiva's anger caused by Indra's high-handedness. With no guardians around, he nurtured the boy.

Śiva kills Jalandhara in Kailaśanātha Temple (Tamil Nadu) sculpted in the Pallava dynasty (17th century CE)

Once, the boy gripped Varuṇa's neck tightly like a noose, causing tears to flow down his cheeks. Thus, the boy was called Jalandhara, the one who induces tears. At the right age, he was married off to Vrindā. He turned against the Devas claiming that they had churned the oceanic waters without his father, Varuṇa's consent. Despite his angst at them, he liked Nārāyaṇa for being Lakṣmī's consort. But why? Because he believed Lakṣmī was his sister, as she emerged from the oceanic waters. Jalandhara's activities did not conform to the shastras. His atrocities reached their peak when he started developing amorous feelings for Pārvatī. Śiva who took notice of this, beheaded Jalandhara with Sudarśana cakra. This is how Śiva brought an end to Jalandhara.'

54

Sudarśana, the Eternal Cycle

'Sudarśana was used by Śiva to kill Jalandhara. But isn't this the weapon of Nārāyaṇa?' asked Vālmīki.

Nārada said, 'True'.

This further increased Vālmīki's curiosity, who pleaded that the history of Sudarśana be known to him.

Nārada said, 'Viśvakarmā, the architect of the devas gleefully got Saṃjñā, his cherished daughter, married to Sūrya. Saṃjñā's desire to stay with her husband didn't last long. She couldn't withstand the heat that Sūrya's body emitted. Looking at his daughter's sufferings, and her repeated plea to keep her away from Sūrya, made Viśvakarmā think of a panacea. As he was walking by various mountains, he stopped by Cakravān. He noticed a group of hunters talking among each other gesturing at a few grey-hued chunks in their hands. Viśvakarmā engaged in a conversation with them, and sought their help in making weapons from these chunks. The vyādhas were moved by Viśvakarmā's humility and provided assistance in the making of weapons. Viśvakarmā created multiple sharp, thin but long metal strips. He arranged them in a circular fashion. This thousand-spoked cakra was taken to the place where Viśvakarmā organized a yajña to reduce the heat emitted by Sūrya. He requested that the devas direct the excess heat in Sūrya to the newly designed cakra which was placed in the fire.

Towards the pūrṇāhuti, those present were able to see the cakra turn red. Coincidentally, Saṃjñā noticed that the heat from Sūrya's body had abated. Hence the excess heat from Sūrya's body was injected into the cakra.

As Viśvakarmā was walking back to his abode with the intent of presenting the cakra to Nārāyaṇa, he stopped by Kailāśa. Enamoured by Śiva's yogāsana, he presented the cakra to him. It was this cakra which Śiva had deployed in the killing of Jalandhara. Later, Nārāyaṇa is said to have asked Śiva for the cakra, in his inimitable manner. The three-eyed Śiva, wholeheartedly gave away the cakra to Nārāyaṇa, whom he used to fondly refer to as the "lotus-petal eyed" one.'

'But,' interjected Vālmīki very hesitatingly.

Nārada, with a smile, said, 'I know your doubt. I will tell you all that Ahirbudhnya has detailed in the āgama.'

Nārada walked to the āśrama wall and drew a circle. Within the circle, he drew two intersecting triangles. 'Ahirbudhnya proclaims that this is the depiction of Sudarśana. Nārāyaṇa has beautiful lotus-petal-like eyes. His mere glance bestows auspiciousness on his bhaktas. His glances are capable of granting mokṣa too. He is fondly venerated by ṛṣis as Sudarśana. His sankalpa of the divine will to protect his bhaktas is viewed as this weapon which is also called by the same name.

Mūlamūrti in Cakrapāṇi in Kumbakonam (Tamil Nadu)

Just like Nārāyaṇa who is seen in different states, Sudarśana, too, presents himself in such states. In the state of para, he exists with Vāsudeva. In the state of vyuha, he accompanies Pradyumna, Aniruddha and Saṅkarṣaṇa. Sudarśana resides in the horn of Matsya, the tusks of Varāha and in the nails of Nṛsiṃha. Like Nārāyaṇa chooses to be the Matsya, Kurma, Varāha, and many others like the present Rāma, Sudarśana, too, has such forms. One such form is the thousand-spoked cakra that was developed by Viśvakarmā and presented to Śiva. Nārāyaṇa is eternal, and so is Sudarśana. This cakra of the paramātmā represents the continuity and cyclic nature of time, just as we see in the seasons. I have heard that Sudarśana is representative of manas, the state of mind,' concluded Nārada.

'Who is Ahirbudhnya?' interrupted Vālmīki.

'Śiva,' replied Nārada.

Vālmīki thanked Nārada for the narration on Sudarśana that dispelled his queries. To his śiṣyas seated in the front, he continued, 'Bharata and Śatrughna were treated with absolute honours in the āśrama by Suyajña and Dīrghāyu. After taking leave of the ṛṣis, the duo, along with their wives, crossed the Ikṣumatī and Vipāśā rivers. Finally, as they reached Rājagriha, they noticed Aśvapati eagerly awaiting their arrival. Bharata's eyes swelled up in respect for his wise grandfather while Aśvapati's eyes feasted on Bharata's humble conduct.'

'But I haven't spoken about Śatrughna in detail, as yet. Have I?' asked Vālmīki. The śiṣyas who agreed with Vālmīki expressed their desire to know more about Śatrughna. Vālmīki continued, 'Yudhājit invited his nephew Bharata to Rājagriha. Śatrughna, too, followed him. Did Bharata invite Śatrughna to Rājagriha? No. Like how he took the sword and its scabbard along, he took Śatrughna with him. This may seem as if Bharata was not mindful of Śatrughna's consent. But it testifies to the fact that Śatrughna sought Bharata's association everywhere and at all times. Lakṣmaṇa and Bharata were extremely fond of Rāma. Though Bharata did start to Rājagriha from Ayodhyā, his thoughts were fixed on Rāma. He wanted to act as per Rāma's wishes at all times. He was just like Lakṣmaṇa, serving him from a distance. Śatrughna was like neither of them. His bhakti and kaiṅkarya were reserved only for Bharata. In a way, Śatrughna had dared what no other person could easily attempt. It was to divert his attention from Rāma to Bharata. If Bharata is devoted to Rāma, it is bhakti towards paramātmā. If Śatrughna is devoted to Bharata, it is bhakti towards the bhakta of paramātmā. The latter is pristine and flawless in many ways, so is Śatrughna. Like Sudarśana who obliterates the enemies of śāstras, so does Śatrughna keep his path of bhakti to Bharata without any impediments.'

There was silence in the āśrama.

'Like Nārada is extremely attached to Nārāyaṇa, and we are all fond of Nārada,' stated Vālmīki, to which Nārada beamed meekly.

Bharata with Māṇḍavī and Śatrughna with Śrutakīrti spent the next twelve years at Rājagriha.

55

A Cursed Prince

Like Indra who was worshipped for inducing the clouds to shower rains, so was Aja equally respected by his subjects for showering prosperity. He placed his crown aside while performing the Aśvamedha yajña as a mark of respect to the devas. A horse was tied to the yupa stambha gilded in gold and erected beside the Sarayū. Just like his father, Aja, Daśaratha of Ayodhyā, too, went in different directions to display his prowess. The thunderous twang from the rājakumāra's bow string followed by a shower of arrows made people wonder if he was Indra incarnate, who was believed to have chopped the wings of mountains. The yajña's culmination coincided with dark clouds that lowered themselves, unable to bear the weight of waters like the rutted elephants that perspire from their temples. Commoners attributed the rains to the rājā's good governance and the successful expedition of the young rājakumāra.

'Could he have been speaking to her despite my warnings? I know of his lascivious acts. He now sleeps like an innocent. I know that he isn't one,' murmured a woman sleeping next to her snoring husband inside the hut. It was just another day after the bickering.

A sudden thunder brought shivers in her, and she quickly embraced her husband.

The crystal-clear rain waters gathered force from the hills while turning brown in the forests. Drenched in the rains, the birds sought shelter in the branches and extended their wings to dry them off. Blue-hued flowers fell into these waters that were already taking a serpiginous course towards the sāgara. A pack of frogs were petrified in crossing these waters assuming it was a long python whose head and tail couldn't be seen. Such was the advent of monsoons and so were its effects.

Daśaratha, with a headgear stitched in wild flowers and leaves, carrying a bow and a quiver of arrows, looked more athletic than before. At dawn, he forcefully followed a herd of deer that led him into thickets. Suddenly, there was stillness all around. Daśaratha, inept in deciphering animal sounds, and adept in shooting the śabdavēdi, readied his bow and poison-smeared arrow. He heard the elephants filling their trunks. Nescient of the śāstra that an elephant should not be hunted anywhere but the battlefield, he released the arrow that levitated towards the source of the sound. To his utter shock, he heard the frail voice of a human. He rushed at lightning speed to the spot, and witnessed a boy whose chest was pierced with the virulent arrow. The boy with jaṭā was dressed like a sannyāsī in deer skin. He was crying in withering pain as he was covered in Bhūmi, and Bhūmi was smeared in his blood. Daśaratha took the boy's head on his lap. The boy quickly realized that he was on the lap of a kṣatriya. As a mark of respect, he tried to put his palms together, but struggled and said, 'Ah, I am a tapasvī who has relinquished comforts. I have not done anything that is worthy of earning such strong enemies. I am the only child of my infirm parents who are both blind. I had come to the stream to fetch water for them. Kindly carry the pot that is lying on the ground to my parents. They will be thirsty.'

Daśaratha carefully placed the tapasvī's head on the ground and brought the water pot. As he was about to rush to the āśrama, the tapasvī said, 'Like the swift river currents that erode a sandback, so does this piercing arrow cause grave pain in me. Please remove this arrow from my chest.'

Tapasvī carries his parents in Hazāra Rama Temple (Karnataka) sculpted in the Vijayanagara dynasty (15th century CE)

Daśaratha very hesitatingly acceded to this plea. Keeping his reddened face away, the rājakumāra pulled the arrow out. The tapasvī cried in unendurable pain as blood gushed out. Daśaratha sensed death approaching the boy. The tapasvī was moribund, and in a hopeless voice said, 'I will not survive for long. My parents can't survive without me. In one arrow you have killed me and my parents. Like one tree that helplessly watches another tree being toppled in the winds, so will my father have to watch me die. Your hunt has not yielded anything fruitful as well. My parents will be unaware of my state. Let you not worry. I am not a brāmhaṇa and you will not incur bramhahatyā. This path will lead you to our āśrama. Reach me to my parents.'

Daśaratha, with a heart filled with sorrow for the tapasvī, carried him to the āśrama. The tapasvī breathed his last moments on the way.

'I can hear your footsteps, my dear boy. Your mother was worried about your safety. I had assumed you were hurt by my words spoken yesterday. Don't take it to heart. We see the world through your eyes. You are our refuge, my son,' said the blind father.

Stillness around.

Fumbling for words, the distraught rājakumāra said, 'I am the son of Aja. My hunting expedition has resulted in a disaster. I thought of aiming at an elephant but ended up killing your son.'

The father and mother crawled to the place where their son's body was lying. The mother lamented saying, 'You cooked the lotus stem and kacu this morning. You fed me with love. My lips haven't lost the taste, and the air hasn't lost the smell, as yet. But, you are gone. Why is my vidhi so cruel?'

'Your praṇāmas to the both of us in the morning compensated for your duty of performing the mandated saṃskāras. Having killed Dhundhu, the tyrant son of Madhu-Kaitabha, Kuvalaśva provided solace to Uttanka. He was called Dhundhumāra from then on. Śibi took mercy on a dove that was being chased by a kite. Both Dhundhumāra and Śibi were received with honours by Indra. Nahuṣa, Sagara and Dilīpa performed Aśvamedha yajñas, and they were also accorded due honours by Indra. I am sure you will follow suit. Why not? You are killed by a "Satyavrata" rājā who did not hide the news of your death. He was generous enough to serve us the news,' said the father.

He turned towards Daśaratha, and said, 'Had you hidden the news of our son's death, your vaṃśa would have been wiped out. By serving us, my son has accrued the puṇya of those serving their preceptors, offering cows as charity, sticking to one partner and shedding their mortal coils at the prayāga.'

The father burst into a fountain of tears. They weren't stopping. He wiped his tears awkwardly and said, 'Inspite of my austerities, I wasn't aware of my son's death until you told me. The pain you have inflicted on me cannot be described in words. You will realize this pain of mine only when you undergo separation from your son. That parting will bring you death.'

In no time, the parents were dead. Daśaratha performed the final rites of the three of them.

The bodies were gone. The voice of the dying father hadn't. As Daśaratha stood in the curtain of smoke, the dead man's curse conveyed two things. One, that Daśaratha, the young rājakumāra, would have a son. And second that he would die because of his separation from his son.

56

Dhruva: Viṣṇu's Youngest Bhakta

'You will die of separation from Rāma' screamed a voice, quite familiar, that was once heard in the forests covered in smoke. Daśaratha, the rājā, mumbled, 'Rāma, don't go away'.

Kausalyā, who noticed this discomfort in her sleeping husband, touched him.

The rājā woke up in a state of shock. He asked, 'Where is Rāma?' and before Kausalyā could reply, Daśaratha said, 'He must be in Kaikeyī's apartment. You will not know.'

As he got up, and was about to exit his chamber, he heard a voice that said, 'Rāma is in the temple of Nārāyaṇa.' It was Kausalyā with a straight face, who said this.

'Dhruva nakṣatra, what is it?' Daśaratha heard the voice of Lakṣmaṇa from the abhiṣeka maṇḍapa. He didn't want to be a block in the conversation of his sons with Vasiṣṭha, their ācārya. He sat on a pedestal, very close to the maṇḍapa, yet hidden from his sons.

Vasiṣṭha said, 'This is as much about the nakṣatra called Dhruva, as it is about Dhruva, the bhakta.'

Lakṣmaṇa implored the ācārya to speak about both. Vasiṣṭha willingly commenced the narration.

~

Svāyambhuva's son, Uttānapāda, had two wives called Sunīti and Suruci. Dhruva was the son of Sunīti while Uttama was of Suruci. One fine day, Dhruva, with some pebbles and a sling in his hands, went past the bhavana. He caught a glimpse of Uttama sitting on his father's lap. As the father cuddled and coddled Uttama, Dhruva, too, desirous of receiving this love, ran towards him. He sat on Uttānapāda's other lap, waiting for those fatherly fingers to run over him. To his shock, someone caught his neck from behind. It was Suruci, his step-mother. She was always envious of the little boy's brilliance and skills. She held the boy like a butcher would hold a rabbit. Her face showcased her arrogance and her tone showed her envy for the little boy. She said, 'Boy! You neither deserve to sit on the throne nor on your father's lap. You know why? You were not born of my womb. You are hence doomed to fail.' She threw him on the floor, and walked away.

The little boy's lips turned pale and were quivering with the fear of being orphaned even with his father by his side. He left the place to seek asylum and solace with Sunīti, his mother.

'What happened, Dhruva? Why are your eyes reddened and your cheeks hot?' The boy stood motionless, while Sunīti's attendants briefed her about Suruci's acrimonious meltdown. A hapless Sunīti said, 'Dhruva, we can't escape the effects of karma, accrued from our previous births. I am your father's wife for namesake, like you are his son. He is ashamed to call me his wife. Your birth from this unfortunate woman has ruined your life.'

She burst into tears and fell on the ground, showing her helplessness. Dhruva, the boy, barely five years of age, left the bhavana and walked into the woods. Blind to the danger in the forests and directionless, this boy just kept walking.

Nārada was informed about the incident that had transpired in the bhavana by Sunīti, and was also told that the soldiers had been dispatched to fetch Dhruva. Nārada assured Sunīti that he would guard Dhruva wherever he was. As he left for the forests, he spotted a little, determined boy walking along the Yamunā. He thought to himself, 'How glorious are these kṣatriyas who can't take even the slightest of insults,' and stopped Dhruva. He asked, 'Dhruva, why this much anger?' There was no reply from Dhruva.

Nārada compelled the boy to spell out his plans.

'I wish to attain the position which my father, grandfather and great-grandfather haven't,' swore Dhruva. Nārada said, 'Bramhā, your great grandfather obtained the blessings of Nārāyaṇa. Svāyambhuva, your grandfather, attained mokṣa by performing yajñas and bhakti yoga. You, too, can perform sādhanā. Go and bathe in these Yamunā waters and I shall direct you from there on.'

After bathing, Dhruva came forward and went around Nārada in a pradakṣiṇā. He mastered the twelve-syllable mantra of Vāsudeva. He erected a mūrti of Nārāyaṇa, and started tapasyā. He relinquished his food preferences while surviving on the kapittha and badara fruits. He ate dry leaves and did not drink water unless it was direly needed. His tapasyā rattled the devas, who pleaded to Nārāyaṇa to bless him. Paramātmā agreed to bless his bhakta.

The impoverished Dhruva felt a cool breeze brush him. He slowly opened his eyes to notice the entire place enveloped in sparkling light.

As he squeezed his eyes open to a slit, he saw someone seated on a bird.

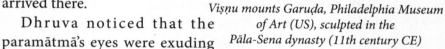

Viṣṇu mounts Garuḍa, Philadelphia Museum of Art (US), sculpted in the Pāla-Sena dynasty (11th century CE)

Upon inspection, he saw a body that looked like sapphire, and toe nails that resembled rubies. A smile that gave way to teeth that glittered like diamonds. As that person alighted from the bird, and walked up to Dhruva, the little boy kept staring.

It was Nārāyaṇa who had arrived there.

Dhruva noticed that the paramātmā's eyes were exuding love, a true father's love. His scars were healed and his body energized. He was choked with contrasting emotions and he couldn't speak a word. Only tears were rolling down his cheeks.

Nārāyaṇa lifted him up, this youngest of his bhaktas. He clasped the boy to him, with his cheeks rubbing over the little one's. Keeping Pāñcajanya suspended in the air, he patted the boy's cheek. With the paramātmā's eyes fixed on him, the little Dhruva said, 'I would like to perennially keep seeing you, hearing about you, smelling your tulasī garland, and always staying at your lotus-like feet.'

Paramātmā smiled broadly.

'Dhruva, from now on, the ṛṣis shall call the polestar by your name. At your paṭṭābhiṣeka, ṛṣis like Kaśyapa and Śukra shall do a pradakṣiṇā around you. You are very dear to me, Dhruva,' said Nārāyaṇa.

As Dhruva, with his head held high, reached the precincts of his rājya, Uttānapāda welcomed his son, for having performed a feat that unnerved even the ṛṣis. The rājā handed over the administration of his rājya to Dhruva and retired to the forests. Dhruva's tapasyā averted the inauspicious events in his rājya. He bore no enmity towards Uttama, his brother. He retired to Badarikāśrama to spend the rest of his life in sādhanā.

'Ācārya, this is inspiring,' remarked Lakṣmaṇa. 'I wanted to know if those forests where the spirited Dhruva performed tapasyā still exist?'

Vasiṣṭha said, 'Those forests where Dhruva performed tapasyā were inhabited by the asuras immediately. Lolā was their leader. He had a son called Madhu. Madhu's bhakti to Śiva fetched him a trident that was as powerful as Śiva's trident. He established a rājya in these forests of the asuras that was called Madhuvana, after him. He has been benevolent towards his prajā. I heard from ṛṣis that he is planning to retire to an island in the oceans, by handing over the rājya to Lavaṇa, his son. I have also heard tattles that his son is a tyrant, so Madhu is a bit hesitant.'

Rāma asked, 'Ācārya, what karma of Dhruva's previous birth made him a victim of his step-mother's diatribe?'

'He was a brāmhaṇa, serving his parents with utmost love. He was acquainted with a rājakumāra, witnessed all his opulence, and wished he was also one. This wish made him a rājakumāra in this birth, and his avarice may have resulted in this rocky relationship with Suruci,' said Vasiṣṭha

Daśaratha noticed his two sons taking leave of Vasiṣṭha. Then he approached Vasiṣṭha and paid his praṇāmas.

Looking at his face, the ācārya asked, 'Why do you look worried?'

Daśaratha said, 'I have not divulged the details of the circumstances that led to my vivāha with Kaikeyī. And that keeps haunting me.'

'That must have occurred many years ago. Why are you bothered now?' asked Vasiṣṭha. 'It may have occurred in the past. But I am worried if there will be repercussions now,' replied Daśaratha.

Vasiṣṭha nodded, allowing Daśaratha to narrate his agonizing past.

57

A Troublesome Past Revisits Daśaratha

Parting with one's child can be traumatizing for any mother. Kausalyā had to undergo this, when her daughter, Śāntā, was given away in adoption to Romapāda. Daśaratha, fully cognizant of her pain, wanted to cheer her up. So he went on an expedition to Rājagriha, to fetch the unseen, precious emerald stones for her.

As Daśaratha was camping by the foothills of Rājagriha, one fine morning he walked by the river Sudāmā. He noticed a group of apsarās playing in the river sands. One of them said, 'Show me your palm, I shall see what the future entails for you.' As the other apsarās extended her palm, she said, 'You will be married to the leader of the tribals soon, and you will sport a tiara made of crow feathers.' The group burst into an infectious laughter.

Suddenly, this apsarā saw a sturdy palm extend itself from her back. As she turned to check whose palm it was, she noticed a muscular, strong man with ravishing looks standing behind her. She couldn't take her eyes off him, while he said, 'Foretell, O young lady.'

As her right palm was clutched to his, an elderly woman arrived at the scene. In a vexed tone, she said, 'What is going on? May I know who this man is?'

The young women rose from their seats in reverence, and muttered, 'Kaikeyī, your mother has arrived. Leave his hand.'

'Why did you hold my daughter's palm? Do you know she is the rājakumāri of Kekaya rājya?' spoke the elderly lady.

'I am the rājā of Kosala whose rājadhānī is Ayodhyā. I had come to these hills seeking emeralds for Kausalyā, my wife, and as I ...,' said Daśaratha, while he was interrupted by a hoary voice that exclaimed, 'Welcome, Daśaratha. Kekaya is blessed with your presence.'

It was Aśvapati, the rājā of Kekaya who had arrived at the scene. Both the rājās exchanged pleasantries.

Before the conversation could continue any further, Aśvapati's wife said, 'Daśaratha, you will need to marry my daughter.'

'But why?' asked Aśvapati.

'He held our daughter's right hand. This is called pāṇigrahaṇa, right? Aśvapati rājā, you are well-versed in the śāstras. This is what others have to say about you.'

Daśaratha, in bewilderment, said, 'But Kaikeyī was just holding my palm to foretell my future, how can this be tantamount to ...'

'Foretell? I know no such skill in my daughter. You are older than her. As a rājā, you must have known that holding a rājakumāri's palm is as good as getting into a vivāha with her,' said Aśvapati's wife in a lofty tone.

'Daśaratha is already married to Kausalyā and Ṣumitrā,' said a helpless Aśvapati.

'It doesn't matter,' she said.

Daśaratha who had fallen prey to Kaikeyī's beauty was not averse to this proposal. 'What kanyāśulka should I pay?' asked Daśaratha.

'Don't insist on such formalities, my friend. You are one of the best rājās of our times. Kaikeyī must be blessed to be your wife,' said Aśvapati.

'No, I don't think we can abandon such traditions. I would insist that the kanyāśulka be given. I am told Kausalyā and Sumitrā have not mothered sons, as yet. In case Kaikeyī gives birth to a son, he should be made the heir-apparent,' said Aśvapati's wife.

Daśaratha agreed to this proposal, and married Kaikeyī.

It was this past that was bothering him.

Vasiṣṭha said, 'I have heard this entirely. While Kaikeyī's mother insisted that traditions not be broken, wasn't she aware that the eldest of the sons being the heir-apparent was also an established tradition? Well, it is better that I refrain from talking about people who have shed their mortal coils.'

Daśaratha asked, 'Should I worry about this promise?'

Vasiṣṭha replied, 'I don't think so. This promise was made to her in the presence of Aśvapati and his wife. Now that Aśvapati is the only surviving witness, it is pertinent on his part to remind you.'

'But a promise given is to be fulfilled immaterial of reminders, right?' asked Daśaratha.

Vasiṣṭha closed his eyes in a pensive mood, and said, 'Promises made on five occasions can be circumvented if the need arises is what I have heard many ṛṣis opine. In that list of five occasions, one is the promise made for a vivāha to happen. So this śāstra comes to your rescue and annexed to that is the absence of Kaikeyī's mother. Above all, Aśvapati is an enlightened individual who will never interfere in your matters.'

Daśaratha, who sighed in relief, asked for the remaining four occasions when promises don't have to be adhered to. Vasiṣṭha refrained from mentioning those, but asked Daśaratha to keep him abreast with such commitments made in the distant past. Daśaratha assured Vasiṣṭha that he knew of two private incidents which no one else knew, one was the promise made to Aśvapati during his vivāha to Kaikeyī, and the other was the curse pronounced upon him by the tapasvī's father.

'What coaxed you to finally disclose this incident to me?' Vasiṣṭha asked in a sarcastic tone.

'Frequent dreams with the wailing father's curse coupled with your narration of Suruci's disgraceful treatment of Dhruva, her stepson, made me divulge the details,' said Daśaratha.

'Do not make such promises which will trouble you any further,' warned Vasiṣṭha, only to conclude the conversation with an ominous warning. 'Rājā, note that your nakṣatra[1] has been aspected by Sūrya, Aṅgāraka and Rāhu recently. Most śiṣyas of mine don't view this development in a positive light. Let your well-thought decisions be quick.'

1 Revati naksatra.

58

A Learned Council Extols Rāma's Virtues

'Why has Daśaratha called us for this meeting?' asked Jayanta.

'I feel Daśaratha may want us to check on Lavaṇa's activities in Madhuvana,' replied Vijaya.

'I am not sure if this is his intent, for Lavaṇa is too young. His childhood pranks should not be blown out of proportion,' said Aśoka.

The rakṣaka informed the mantris that the rājā had arrived. The mantris rose from their seats that were laid in front of the rājā, and waited till he sat.

'What are the qualities that you cherish in Rāma?' asked Daśaratha. He was doubtful if his mantris would construe the question in the right manner. He lowered his head expecting sombre answers.

'Rāma is well-spoken. He chooses the sweetest of words. To any person who is shy to speak, he initiates the conversation. He has mastered the art of speaking, like Bṛhaspati,' said Siddhārtha.

'He is a true kṣatriya who sports his valour like an armour. He fights his enemies in their chosen areas. The wicked sons of Tāṭakā saw this. I see an Indra and a Yama in him,' said Vijaya.

'He never gets angry. Rather, he has control over his anger. And if he gets angry, he is sure to make the world tremble,' said Driśti.

'He is the best in archery. I have heard Vasiṣṭha say this,' said Jayanta.

'He adheres to the truth. He speaks that beautifully. His belief in this virtue is so strong that he will never speak the untruth even in adversity,' said Sumantra.

Daśaratha's face slowly brightened up.

'I have seen him amidst elderly people, conversing with them. His respect for personalities of superior conduct and enviable wisdom is palpable. He respects the prajā immaterial of their highs or lows,' said Aśoka.

'He can gauge the needs of his prajā from their faces. But no one can guess what he is thinking by the look on his face,' said Mantrapālā.

'He values prapatti dharma as his ātmā. No one who arrives at his doorstep seeking asylum will ever go empty-handed,' said Aśoka.

'He isn't jealous of any one for he is the trove of prosperity. He is so complete that he is beyond the realm of everyone else's jealousy,' said Sumantra.

'He remembers even a small help extended to him, and forgets any anguish caused to him. He proves that his thoughts and actions are meant for the good of even those who don't want any good for him. He brings happiness to our prajā by his mere presence. They love him more than they love their family, this rājya and even themselves. They see their ātmā stationed in Rāma's body. Who on this Bhūmi can boast of such a compliment?' said Siddhārtha.

'Rāma knows the art of collecting taxes from people without putting them in distress, like the bees that collect nectar from flowers. He has also mastered the art of giving back benefits to them bountifully like the clouds that suck the waters from the seas, and shower copious rains back on Bhūmi,' said Arthasādhaka.

'He is adept in taming elephants and riding horses. He leads the army from the front. And his resolve is as sturdy as the mountain,' said Jayanta.

Daśaratha's eyes were moist. He was filled with pride. He felt that a barrage of Rāma's qualities was thrown open by his mantris.

'But why do you ask about these qualities of Rāma all of a sudden? Do you plan to send him on any expedition? Do you plan for a rājasuya or another Aśvamedha?' asked a curious Sumantra.

'The circumstances demand Rāma becoming the heir-apparent,' thundered a voice. The mantris turned their heads, and checked who the person was.

Vasiṣṭha and Vāmadeva walked into the assembly. The mantris rose from their seats, and so did Daśaratha.

The duo blessed them and took their seats. Vāmadeva said, 'The nakṣatra of Daśaratha has been aspected by Sūrya, Aṅgāraka and Rāhu. This doesn't augur auspiciousness for the monarch. The skies have been gloomy before sunset. The rain-bearing clouds envelop the skies when it isn't the monsoon season. Lately, many parts of our rājya have experienced tremors. I have consulted with astrologers who decipher such nimittas. They feel that the rājya should see a shift in power.'

Daśaratha said, 'I respect this suggestion. I have heard about Rāma's qualities from my mantris. Ācārya, I pray to listen to your views.'

Vasiṣṭha said, 'He is adept in the vedas. He is appreciative of the śāstras of music and dance. He has vowed to be in a relationship with only Sītā. Who else have we known in the kṣatriyas to honour their women in such light? Above all, his wife is an epitome of superior virtues. She was spotted in Bhūmi by Janaka. Today, she has gifted the patience of Bhūmi, her birthplace to her consort. No one in the present world can match Rāma, and…'

Daśaratha said, 'and…'

Vasiṣṭha said, 'He is peerless. That's all.'

Daśaratha thanked Vasiṣṭha and his mantris for unhesitatingly sharing their views on Rāma.

Later, in the āśrama, Vasiṣṭha was asked by Vāmadeva if there was any aspect of Rāma which he didn't want to divulge to the assemblage. Vasiṣṭha nodded affirmatively and said that Nārāyaṇa, the paramātmā, had come down as Rāma to rejuvenate dharma.

59

Rāma's Coronation Announced

'In the illustrious lineage of Bramhā, Marīci, Kaśyapa, Vivasvān, Manu, Ikṣvāku, Vikukṣi, Kakutstha, Dhundhumāra, Prasenjit, Māndhātā, Tryāruṇi, Triśaṅku, Hariścandra, Rohitāśva, Sagara, Aṃśumān, Bhagīratha, Ṛtūparṇa, Mitrasaha, Aśmaka, Mūlaka, Dilīpa, Raghu and Aja comes our beloved rājā, Daśaratha. Arise from your seats, and bow your heads to him,' announced a rakṣaka.

With the prajā gathered on either side, Daśaratha walked past them with folded hands that looked like lotus buds. He walked up the gold-gilded steps, with one of his hands on Sumantra's shoulder. His face carried the aura of having listened to Rāma's qualities from his mantris, while his breathlessness revealed his senility. He sat on the throne, which he had adorned for many years now.

'Prajā, I hope you are all keeping good health, and witnessing prosperity by the benign blessings of Nārāyaṇa, our presiding mūrti,' Daśaratha said this in his voice that sounded like a kettledrum. He paused for a while, and then continued with his speech. 'This white umbrella that you see above me has witnessed numerous rājās in our vaṃśa. Numerous decisions favouring the welfare of prajā, and umpteen judgements that stood by dharma, were pronounced in its shade. I desire rest. I must eventually retire to the forests. But I must ensure that this throne of Ayodhyā is bestowed on the right person, who will be my heir-apparent.' He again paused, but this caused some restlessness in the prajā. Sumantra raised his hand, pointing to the prajā to remain patient.

'After due consultation with my mantris and the brāmhaṇas in our rājya, I have decided that Rāma, the eldest of my sons, shall be the next rājā of Ayodhyā. Let him hold the sceptre in his hands while ensuring dharma in this rājya,' said Daśaratha.

There was a rapturous applause in the audience. For a moment, Daśaratha noted the same happiness as the peacocks would display upon seeing the rain-bearing clouds. He beamed with happiness, looking at Sumantra, who was equally elated.

One man said, 'We as prajā could only wish that Rāma was our rājā. But it is you who has fulfilled it. We were apprehensive to voice this out to you, for we didn't want to hurt you. But when you have decided it our way, we are supremely pleased.'

Another man said, 'Rāma's adherence to dharma is well-known. His long arms point to his ability to protect this rājya from all enemies. It is said that Madhu and Kaiṭabha had once caused immense harm to Bhūmi, and she is said to have lost her intrinsic fragrance. We are sure she shall regain that with Rāma's presence as our rājā.'

An old lady came forward with her hands on her granddaughter, and spoke in a feeble tone, 'All the women I know, who are used to propitiating to only Nārāyaṇa, are now, for the sake of Rāma's good health and fame, propitiating every devatā. Rājā, did you notice the mild tremors in our assembly when you announced Rāma's paṭṭābhiṣeka? It was indicative of the excitement among the prajā. We have only one more desire, that he should be seated on Śatruñjaya, our royal elephant. As he is seated on the elephant, it will be a heavenly sight. Make sure that his face is covered by the cloth that hangs from the umbrella, to protect him from scorching rays.'

When it was believed that the prajā had finished voicing their opinion, the young girl continued from where her grandmother left off, and said, 'Rāma has long arms which we have never seen in any other kṣatriya. Doesn't that mean he will protect us at all times? His walk is as majestic as an elephant, just like our Śatruñjaya. His face is as beautiful as the Candra, bereft of its spots. He simply steals our eyes with his beauty, that is nonpareil. He listens to us, and is very accessible. His demeanour steals our hearts. His presence provides us the relief of showers when it is sweltering hot, all along. When is the paṭṭābhiṣeka scheduled?'

The old lady chided the young one in disapproval of talking precociously before royalty.

Sumantra and Daśaratha looked at each other in satisfaction.

60

A Rājya Rejoices

Mango flowers were kissed passionately by the singing kokilas, and so was the nectar in the lotuses savoured by the bumblebees. Women adorned their tresses with the flowers of karnikāra, aśoka and mallikā in the Caitra month. Beautiful floral patterns were drawn outside the houses, and the smell of incense sticks engulfed every corner. Tents were erected in street corners of the nagarī, where mashed rice with milk and curd was cooked to serve the incoming guests. In the maṇḍapa's adjoining temples, dance performances and music recitals were organized. Sumantra ensured that the arrangements were in order.

Vāmadeva, on the other hand, was responsible for keeping the materials required for the paṭṭābhiṣeka in order. He deployed the goldsmiths in polishing the white umbrella, and the sceptre. A hundred golden pots filled with the Sarayū waters were arranged in the assembly hall.

Daśaratha summoned Rāma to his apartment. The eldest of the sons reached his father's presence. Rāma's wisdom shone like Sūrya who illuminates the Meru mountain, and like the invigorating rays of Candra who is the crest jewel amidst nakṣatras. He prostrated at Daśaratha's feet with folded hands and submitted his abhivādana, introducing himself as 'Rāma Varmā', in accordance with the kṣatriya handbook.

Daśaratha embraced his dearest son, kissed him on the forehead and said, 'Rāma, you are the fruit of my accrued puṇya in countless births. By fathering you, I fulfilled the wishes of pitṛs. In this lifetime, I have conducted many yajñas, and offered generous dakṣiṇā to the officiating ṛtviks. In this manner, I have impressed the devas and brāmhaṇas. Having undergone adhyayana in the vedas, I have gotten rid of the debt to the ṛṣis. I have enjoyed all the comforts in my life. When I look at you, I feel I am looking at myself in the mirror. Rāma, you are the repository of all auspicious attributes. This morning, when I stood before the mirror, I realized how old I have turned. It felt as if my white hair was telling me to relinquish the throne. While it is my desire to anoint you as the heir-apparent, the prajā, too, concur with this view wholeheartedly. This crown will suit you the most, my dear son Rāma, the one with eyes like the petals of a red lotus. Yet, as your father, I am bound to share my learnings. Unabated anger and irresistible lust leads us to acts that are completely avoidable. Treating women as harlots, spending productive time in gambling, addiction to hunting animals, falling prey to vāruṇi, being harsh when speaking and punishing prajā in the cruellest manner are some of the vices a poor rājā possesses.'

Rāma prostrated at his father's feet again. Having obtained his father's approval to speak, he said, 'Father, you have underestimated your powers. You are a man of immense prowess and unparalleled wisdom. You must rule Ayodhyā for many more years. We feel safe in your rājya.'

Daśaratha told Rāma that he had been experiencing dreadful dreams, and mentioned meteor showers in the surrounding villages. He added that the ṛṣis deciphered such incidents as signs of death for the reigning rājā.

Rāma was shocked to hear of the prophecy. He exercised high restraint in not letting the tears trickle out of his lotus-like eyes. He mustered courage, and humbly accepted the decision of Daśaratha, the famed rājā of Ayodhyā.

With some hesitation, he said, 'The four of us have grown up together. Bharata and Śatrughna are away in Kekaya. It will be my fortune to have them as well at the paṭṭābhiṣeka. It will be licit too.'

'You know, your paṭṭābhiṣeka is arranged on the day aspected by the Puṣya nakṣatra. It is Bharata's nakṣatra, don't you know that?' asked Daśaratha convincingly.

Knowing that Rāma would still want his brothers to be present, the rājā said, 'Bharata is my treasure. He has always been respectful to me. He loves you the most. He is always accompanied by Śatrughna, like you are always followed by Lakṣmaṇa. I am eager to see him in Ayodhyā, after twelve years. I will dispatch a messenger to bring your cherished brothers back, but let not the paṭṭābhiṣeka be paralysed citing his absence. The caprices of humans are well known to you, Rāma. My instinct asks me to carry out this auspicious event at the earliest, when Bharata is away in Kekaya. Please meet Vasiṣṭha, our purohita and follow his instructions.'

Rāma nodded positively, and left the apartment.

61

A Mother's Pride

Nārāyaṇa, the presiding mūrti of Ayodhyā, was looking like a lotus pond with his eyes, face, hands and feet all resembling freshly blossomed lotuses. The flanking of Lakṣmī and Bhūmi on either sides looked like pristine haṃsas swimming in the lotus pond. From another slant, Nārāyaṇa looked like the wish-yielding kalpaka tree, with his consorts who looked like the creepers entwined around it. Kausalyā was quenching her spiritual thirst in his presence, and seeking mystic solace in his shade.

Rāma reached the temple of Nārāyaṇa. He noticed his mother seated in front of the mūrti, with eyes closed. He approached her, waiting for her to take notice of him. As she gracefully looked at him, Rāma offered his praṇāmas to her and submitted his abhivādana. He said, 'Mother, I have been ordered by Daśaratha, the ruling rājā of Ayodhyā, to undergo the paṭṭābhiṣeka. This order states that I will be the rājā from tomorrow. I need your guidance to this effect.'

Kausalyā was already aware of this news through sources privy to her. Meanwhile Sumitrā, Lakṣmaṇa and Sītā rushed to the temple premises. Kausalyā said, 'May Nārāyaṇa shower his choicest blessings on you. Rāma, you are a fountainhead of knowledge. Do you think I will have the acumen to advise you? I am always in awe when you speak. I would prefer to be like Devahūti, whose path to sākṣātkāra was steered by her very son, Kapila.'

Rāma turned towards Lakṣmaṇa and told him that Lakṣmaṇa was indispensable to the rājya. Rāma added that without Lakṣmaṇa's services, he wouldn't be able to execute any order for the welfare of his subjects. Lakṣmaṇa was bashful on hearing the compliment, and nodded his head in agreement.

Utsava mūrti of Namperumāḷ in Śrīraṅgam (Tamil Nadu)

Vasiṣṭha entered the temple with his śiṣyas. Kausalyā, Sumitrā, Rāma, Sītā and Lakṣmaṇa stood in reverence to the bramharṣi with folded hands. As the purohita sat on the maṇḍapa pedestals, he looked at Rāma with a sigh of satisfaction. He said, 'Rāma, I am sure you would have been informed about your paṭṭābhiṣeka by Daśaratha. Your father is as excited as Nahuṣa who performed paṭṭābhiṣeka to Yayāti, his son, in the days of yore. I have a few orders to be conveyed to you. Along with Sītā, you will need to fast till the paṭṭābhiṣeka takes place. I will ask my śiṣyas to bring a pair of mats made out of darbha grass for the both of you. To sleep, use that tonight.'

The purohita then turned to the rest of them and said, 'I can see the glee in all your faces too. After all, it is Rāma, my dear śiṣya, who is going to be anointed the rājā soon. Kausalyā and Sumitrā must take charge of giving away cows in charity to the needy. Lakṣmaṇa must keep an eye on the incoming guests to Ayodhyā for auspicious events such as the paṭṭābhiṣeka are marred by unforeseen obstacles.'

As Sūrya was about to set, Rāma and Sītā left for their bhavana. After bathing, with Sītā by his side, Rāma offered ghee to the blazing āhavanīya fire while saying, 'Agni, I offer this to you, who is accompanied by Svāhā, your dear wife. Please carry this havis to Nārāyaṇa, who is accompanied by Lakṣmī, also known to the ṛṣis as Svāhā. I offer this to Prajāpati as well, who has Nārāyaṇa as his antaryāmī.' Rāma completed the evening ritual by consuming the ghee prasāda. The daṃpati returned to the temple of Nārāyaṇa. Rāma and Sītā sat in the presence of the mūrti, and performed arcanā with lotus flowers. As Rāma was involved in reciting the puruṣa sūkta, a portion that celebrates the glory of Nārāyaṇa, Sītā couldn't take her eyes off Rāma. She saw the dexterity with which Rāma was performing ārādhanā and hārati to the mūrti. She noticed the resemblance in the mūrti, and Rāma, its ārādhaka. Her eyes dilated in amazement and her heart swelled in pride. As they retired to their darbha mats in a maṇḍapa, Sītā with a smile asked, 'Rāma, my know-it-all husband, can you tell me about Devahūti and Kapila, whom your mother was referring to?'

62

Kapila and the Sāṅkhya Philosophy

Svāyambhūva Manu along with Śatarūpā were living in Barhiṣmatī. The nagarī derived its existence from the Varāha avatāra of Nārāyaṇa where as a running wild boar, his body hair fell in multiple areas. The ṛṣis regarded the darbha grass spread in the nagarī outskirts as offshoots of Varāha's body hair. Manu ruled this province called Bramhāvarta from Barhiṣmatī, its rājadhānī. The land mass was sandwiched between two rivers, Sarasvatī and Dṛṣadvatī. The daṃpati left for Bindu[1], the holy lake, in their chariot. After sprinkling water from the lake on their heads, they noticed a handsome personality with jaṭā and large eyes, dressed in rags. Manu could perceive the halo around this person, and approached him with folded hands. He said, 'Praṇāmas to you. I am hopeful that you are an upakurvāṇa, as you wouldn't have taken any vow of endless celibacy. I am in search of a groom for Devahūti, my daughter. Her bodily glow excels the glitter of her ornaments.'

The ṛṣi opened his eyes, and said, 'My name is Kardama. Yesterday, while I was engrossed in dhyāna, I heard an inner voice that said I will be marrying the daughter of Manu soon. When my eyes opened,

1 Siddhpur is a town in the Indian state of Gujarat.

I heard the sound of brihat and rathantara, the sāma vaidika chants. As I turned back, I saw Garuḍa leaving the spot with the flapping of his wings. I knew this was a command given to me by paramātmā.'

The gratified father conducted the vivāha between Devahūti and Kardama, as per vaidika norms. To this daṃpati, paramātmā chose to be born as a little boy manifesting some of his unique qualities. He was born with hair that resembled gold, and eyes that looked like petals of lotus. His tawny complexion earned him the name Kapila. He flourished as a handsome boy and, to everyone's surprise, he was able to grasp the amṛta of the vedas with mere intuition. Kardama noticed his son's prodigal abilities and proclivity to sākṣātkāra. Realizing that his son was immensely blessed by the paramātmā, Kardama took leave of his family and assumed the role of a sannyāsī.

Devahūti was disheartened at Kardama's departure. Seeing his mother in distress, Kapila said, 'The material body is a conglomerate of sense organs, with the mind whose innate quality is to engage in servitude to paramātmā. Due to perpetual karma, the material body and the puruṣa are treated as one and the same. This is ahaṁkāra, say the ṛṣis. Your attachment to Kardama, my revered father, was only limited to his material body. In reality, he has acted true to the śruti injunction that ordains a person to engage in bhakti towards the paramātmā. This terrible cycle of birth and death can never be disbanded until there is the benign grace of Nārāyaṇa.'

As Devahūti heard this, she was enlightened about the purpose of puruṣa's bhakti to paramātmā. She practised upāsanā towards paramātmā, and her jīvātmā shed its mortal coils at the destined time. The āśrama where Devahūti obtained mokṣa was called Siddhapada from then on.

Kapila proceeded from the banks of Sarasvatī to the banks of Gaṅgā. Kapila's grip on the vaidika quintessence earned him the name Maharṣi, and his sermons were the most sought-after by rājās of different quarters. Kapila's proficiency in the yoga śāstra earned him the reverence of many siddhas.

Over a period of time, Kapila became the progenitor of sāṅkhya school of philosophy. The central doctrine of sāṅkhya philosophy revolved around the prakriti, puruṣa and paramātmā. This further delved on the uncaused mūla prakriti giving rise to evolutes that are twenty-three in number, and the puruṣa that is neither caused nor is the cause of anything else. This prakriti and puruṣa were deemed fit under the dominion of paramātmā. But in due course of time, the sāṅkhya school of philosophy underwent revisions, and the role of paramātmā was masked entirely.

63

A Hunchback's Arrival at Jubilant Ayodhyā

In the early hours of dawn, Rāma said, 'Sūrya, I perform dhyāna on you, who is respected by us all; your rays provide us energy, while praises on you are enchanting to our ears,' as he invoked the 'mitrasya cārśini dhrutaḥ' mantra from Śukla yajurveda. Sītā's eyes were fixed on Rāma doing his daily karma. She was looking at him as if she was seeing him for the first time. Dressed in silk clothes, the daṃpati performed the morning ārādhanā to the mūrti in the temple. Later, they rode in the chariot to their bhavana, on well-sprinkled pathways. The daṃpati noticed the houses decorated in beautiful flowers. Banana trees were placed on both sides of the gateways, and the walls were covered in areca leaves. The daṃpati noticed smoke

Lakṣmī amidst elephants in Sanci stupa (Madhya Pradesh) sculpted in the Sātavāhana dynasty (1st century CE)

emanating from a certain house laced with the smell of burnt lotuses. As the chariot stopped, they heard the brāmhaṇas say, 'Lakṣmī, we pray to you, the one with the cool rays of Candra. Like the lotus that emerges from the serene waters, so do our minds rise above the material realm when they meditate upon you, who is mercy incarnate. You are the personification of the vaidika riks which we invoke looking at Sūrya. Your divine will, called the saṅkalpa, has given birth to the vilva tree, and its fruits are used in the vaidika yajñas. Your amiable grace ensures that our basic requirements like water and food are met with ease.'

Alakṣmī with the symbols of crow and a broomstick sculpted in the Pallava dynasty (8th century CE)

Please drive away Alakṣmī, the personification of everything inauspicious from our lives.

Sītā simpered as if the brāmhaṇas were speaking to her and invoking her grace. Rāma smiled in acknowledgement, as the chariot continued to the bhavana.

An elderly woman with white hair was stooping, holding a stick in her hand. Her eyes were blue, burning with anger for an unknown reason. Her eyes were coloured in the collyrium of greed and her lips were painted in the paste of envy. A swarm of bees hovered around her palasa flower-decorated chignon. A prominent hunch adorned her back. She belonged to Kekaya, and used to babysit Kaikeyī. Unable to bear separation from Kaikeyī, she used to visit Ayodhyā. But Bharata's extended stay in Rājagriha did not bring her to Ayodhyā that often. Her antecedents were unknown, but her name wasn't. She was called Mantharā.

Mantharā falteringly walked towards a woman who was drawing floral patterns outside her dwelling. She asked, 'Why is Ayodhyā wearing a festive look?'

The woman replied, 'Don't you know? It is Rāma's paṭṭābhiṣeka tomorrow. We are all gearing up for this momentous event that we have been waiting for all our lives. You should also get ready. The rānī is giving clothes and jewellery to charity. You can also receive them, if you go to her bhavana.'

'Rānī, who?' asked Mantharā.

'Kausalyā', came the answer.

Mantharā noticed no signs of festivities outside Kaikeyī's bhavana. She walked up the stairs and spotted Kaikeyī, who was sleeping peacefully on her bed. She shouted, 'Wake up you fool. A barrage of calamities is waiting to strike you.'

Kaikeyī opened her eyes and looked at Mantharā. But the latter unhesitatingly continued, 'Your husband talks about adherence to the truth in public while he is deceitful in private. He will come running to you and will place his head on your lap. You will run your fingers through his hair, unaware that you have been romanticizing a snake, that too a venomous one. You will act as if you are the closest to Daśaratha. But his love for you is like the river waters in the summer, which is meagre and doesn't quench the thirst of the passersby. He will charm you with sweet words. But you are too naive to understand his ploy. You and your son are gone to rack and ruin. But remember, anything that afflicts you brings me sorrow.'

'Sorrow, why? You have the gift of the gab. Tell me at once, what has caused this pain?' asked Kaikeyī while still lying on the bed.

'Don't you know about the paṭṭābhiṣeka that is being arranged for Rāma? Do you know that this event, of great importance, is being carried out in the absence of Bharata, your son?' asked Mantharā with a straight face. Like Candra who appears spotless during the autumn, so did Kaikeyī's face brighten up upon hearing the news of Rāma's paṭṭābhiṣeka. She was unable to contain her joy. She took a pearl necklace from her neck, and gave it to Mantharā as a present. Then, Kaikeyī said, 'Mantharā, the news that you bring is like amṛta to my ears. Please let me know if I can give you something else?'

64

Mantharā's Poison Consumes Kaikeyī

'You foolish woman, do you realize a big calamity has struck you? While you will be drowning in the ocean of sorrow very soon, you are happily celebrating the news of the paṭṭābhiṣeka. Honestly, I do not know if I have to laugh at your stupidity or cry about how gullible you are. Rāma is not your son. He is Kausalyā's son,' said an irate Mantharā. She threw the pearl necklace on the floor, with the pearls scattered in all directions.

Kaikeyī said, 'I don't see any difference between Rāma and Bharata.'

'But your husband does! Puṣya is your son's nakṣatra, and the paṭṭābhiṣeka is exactly happening tomorrow on the day aspected by this nakṣatra, and in Karkata lagna. To the rājā, there is something in Bharata which worries him, and that reason is unknown to me. If my notion is wrong, why isn't Bharata invited for the paṭṭābhiṣeka?' said Mantharā.

Kaikeyī said, 'Rāma is the repository of all virtues. He is grateful and adheres to the truth. He deserves to be the rājā. He protects his brothers, just like Daśaratha now takes care of his sons. After many years of ruling Ayodhyā, Rāma will consider Bharata to be his successor. We shall continue staying prosperous at all times, be rest assured.'

Mantharā said, 'Forget about this distant dream of yours. I am petrified thinking about your immediate future. I see you with folded hands serving Kausalyā, Māṇḍavī serving Sītā, and your son serving Rāma. All your time will be spent serving them.'

Kaikeyī said, 'Rāma is worthy of becoming the rājā. In my opinion, worthier than Bharata. Haven't you seen how sincerely he would serve me? Bharata is very dear to Rāma. If Rāma is going to be the rājā, it is as good as Bharata becoming one.'

Mantharā said, 'You are truly an imbecile. Don't you know it is Rāma's son who will succeed him, and not your son? If you believe all the sons of a rājā will be instated as rājās, trust me, there will only be anarchy.'

There was silence.

Mantharā continued, 'Rāma is obtaining the rājya with little effort. But I am sure, his objective after becoming the rājā will be to banish Bharata from Ayodhyā. It is Bharata, your son, who will be more despondent than both of us.'

'What substantiates your conviction, Mantharā?' interjected Kaikeyī.

Mantharā asserted, 'Just because your father Aśvapati wanted to have spiritual discussions with Bharata, he had to leave Ayodhyā. It is over ten years now. How long will these discussions continue? My attempts to send him to Ayodhyā were futile. Did Daśaratha call him back from Kekaya, even once?'

'So is Śatrughna,' said a confident Kaikeyī.

'Bharata and Śatrughna are inseparable. So are Rāma and Lakṣmaṇa. They are like the Aśvinikumāras. They have always been that way, from their younger days. Even trees respond to our proximity to them, don't they? Rāma protects Lakṣmaṇa, like a father guarding his son. But where is that brotherhood between Rāma and Bharata?' asked Mantharā.

Mantharā counsels Kaikeyī in the Hazāra Rama Temple (Karnataka) sculpted in the Vijayanagara dynasty (15th century CE)

'You must know that my father is indisposed. I am sure Yudhājit would have been invited instead. Bharata will come along with them,' maintained Kaikeyī.

'Kaikeyī, the decision was made recently. I am sure no invitation was sent. Even if the invitation was sent, it will take over seven days for them to reach Ayodhyā. What purpose does it serve then?' asked Mantharā.

Kaikeyī was left speechless.

'Daśaratha neither invited your father nor your brother for the paṭṭābhiṣeka. Your husband did not bother to wait till Bharata arrived. What does this prove? It simply means that the rājā is hiding something that is known to your father which he doesn't want us to know. It also brings out his aversion to Bharata. Your son is going to be hunted by Rāma, once he assumes power, like a lion that waits for an opportunity to pounce on a wounded elephant,' roared Mantharā.

Kaikeyī's eyes slowly turned moist. Turning herself away from Mantharā, she asked, 'I am sure Kausalyā will never let Rāma go astray.'

'Completely baseless. After his vivāha with you, Daśaratha has been ignoring Kausalyā. Like a wounded snake that waits to fight back its enemies, so will she wait for an opportunity to hit back at you or your son. She will rather induce more hatred in Rāma towards Bharata. She will also seek to annex Kekaya with this rājya. Rāma, to fulfil her aspirations, will summon your brother for a war. And as you keep singing praises about Rāma's valour, he will prove you right on the battlefield. From your son, father and brother's deaths at the hands of Rāma to the seizing of Kekaya, you will be responsible. But you will not be allowed to question even then. You know why? Because you will be the attendant to Kausalyā or Sītā in their apartments,' said Mantharā.

65

A Diabolical Plan Unfolds

'While I was under the wrong assumption that Rāma, who will become the rājā of Ayodhyā, will guarantee us a good life, it is you who has removed this veil of ignorance,' said Kaikeyī in a grateful tone, as she sat on the settee. Kaikeyī was taking deep breaths, but was unaware of the way ahead. She was soaked in ire, but did not know whom to direct it at.

'What is the way ahead for my Bharata, and what is it for that Rāma?' asked Mantharā.

'Bharata should become the rājā of Ayodhyā, and Rāma must go somewhere,' said Kaikeyī.

'Somewhere, where?' asked Mantharā.

'Maybe to the forests,' paused Kaikeyī, and continued, 'but I don't know the plan of action.'

'Kaikeyī, do you remember the battle at Vaijayanta?' asked Mantharā.

'Vaguely, yes, but how does that help me now,' asked Kaikeyī.

'I will narrate whatever I heard from you long back. Daśaratha had volunteered to assist Indra and the devas when they were fighting the asuras at Vaijayanta[1], south of the Daṇḍaka forests. The asuras were led by Śambara, the one whose flag had the whale motif. After fighting through the day, when you were sleeping with Daśaratha in the tent, you spotted the movement of asuras. You instantly woke Daśaratha up from his sleep. When Sumantra could not be spotted, you rode the chariot for the rājā. The asuras shot many arrows from behind at Daśaratha, and you instantly escorted him to the medical practitioner. While Daśaratha was being administered with medicines, the asuras attacked him there too. It was you who courageously drove them away. The rājā took cognizance of your bravery, and offered you two boons. You didn't know what to ask then, and you politely brushed them aside. Isn't it time for you to seek those boons, Kaikeyī?' asked Mantharā.

Kaikeyī's face lightened up.

'I will ask the throne for Bharata, and …' said a dithering Kaikeyī.

'And what, Kaikeyī?' asked Mantharā.

'That Rāma has to go to the forests,' completed Kaikeyī.

---

1 Scholars opine, this could be Banavasi in Uttara Kannada of the Indian state of Karnataka.

'Well, Rāma shall go to the forests for a year and will return. Do you think that will help? Instead, Bharata needs time to convince the prajā with his administrative skills and generosity in kind. He must prove his valour by bringing the neighbouring rājyas under his control. These shall win the hearts of the prajā and the army. Meanwhile, Bharata should be blessed with a son, whose skills should be honed to perfection. Rāma's exile will distance him from Sītā, and will isolate him from the prajā. Even if Rāma returns to Ayodhyā from exile, there will be no intent in the prajā to witness his paṭṭābhiṣeka for they will be habitualized with Bharata's regime. This is the only way Bharata and his son can firmly establish their legacy in Ayodhyā,' said Mantharā.

'How long should this exile be?' asked Kaikeyī innocently.

Turning her face towards Kaikeyī, Mantharā, the one with a thunderous voice, and diabolic pair of eyes said, 'fourteen years'.

Kaikeyī looked as if an impossible feat was achieved. She brought a cup of gold paste, smeared it on Mantharā's hump, and circled a golden garland studded with precious stones on it. She said that she wouldn't have known of Daśaratha's despicable plans had Mantharā not apprised her. She added that she then realized why Mantharā's hump was huge, for it carried all the brains required for a kṣatriya, and many other magical powers. To the very bashful Mantharā, Kaikeyī said, 'Mantharā, like a lotus that bends itself to a breeze, so do you look with your hump. It seems to me as if you are the prettiest hunchback woman this world has ever seen.'

66

Deadly Promises Redeemed

Daśaratha's chariot arrived at Kaikeyī's bhavana. The sounds of peacocks and parrots reverberated throughout. He ascended the stairs to the apartment that was plastered in white limestone paste. He entered the apartment like Candra who awaits Rāhu during grahaṇa. Kaikeyī was neither spotted welcoming the rājā nor was she seen on the bed. He asked the rakṣaka about Kaikeyī. With shivering hands and a quivering voice, the rakṣaka said, 'She is in the chamber of wrath'. The perplexed rājā had myriad questions running in his mind as to what could have caused his dearest wife this unabated anger. Gems of multiple colours were scattered on the ground, like the colourful nakṣatra*s* that embellish the night sky. With unkempt hair that was tied as a single braid and draped in a soiled saree, Kaikeyī was lying on the floor, bereft of her usual ornaments. Like a poisonous snake waiting to strike its enemy, Kaikeyī had resolved to seek the boons at any cost. He lifted her gently with both his hands as he exited the chamber of wrath and placed her on the bed. With his hands caressing her, he said, 'Kaikeyī, my dear, why are you angry? Whom are you angry with? Who has disrespected you? I am pained to see you smeared in dust. If you are afflicted with body ailments, I will summon the best medical practitioners to attend to you. If you wish to help somebody, I am ready to execute that. And in case you are displeased with someone, I am ready to bring an end to him. But you shouldn't spoil your health for such petty reasons. I can't see you shed tears. I am waiting for your eye gestures to execute anything that pleases you. Besides Kosala, my authority extends to the rājyas of Aṅga, Vaṅga, Magadha, Matsya, Saurāṣṭra, Sindhu-Sauvīra and to the southern ones too.'

Daśaratha was baffled by Kaikeyī's firmness. But he couldn't withstand her stillness anymore. Lifting her head and placing it on his lap, he said, 'Among my sons, I love Rāma the most. I can't live without him for a moment. I promise in his name that I will fulfil your desire. I lay all my accrued puṇya at your feet, but relieve me from this suffering. I will do as you please. Kaikeyī, touch my chest and feel my pain.'

Like a deer waiting to jump into the net laid by the niṣāda, Daśaratha was inviting Yama through this hasty promise. Kaikeyī finally looked at Daśaratha, sat up and said, 'Sūrya, Candra and the Devas are witness to your commitment. There is no puṇya greater than fulfilling one's promises. You assured me of two boons at the battle of Vaijayanta. I wish to retrieve them now. I want Bharata's paṭṭābhiṣeka performed instead of Rāma's. I also want Rāma to relinquish his riches and live like a tapasvī in the forests for fourteen years, and he must leave for the forests this very day.'

Struck by the harrowing words of Kaikeyī, Daśaratha fell unconscious. In a few moments, he awoke to the reality that what had transpired a while back wasn't any dream.

'Bharata, our virtuous son, has been away in Kekaya for twelve years now. It is Rāma who has been serving you throughout this period. He has served you much more than serving his very mother, Kausalyā. You have told me several times that Rāma is very dear to you. Probably as dear as Bharata. Kaikeyī, you may have several attendants, but tell me one person who attends to all your needs like Rāma does? He has not just served you, he has secured a significant space in the minds and hearts of our prajā. I was talking to them recently. They could not point out a single flaw at my dear

Rāghava. He is charitable to the poor. He serves his ācāryas with utmost respect. He displayed bravery while fighting Tāṭaka, Mārīca and Subāhu. Have you heard of one person being the reservoir of qualities such as truth, tapasyā, wisdom, respect for elders, gratitude, forgiveness and care towards every living being? It is my Rāmacandra. Even the devas hold him in the highest respect for his archery skill. Kaikeyī, have you ever heard Rāma speak any unpleasant words? You have told me many times, "Rājā, my eldest son is Rāma." Did you want to please me with such sweet words? No. You genuinely loved Rāma. You have never spoken anything that was irksome in the past. There was always probity in anything you did.

'But today, you entered the chamber of anger, and you have sought such undesirable boons. Kaikeyī, you want our dear Rāghava to live in the forests for fourteen years? Why should he be sent on exile, that too for fourteen years? Is this a punishment for his love shown to the both of us or for his adherence to the truth? Kaikeyī, what crime has Rāma committed to draw your anger?' asked Daśaratha.

Kaikeyī did not answer. She was looking at the wall with a straight face.

Daśaratha continued, 'You have surely come under the influence of someone who decided to bring death to me. This bad company of yours is also bringing disrepute to our Ikṣvāku vaṃśa. I shall secure many more rājyas for your pleasure. I can live without Kausalyā or even Sumitrā. But I can't live without Rāma. Like Sūrya who is imperative for our existence, so is Rāma to me. Your words soaked in anger hurt me like the sting of a scorpion. Save Rāma from all turmoils. With folded hands, I plead to you. I will touch your tender feet with my head. Please show mercy on this old man who wishes to welcome death peacefully.'

Kaikeyī looked at Daśaratha touching her feet and disapprovingly stepped away.

She sat on her couch looking at the frail rājā, and said, 'In the vaṃśa of Yayāti, Uśīnara was born. Through his vivāha to Mādhavi, he had a son called Śibi. Tales about his generosity reached different quarters. Once Nārada even advised an elderly king called Suhotra to pave the way for Śibi's chariot as a tribute to his generosity. During an engaging conversation with his ācārya, a dove came and fell at his feet. Looking at blood stains on its feathers, Śibi noticed a kite flying in circles over the spot. Taking cognizance of the kite's hunger, and the helplessness of the dove, Śibi instantly cut some flesh from his thigh and threw it at the kite. Have you heard about Śibi?

Śibi's thigh flesh on a measuring scale in Borobudur (Indonesia) sculpted in the Śailendra dynasty (8th-9th century CE)

'When a rājarṣi called Alarka was supervising his rājya on a horse back, he noticed a blind man struggling to spot his kamaṇḍalu. He escorted the blind man to a physician's dwelling, asking that his eyes be transplanted in the man's sockets. I am sure you wouldn't have heard about Alarka too.

'The seas don't cross the shore for fulfilling a simple promise made to the devas. Don't you ever gloat about righteousness anymore. Learn to fulfil the promises that you have made. I can't see Kausalyā being accorded respect if Rāma were to be made the rājā. If there is one thing that can bring joy to me, it is Rāma's exile to the forests. In case you go ahead with Rāma's paṭṭābhiṣeka, I promise in the name of my dear Bharata, you will see me dead.'

Daśaratha said, 'Rāma's elephant-like gait towards me always brought me joy. His very presence would make me grow younger by many years. When children of his age were out playing, I asked him to go to the forests with Viśvāmitra. He withstood all the hardships at that age. How will Rāghava, who would have relinquished his chariots, elephants and horses, walk on the rugged path of the forests infested with thorns and stones? How can he survive on the fruits and tubers leaving the lavish food in the bhavana? How will he abandon the stylish clothes and put on the clothes of a tapasvī? Today, if I ask him to go on exile to the forests, he will surely do it for my sake. How ill-fated I am, to have such an obedient son like Rāma! He has become fatherless, when his father is still living.

'Like a niṣāda who uses music to trap a deer, so have you enticed me with honeyed words all these years. Our prajā castigates a brāmhaṇa for consuming vāruṇi for he is forbidden to do so. They will subject me to a similar treatment when I deviate from the practice of performing paṭṭābhiṣeka for the eldest son. Rājās from the neighbouring rājyas would have already reached the outskirts of Ayodhyā. What will I answer them in case the paṭṭābhiṣeka is cancelled? I have never courted Kausalyā the way I ought to have done. Despite her care for me, I have focussed my attention only on you. Today, I regret having neglected her all these years. What can justify Rāma's exile to the forests to his mother Kausalyā? Sumitrā will also equally lose her trust in me. I can't see Sītā, my daughter-in-law, suffering for no fault of hers. Tears in her eyes will bring death to me. Kaikeyī, your son is unlike you. Under no circumstances will Bharata occupy the kingdom. If my dear Rāghava's face is compared to Candra, you are that grahaṇa which has possessed his lustre. How can I command him to go to the forests? I am sure the accrued pāpas of my previous births have come in your form. Thinking of you as a rope, I have actually been nourishing a poisonous snake in my house.

'"For the sake of his lust for an undeserving woman, Daśaratha has sent 'the best among all men' to the forests" is how the world will pass comments at me. By sending Rāma to the forests, and bringing death to me, what happiness are you going to harness? You can burn Rāma, Kausalyā, Sumitrā, Lakṣmaṇa, Śatrughna and me in a large pyre. This will bring peace to us, and happiness to you and Bharata.'

Kaikeyī stayed undeterred, and said, 'Fulfil your promises instead of giving me sermons.'

Daśaratha said, 'You are talking as if your plans are known to Bharata. In case he is hand in glove with you in this nasty game, he should not perform my funeral rites. You and your son can happily rule Ayodhyā after my death. I feel like calling out the women in this world, but how can I hold all of them responsible for your heinous act? I wish your teeth fell when you uttered those boons. I wish the fire consumed you even before you thought of these boons.'

67

An Impotent Rājā Bows to Greed

'You keep singing verses about your steadfastness to truth, and fulfilling promises. Where is all that gone?' asked Kaikeyī.

Like Yayāti who looked exhausted when he was sent back from Amarāvatī upon his puṇyas getting over, so was Daśaratha looking, as he was lying on the floor. He said, 'As my Rāghava will leave to the forests, the jīvātmā in my body will also trace its journey outwards. Rāma's birth brought an endless joy in me and today I have to see him suffer in the forests. I wish I was dead this very moment for that will save me from uttering those cruel words of banishment to Rāma. Kaikeyī, save Bharata and yourself from this ignominy. I am a frail rājā now. Please show mercy on me too.'

'Send Rāma to the forests. I do not want to keep repeating the same sentence. If you fail to do as promised, I will commit suicide right in front of you,' warned Kaikeyī.

Bali had promised Vāmana three measures of Bhūmi. Despite warnings from Śukra, his purohita, Bali went ahead in implementing his commitment. Similarly, Daśaratha was bound by the promise he had made to Kaikeyī. But in Bali's case, the promise was made to paramātmā while in Daśaratha's, it was made to Kaikeyī, who was avarice incarnate.

'Kaikeyī, do you remember our vivāha in Kekaya was performed in the presence of your parents, and the prajā? I was mesmerized by your beauty, and by your nuanced speaking skills then. In the presence of the fire, the purohita asked me to hold your right palm, and say these words looking at you, "While giving you to me, Bhaga, Aryamā, Savitā and Indra, asked me to be a responsible gṛhastha. Let Sarasvatī protect our relationship. Agni married Svāhā and so should I exemplify as a gṛhastha like him. May Vāyu, the good friend of Agni, unite our minds." I was not aware that I was marrying a devil. Realization has dawned very late in me. I now disown that hand of yours, whereby I also disown Bharata, the one spawned by us. He should not perform any rituals on my death, not even the mandated ones like offering water in the mouth of my dead body,' said Daśaratha.

Bali promises three measures of land to Vāmana in Halebiḍu (Karnataka) sculpted in the Hoysāla dynasty (12th century CE)

The lamenting rājā lay on the floor all night, gazing at Candra and his nakṣatras in the sky.

Daśaratha's prayers to Sūrya that he should never rise did not fructify though. As the rays of Sūrya started brightening up the gold lines laced on the lower walls of Kaikeyī's apartment, Daśaratha grew anxious as Puṣya nakṣatra dawned. He did not know how to convince Vasiṣṭha and Vāmadeva. He did not know how to face his prajā who were treating the paṭṭābhiṣeka as their own family event. After their baths, Vasiṣṭha along with his śiṣyas, entered Ayodhyā carrying the golden pots with Sarayū waters to the music of ānaka and dundubhi. Vasiṣṭha reached the sabha maṇḍapa, and greeted Vāmadeva who was overseeing the arrangements for the paṭṭābhiṣeka. A chariot drawn by four horses, a cow, a humped bull and a mighty lion were tied to the pillars. A bow with a quiver of arrows, a sword, a śibikā, a pair of cāmaras, a golden vessel with prayāga waters and garland, the tiger's skin and darbha grass were placed on a pedestal in front of the vedikā.

Vasiṣṭha gesticulated at Sumantra to bring Daśaratha to the maṇḍapa. The able charioteer reached the apartment of Kaikeyī, and said, 'Rājā, the night has passed. The most anticipaṭed day of our lives has arrived. Like the devas who sing bards to Bramhā at the foothills of Meru, so am I at your doorstep. Rājā, may you receive abundant blessings of Sūrya, Candra, Śiva, Kubera, Agni and Indra on this day.'

With no acknowledgement from Daśaratha, Sumantra entered the apartment. He was shell-shocked to find the rājā lying on the floor, motionless. While Sumantra was about to bend and check on Daśaratha, Kaikeyī came running to his presence. She said, 'The rājā didn't sleep the entire night thinking about the paṭṭābhiṣeka. He wants to see Rāma. Bring him here.'

Sumantra agreed to execute the order and left the place only to be haunted by Kaikeyī's unusual behaviour that reminded him of her mother.

68

Kaikeyī Lays Down the Law

In the backdrop of a stone panel in which a deer pair was surrounded by fawns was a beautiful bed made in ivory and covered sparingly in gold. In one corner of the apartment were a few lit candana sticks that engulfed the air with an intoxicating fragrance. On either side of the bed were lit ornamental lamps and women holding the chāmara, a fan made of the yāk's hair. On Sītā's

lap was Rāma resting his head. His face looked like the charming Candra while Sītā's face glittered like Citrā nakṣatra. Platters filled with gold ornaments, precious gems, freshly farmed pearls and newly spun silk garments were kept on the floor. The prosperity in the apartment dwarfed Kubera's rājadhāni. This was a classic vignette of Vaikuṇṭha where Nārāyaṇa and Lakṣmī rest on Ananta, the serpent couch. Sumantra was magnetized by this wonderful scene in front of his eyes. With folded hands, he said, 'Rāma, your father who is in the apartment of Kaikeyī, wishes to see you at once.'

Rāma looking at Sītā's eyes, as if seeking approval, said, 'Here is Sumantra, a dextrous mantri, a seasoned charioteer, a confidante of my father, and our well-wisher. If he is asking me to meet Daśaratha, it must be related to the paṭṭābhiṣeka. If Kaikeyī, my revered mother, wishes to meet me, I am sure it will augur fame and prosperity for the both of us.' She followed him till the doorstep and said, 'May Indra, Varuṇa, Kubera and Yama protect you in the east, west, north and south directions. Like Bramhā who guides the rājasuya conducted by Indra, in the presence of ṛṣis, so does your father want to see you perform rājasuya with the blessings of brāmhaṇas.' She went a step closer, and murmured in his ears, 'I will see you smeared in butter and draped in deer's skin performing the rājasuya. I will also see you scratch your back with the antelope's horn.'

Rāma smiled at Sītā.

Armoured soldiers who had applied the paste of candana and aguru on their bodies were standing ahead of the silver-plated chariot. The dark-complexioned Rāma ascended the chariot drawn by four horses. His seat was stitched with tigerskin. Lakṣmaṇa quickly mounted the chariot with an umbrella and a chāmara in his hand. The prajā saw the chariot speeding through with a rumbling sound. They were reminded of Indra seated on Airāvata, the four-tusked elephant, emerging from the clouds, to the sound of thunder and the glow of a lightning. Young women standing on the pathways showered lotus petals on Rāma. Elderly women said, 'You should rule us following your ancestors like Vivasvān, Manu, Ikṣvāku, Kakutstha, Māndhātā, Hariścandra, Bhagīratha, Dilīpa, Raghu, Aja and Daśaratha. You always show equal love for the brāmhaṇas, kṣatriyas, vaiśyas and śūdras. Your mother Kausalyā will feel accomplished today. In the paṭṭābhiṣeka with Sītā by your side, you will look striking like Candra with Rohiṇī nakṣatra in the ascent. Watching you both is like watching Lakṣmī and Nārāyaṇa. If any of us haven't seen you with Sītā, or atleast have not been sighted by the two of you, it is a big misfortune.'

Leaving Lakṣmaṇa outside, Rāma entered Kaikeyī's apartment, and submitted his abhivādana. Daśaratha did not acknowledge Rāma's praṇāmas with his characteristic 'āyushmān bhava Rāma varmā' benediction. Rāma immediately took notice of his father's strange behaviour. Daśaratha's face was agitated like the ocean with successive high tides on an amāvāsya night. His face looked like the Sūrya during grahaṇa, with no sheen. His eyes were like a tapasvī who had turned knavish momentarily. Rāma worriedly asked, 'Mother, is there any disease that has struck my father? Have I committed any mistake that has angered my father? Have I disobeyed any of your words? Has anything untoward struck my dear Bharata or Śatrughna? Is there something that you uttered which is displeasing to him? Please tell me how I can bring Daśaratha to his spirits.'

Kaikeyī said, 'Rāma, don't worry. Daśaratha has no disease. As per the latest information provided to me by my trusted sources, no misfortune has struck either Bharata or Śatrughna. It is only out of fear for you, the rājā is not able to spell out what is in his mind. I am worried that Daśaratha's sail on truth shouldn't go adrift for your sake.'

'Daśaratha is my dear father, cherished ācārya and an eternal well-wisher. He is the rājā of Ayodhyā. In case he asks me to consume the juice of karavīra roots and leaves, I will do it instantly. If he wants me to enter a blazing fire, I will do it too. I promise to fulfil whatever he desires. You, my father and our prajā know that I don't lie. I will never go back on my promised words. I will execute my father's words even if it were to come through you,' roared Rāma.

'You must forsake your paṭṭābhiṣeka at once. Wearing jaṭā and deerskin, you must go to the forests of Daṇḍaka for fourteen years. And Bharata will be made the rājā of Kosala,' uttered Kaikeyī at Rāma, whom she was doting till the previous day.

Rāma's face showed no melancholy. It was as dispassionate as it was when he had heard of his paṭṭābhiṣeka news from Daśaratha. Indeed, there was an aura around his lotus-like face, as if the revised order was a divine providence.

'The one thing that hurts me is that the rājā did not think of me worthy enough to execute his commands. To me there is nothing in this world greater than serving my esteemed father. Bharata is more precious than my very life. I am sure he will rule Ayodhyā very effectively with the blessings of our ancestors. I can vouch he will serve my father with utmost affection. I will wear valkala at once, and leave for the forests,' said Rāma. He performed a pradakṣiṇā around Daśaratha and Kaikeyī, and swiftly left the apartment.

Lakṣmaṇa, with tears rolling down his cheeks, followed Rāma to the temple of Nārāyaṇa, where Kausalyā was stationed. They noticed the rānī, draped in silk apparel, and seated opposite the vedikā. While offering amṛtakalasa balls as havis to the fire, Suyajña said, 'This yajña invoking Garuḍa's blessings will finish soon. Normally, Garuḍa's avatāra is recounted towards the culmination.'

Rāma did not want his mother to leave the yajña incomplete. It was only in such kriyās that she attained solace. Rāma gestured to Lakṣmaṇa that they needed to wait till the narration was over.

69

Garuḍa's Glory

Kaśyapa married Kadrū and Vinatā, the daughters of Dakṣa. They stayed in an āśrama by the foothills of Himālaya. The sisters used to regularly visit the caves with the remnants of the yajña conducted by Kaśyapa. Kadrū used to feed the snakes while Vinatā, who was averse to snakes, used to feed the birds. Kadru earned the confidence of the noxious snakes by nursing them. In the urge to see such obedience in the birds, Vinatā broke open one of the two eggs in the nest on a devadāru tree. A little eagle, with red eyes, and a fresh and dewy look peeped out of the shell. She called him 'Aruṇa' for that reason. To Vinatā's shock, the bird's thighs and legs were missing, and she ran to Kaśyapa for help. Kaśyapa, the ṛṣi with the ability to foresee, advised that Aruṇa be handed over to his śiṣyas.

The śiṣyas used to stand facing the east every morning, and recite, 'May we hear auspicious messages and see auspicious sights; may we live longer to serve you with our bodies; may Garuḍa, Bṛhaspati and Indra, join you in bestowing all auspiciousness on us.'[1] Towards the end of the recitation, the śiṣyas placed a cow, white silk, and bronze vessels with water in front of Sūrya and Kaśyapa, seeking their blessings. As a result, in the course of time, Aruṇa developed the grit to live with his

1 Taittiriya Aranyaka, 1.1.

physical limitations. Habituated to welcoming 'his brother' at the rise, Aruṇa was accorded the status of a charioteer to Sūrya.

Kadrū for long nurtured acrimony towards Vinatā. The two women once noticed a white horse galloping in the waters of Candrabhāgā. Uttering praises about its physical appearance, and colour, the discussion now centred around its bushy tail. Vinatā claimed it was white, while Kadrū vouched for its dark colour. That night, Kadrū quietly seized the horse, and brought him to the cave where the snakes lived. She wrapped the reluctant and lazy dark-hued snakes around the hair strands of the horse's tail. The next morning, as she released the horse for grazing, the gullible Vinatā noticed the horse's dark tail from a distance. Realizing her error, she asked Kadrū to announce a punishment. Kadrū slyly asked that Vinatā become her maidservant which the latter agreed to. Meanwhile, the other egg in the nest hatched and a chick with audacious eyes peeped out. Kaśyapa and Vinatā, who were enamoured by the bird's ravishing form, realized that he was an avatāra of Garuḍa, paramātmā's celestial vehicle. He grew into a giant amid the birds, and his strong claws that could carry unimaginable loads, fetched him the name 'Garuḍa'. Sensing his beloved son-like Garuḍa's incessant hunger, Kaśyapa directed him to coastal regions. After flying a long distance, the bird noticed a daṃpati outside their hut. It was a brāmhaṇa who was courting a woman of the niṣāda jāti. In a fit of hunger, Garuḍa gulped the daṃpati only to realize as he was swallowing them, that the chants of the brāmhaṇa, were akin to that of his father's. So he ejected them, and continued to scout for food by travelling to a distant dvīpa[2]. He made this dvīpa his home. Smaller prey did not satiate his hunger.

One day, he noticed an elephant and a tortoise by a lakeside. They were busy brawling with each other like brothers who fight over property. In a flash, Garuḍa, true to his name, picked them up in each of his claws, undeterred by their body weights. He flew off to a distant dvīpa[3], yet again. As he arrived, he rested on the branches of a

---

2 Flores island (part of lesser Sunda islands) in Indonesia.

3 Pamban Island, belongs to the Indian state of Tamil Nadu.

vaṭa tree. Seeing one of its branches break, and fall with an upended assemblage of vālakhilyas in dhyāna, Garuḍa was shocked. He quickly held the branch with the vālakhilyas between his beaks, averting an accident and the bramhahatyā. Feeling a spree of breezes on their faces, the vālakhilya ṛṣis opened their eyes. These ṛṣis of intense tapasyā but of diminutive sizes were baffled by what they were seeing. Below, from a pair of talons were dangling an elephant and a tortoise, and further down were the deep seas. They looked up to notice a mammoth bird with sharp eyes. They were gratified that someone as mighty as this bird could take on Indra, who had once mocked their petite forms. Safely leaving the branch with the vālakhilya ṛṣis on the Gandhamādana mountain, Garuḍa gobbled up his prey. The ṛṣis performed penance on a nearby mountain[4] for many years, and later made Vasiṣṭha's āśrama their home.

Garuḍa carries an elephant and tortoise in Candi Sukuh (Indonesia) sculpted in the Majapahit dynasty (15th century CE)

Vinatā realized that fetching amṛta alone would please Kadrū, and was confident that Garuḍa could help her achieve this task. She showered ample blessings on her son, and Kaśyapa, too, said, 'May the fruits of my recitation of rik, yajus and sāman of the vedas give you immense strength for your mission.'

A spirited Garuḍa reached the ramparts of Amarāvatī. With fierce gliding flights and sharp-edged claws, he put up a spirited fight with Indra. At the end, he snatched the most-protected

4 Valakhilya mountain near Uttarkashi in the Indian state of Uttarakhand.

Garuḍa consumes a snake in National Museum (Vietnam) sculpted in the Cham dynasty (12th-13th century CE)

amṛta pot from the devas, and returned to the āśrama. Vinatā was released from bondage when the amṛta pot was handed over to Kadrū. But Kadrū's triumph was short-lived as Indra swooped down in his chariot and snatched the pot away from Kadrū. A few drops of amṛta that had fallen on the grass were savoured by the snakes in a flash. Taking cognisance of Vinatā's relief, Kadrū's defeat and the snakes' grief at not consuming amṛta to their satisfaction, Garuḍa soared the skies in glee.

To his śiṣyas, Kaśyapa said, 'Nārāyaṇa uses Garuḍa as his vehicle and a Garuḍa motif on his flag, to bestow auspiciousness on his bhaktas. My son, of such beautiful wings, henceforth will be referred as Suparṇa. The vālakhilya ṛṣis say that one must perform dhyāna on Suparṇa's resplendent form adorned by the snakes, his brothers in a sense, to ward off evil potents.'

70

An Unruffled Prince Adheres to Dharma

Lakṣmaṇa said, 'Rāma, the situation is worrying. We need to seek Kausalyā's permission at the earliest.'

Sensing a murmur at a proximity, Kausalyā turned back. She noticed Rāma, standing with Lakṣmaṇa. Granting permission to the rājakumāras to arrive at her presence, Kausalyā gradually rose from her seat. Her eyes were loaded with the warmth of a cow that yearns to see its calf. Holding him in her arms, she planted a kiss on his forehead. She ordered that ornate seats be placed for them, and food varieties be cooked immediately.

Rāma, who had committed to live like a tapasvī in the forests, did not want to enjoy the comforts anymore. He simply touched the seat as an act of accepting the honours extended by his mother, and said, 'I will need a viśtara to sit.'

Kausalyā, stunned by this request, said, 'Why do you need a seat like viśtara, meant for a tapasvī, stitched with darbha? I have heard that a viśtara is stitched with twenty-five darbha blades. Do you want to remind us of your age by sitting on it?'

Rāma, with utmost humility said, 'This news may be shocking to you, Sītā and Lakṣmaṇa, but not to me. I am asked to live in the forests of Daṇḍaka for fourteen years. As I will be living the life of a tapasvī, I shall abstain from consuming meat unless any kriyā that I perform demands consumption. Instead, I will survive on milk, honey, fruits and vegetables. The paṭṭābhiṣeka will be performed for my dear Bharata.'

Kausalyā, who heard this bombshell, swooned. Her state was like the branch of a sāla tree that falls when slashed by the woodcutter. It was also akin to a woman pushed from the mountains in Amarāvatī when her puṇya was exhausted.

As Rāma helped her sit by the maṇḍapa pedestal, she said, 'Did I wait for seventeen years since your upanayana to see you as a tapasvī? Rāmacandra, I have observed vratas like Cāndrāyana and Kṛcchra multiple times, and from now on I am denied the pleasure of seeing your Candra-like face. The lacuna left by Śāntā was filled with your birth. I now wish that you were never born to me because this pain is unbearable. I was always looked down upon by the irascible Kaikeyī. She ensures that your father never recognizes my presence. Through your banishment to the forests, she is conniving to make me an attendant at her apartment. Death will not come to me, you know why? If the jīvātmā hadn't left my body when it first heard that you were turning a tapasvī, what other reason could aid its departure? I now realize why my eyes were fixed on the bark of a tree that had fallen in the river waters during the last monsoon. It was to announce the fact that, just as a torrential flow causes no harm to a tree bark, my heart faces no death when hearing the news of your exile.' Kausalyā was inconsolable after saying these words.

'Which śāstra is Daśaratha following to strip you of the right to become the next rājā? If such is the case, I will slay Bharata to restore your legitimacy to the throne. I am ready to die for the sake of Rāma. Daśaratha is truly crippled of old age, and has lost his mind. I am not sure what hateful lessons he is being taught by Kaikeyī. Will any father in his good senses ever send a spotless son like Rāma to the forests? When our śāstras order that even an ācārya who goes astray is to be killed, how then can Daśaratha, my demented father escape death? Don't grieve, mother,' said Lakṣmaṇa, breathing out fire like Ananta during the pralaya.

Kausalyā said, 'To fight the asuras, Varuṇa approached Dadhīci, a ṛṣi who had undertaken severe austerities. He requested the ṛṣi to part with his bones that would help make a unique weapon called vajra for Indra, and eventually help vanquish the asuras. Not even giving it a second thought, Dadhīci abandoned his body in the samādhi state of yoga.[1] As Suvarcā, the pregnant wife of Dadhīci, reached the tree where he used to meditate, she noticed flies swarming up to a heap of flesh bereft of its bones. In a state of shock, Suvarcā delivered a boy prematurely, left him to the care of mother nature and died. This boy was named Pippalāda. After growing into a brāmhaṇa of immense splendour like his father, Pippalāda understood the sacrifice of his father. He also realized that his mother died of sorrow. To avenge the death of his mother, he dispatched a krityā to attack Varuṇa. This rākṣasī of high powers went running towards Varuṇa who was afflicted with mātruhatyā, the sin incurred of causing Suvarcā's death. You must be wondering why I am narrating this incident to you. If I die of your separation, you, too, will incur mātruhatyā like Varuṇa, and will be a victim of our prajā's abuses. On the other hand, I have heard of Kaśyapa's descendent who was invited to Bramhā's abode, just because he served his mother till her last breath. Rāma, I know that you must be aware of a śāstra that says "one's mother commands ten times more respect than one's father". It is decreed that from among a list of mother-like beings, namely one's mother, the adoptive mother, the ācārya's wife, the rānī of a rājya, the milching cow and Bhūmi, our land, that one's mother deserves the highest honour. As your mother, I have decided that you cannot leave Ayodhyā. If you have decided to leave Ayodhyā, then take me along.'

After listening patiently to Kausalyā's desolate and Lakṣmaṇa's fuming words, Rāma said, 'There lived a ṛṣi called Kandu. He was respected for his knowledge in the śāstras. His father, in a rage, asked him to slaughter a cow. Despite knowing that he would incur gohatyā, the sin of killing a cow, Kandu performed the unforgivable act, only to fulfil his father's order. Similarly, Paraśurāma beheaded his mother, Reṇukā, to fulfil his father, Jamadagni's, orders. Even

---

1 Dahod, a town in the Indian state of Gujarat.

the sons of Sagara dug up Bhūmi in different places, and went to the extent of killing Kapila, just to keep their father's word.

'There is a saying that "Truth is established adherence to dharma". In my understanding, if I fulfil the promise made to Daśaratha, it is dharma in itself. There are four puruṣārthas that every human should aspire to attain. Dharma, is the foremost of the four, that relies on adherence to the code of conduct laid in our śāstras. Artha, is the wealth that one creates for a prosperous living through the professions prescribed for one's varṇa. Kāma, is the enjoyment and gratification of one's senses through legitimate relationships. Finally, comes the desire to attain mokṣa, a state from which there is no return to this mundane world. One can't attain artha and kāma without any clinging to dharma. Only if I respect the dharma to follow my father's orders will I be able to live a happy and prosperous life with Sītā. Pinning the blame on Kaikeyī is wrong as the rājā did not stop her while she asked me to go to the forests. I take her words as my father's command. You may recall that Yayāti was banished from Amarāvatī, but with the help of his grandsons, arrangements were made for him to trek back to Indra's rājadhānī. Similarly, I am not going to stay in the forests permanently. In fourteen years, I will be back in Ayodhyā to the auspicious music of instruments.

How will Daśaratha complete yajñas without you by his side? After so many years of being together, leaving him in his old age will discredit you. You must ensure nothing untoward happens to my father because of my departure. There is no way you can accompany me to the forests. You could utilize your time in propitiating Nārāyaṇa and performing vratas during my absence.'

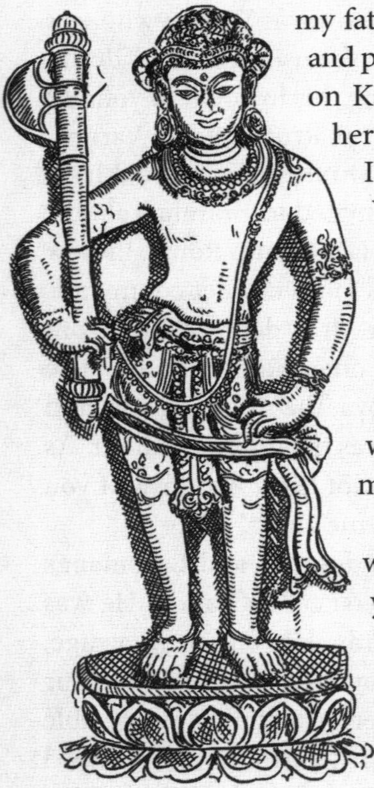

Paraśurāma in Balurghat Museum (West Bengal) sculpted in the Pāla dynasty (11th century CE)

71

Rāma Convinces Kausalyā

Kausalyā, realizing Rāma's resolve to follow his father's words, made up her mind to not obstruct him any further. For having spoken some hurtful words against Daśaratha and Rāma, Kausalyā performed ācamana, the purification rite once. She asked the brāmhaṇas to conduct a yajña praying for the successful sojourn of her son to the forests. Puṇyāhavācana mantras were recited, as white flowers, ghee, curd, honey and white mustard seeds were offered to the fire. She offered them generous dakṣiṇā and obtained their blessings for Rāma. She tied an amulet made from Viśalyakaraṇī, a herb that heals serious wounds, to his right arm. She applied sandal paste throughout his body, and murmured these lines in his ear, 'Aditi pronounced her benedictions on her sons, Indra and Upendra, when they left on an expedition to fight Vṛtra and to bring down the arrogance of Bali. Similarly Garuḍa, in his avatāra left for Amarāvatī to fetch amṛta for his step-mother. Vinatā prayed for her son saying, 'Let the Maruts protect your wings, Sūrya and Candra your back, Agni your head and Vāsus your body.' May Bramhā, Śiva, Skanda, Bṛhaspati, Kubera, Yama, Vāyu, Sādhyā, Viśvedevata, Saptaṛṣis and Siddhas protect you. May Nārāyaṇa, our family mūrti, protect you. May the dharma which you have been nourishing with sheer

discipline, protect you at all times.' She embraced, and kissed Rāma on his forehead. She granted consent to Rāma to leave for the forests and he, with folded hands, performed a pradakṣiṇā around her.

Rāma left the apartment, and ascended the chariot. Lakṣmaṇa quickly followed him. Turning towards Lakṣmaṇa, Rāma said, 'I know your love for me. Remember that only by adhering to dharma I can show the world the true prowess of a kṣatriya.' With folded palms, he paid respects to the prajā gathered on both sides of the pathway. Pointing to the arrangements made on the way to his bhavana, he asked Lakṣmaṇa that they be removed. He did not want any doubt to arise in the minds of Kaikeyī or Daśaratha regarding his intent to leave Ayodhyā. He said that Kaikeyī was always affectionate towards him, and it was only his own vidhi that was sending him to the forests.

Lakṣmaṇa said, 'Rāma, only the weak will point fingers to vidhi. Like a wild elephant that needs to be controlled by aṅkuśa, so does vidhi need to be handled cleverly. Without going astray from dharma, we can hatch a plan to create hindrances to Daśaratha's plan. I heard that Daśaratha had sought our prajā's opinion on your paṭṭābhiṣeka. Did he have the grit to ask for their opinion on Bharata's paṭṭābhiṣeka? Which dharma stopped him from asking? If Daśaratha had made up his mind to fulfil Kaikeyī's wishes, why did he even inform you of making you the next rājā? If the boons granted to Kaikeyī are the reason for the change in decision, why were those not granted in the past? What clandestine event occurred between Daśaratha's original decision and the revised one? This is a plot, totally vengeful in nature. You don't possess a single flaw and thus, you are not able to smell the rotten minds of the man and his wretched lady. The seas are vast with unfathomable depths in comparison to the shores that are visibly insignificant. Yet, the seas don't cross the boundary lines. Similarly, I am your eternal servant. Yet, you can't discount my views. I will summon Daśaratha for a battle. I will present victory at your lotus-like feet.'

The chariot halted at Rāma's bhavana. Wiping the hot tears of Lakṣmaṇa, Rāma said, 'It is my resolve to fulfil my father's commands. I have decided to walk in the forests of Daṇḍaka. There is also another reason for it.'

'What reason?' asked Lakṣmaṇa.

Rama said, 'We are only told of Vikukṣi and Nimi as the sons of Ikṣvāku. But the latter had another son who is not that well-known. This son was a brute whose every act deserved a blow. He was called Daṇḍa, for that reason. Ikṣvāku banished him to a region south of Kosala. One day, Daṇḍa molested a woman serving in the āśrama of Śukra. The ṛṣi's curse resulted in Daṇḍa and his territory perishing in the sudden fires. Forbidden from habitation, this region turned into Daṇḍaka forests that have become the breeding space for rākṣasas. It is not right that a territory under Kosala's jurisdiction is left unattended.'

Lakṣmaṇa said, 'If your objective is to restore dharma in the Daṇḍaka forests, I shall come with you. Do you think these well-developed arms of mine are to beautify me? Do you think my bow and quiver of arrows are simply artefacts?'

Rāma asked Lakṣmaṇa to stop bickering any further, and said conclusively, 'I have learned to exercise viveka at this crucial moment and I don't want to fall prey to anger. While I take to tapasyā relinquishing my status as a rājakumāra, I will abstain from using the holy waters in the golden pots placed at the sabha maṇḍapa. Instead, I will draw water from the well at Vasiṣṭha's āśrama, and become a tapasvī. I am sure I will practise upāsanā during my Daṇḍaka stay.'

72

Sītā's Ire

'Ūrmilā, hasten. Please get those mustaka balls here. Suyajña will perform the mandated ārādhanā to Varāha mūrti, before the paṭṭābhiṣeka. These balls will be kept as prasāda towards the end. He will also narrate the exploits of Varāha. It is after that, that Rāma and I will be walking to the sabhā,' said Sītā hurriedly.

'Sure. I am bringing them. I am eager to listen to Varāha avatāra and its significance from Suyajña,' said Ūrmilā as she placed the platter in front of the mūrti.

The sound of footsteps indicated to Sītā that Rāma was entering the apartment. But the rhythm didn't suggest the gait of a rājā. As she looked at the door, she noticed Rāma arrive. His face did not hint at any unanticipated turn of events. Sītā, adept at reading Rāma's mind, noticed his hair tresses too. They were bereft of the admixture of honey and curd, normally sprinkled a muhūrta before the paṭṭābhiṣeka. She knew that there was a sudden development in the rājya whose details Rāma did not want to divulge immediately. Ūrmilā noticed the blank expressions on Rāma and Sītā's faces. With her hands, she strongly gestured at the rakṣakas and maids to leave the apartment. Not uttering a single word, Ūrmilā too exited the apartment.

She was pulled in a flash against the wall, and her mouth was quickly covered by a hand. In shock, her eyes didn't blink while a voice said, 'Stay quiet. The situation is grim. I can't leave my brother's apartment without knowing his further course of action.' Ūrmilā removed Lakṣmaṇa's hand in a flash, disapproving of his uncouth behaviour. But equally worried for Sita, she too stood outside the apartment wanting to know what had transpired within the royal court.

Rama: Sītā, you were born to Janaka, the rājaṛṣi. Your knowledge of dharma comes as no surprise, for it is something he has bequeathed to you.

Sītā: I am pleased that you have always taken my father's name with such respect. I was taught by my father that each of us has a dharma to follow. I aspire to be a conscientious wife to you, like Arundhatī is to Vasiṣṭha, Lopāmudrā is to Agastya, Sukanyā to Cyavana and Śrīmati to Kapila. Amongst the kṣatriyas, Madayantī to Mitrasaha, Keśinī to Sagara, Sāvitrī was loyal to Satyavān and Damayanti to Nala. Rohiṇī is fond of Candra like Suvarcalā is fond of Sūrya.

Rāma: Each one interprets the dharma as per their convenience.

Sītā: Āryaputra, what has happened? Why is our conversation revolving around dharma today?

Rāma: I have come to explain your dharma in my absence.

Sītā: In your absence?

Rāma: I am asked to live in the forests of Daṇḍaka for fourteen years. The paṭṭābhiṣeka will be performed for Bharata, and he will rule Ayodhyā. Look at Bharata as your brother, but do not expect any extra attention from him. Look at Śatrughna as your son, but do not give him herculean tasks. Anything that is displeasing to Bharata and Śatrughna is best avoided. You can engage your mind in observing vratas, and in the company of tapasvinīs. Ensure that you provide good care to Daśaratha and Kausalyā. You should also treat Sumitra and Kaikeyī with respect.

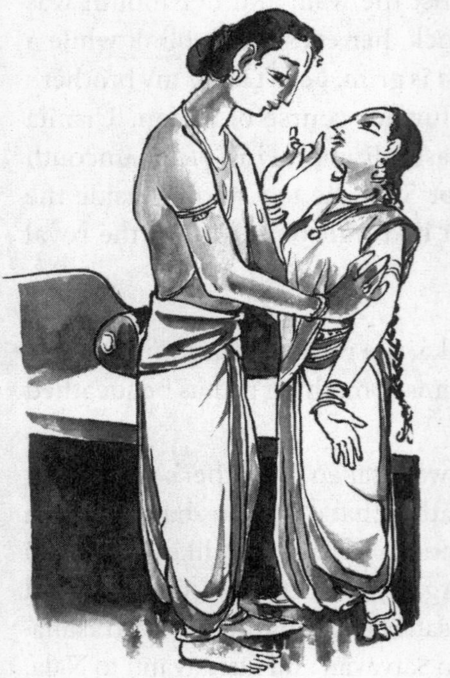

Sītā: Āryaputra, how could you have spoken such witless words? I will also accompany you to the forests of Daṇḍaka.

Rāma: Sītā, the command of Daśaratha is to me. Only to me.

Sītā: Though Mitra and Varuṇa are two devatās, they are treated as one, as Mitrāvaruṇa, in case the mantra indicates thus. Similarly, Indra and Agni are treated as one, as Indrāgni, if the mantra says so. I have heard many ṛṣis explain this in my father's presence. You have thorough knowledge of yajñas. Don't you know this?

Rāma: What are you implying?

Sītā: When the command is for you to follow, it implies that I am also a part of it. I, too, need to accompany you to the forests.

Rāma: A rule deployed to understand the yajña and its mantras can't be imposed on us.

Sītā: Why not? In the yajñas classified as prakṛti and vikṛti, a certain set of rules are individually adhered to. But in the vikṛti yajña alone, the rules of the prakṛti are also applied. Similarly, when it is said "Lakṣmī is inseparable from Nārāyaṇa, follows him everywhere", all that which applies to Nārāyaṇa, applies to Lakṣmī as well. When we were married, the purohita saw you as Nārāyaṇa, and me as Lakṣmī. If that is the case, I should follow you to the forests, because every command issued to you, has me inherently mentioned in it. Śāstras mandate the presence of one's wife while performing agnihotra. So have you decided to render these śruti injunctions futile, and thereby abandon agnihotra?

Rāma: I don't need to conduct agnihotra, as I have decided to live the life of a bramhacārī, a celibate for fourteen years. I will relinquish jewellery and silk clothes. Instead, I will don the valkala and sport a jaṭā.

Sītā: I vividly remember the incident where the ṛṣis in Mithilā anticipated my stay in the Daṇḍaka forests. Don't worry. I, too, shall live the life of a bramhacāriṇī, wearing the valkala.

Rāma: To keep my senses in control during the day and through the night, I will live on fruits that have fallen from the trees.

Sītā: I, too, can live on fruits.

Rāma: Not just fallen fruits, do you know I have to sleep on the fallen leaves over a bumpy ground.

Sītā: I can sleep on them too.

Rāma: The forest paths are infested with thorns and kuśa grass.

Sītā: I can remove the thorns and make the kuśa grass soft for you, by treading over them.

Rāma: Crossing rivers and lakes is not easy. The roar of the waterfall can be chilling for the weak hearted.

Sītā: I am excited to cross rivers and I have always wanted to bathe in waterfalls. I am eager to see lakes, dotted with haṁsas and filled with fully blossomed lotuses.

Rāma: Hissing serpents, buzzing bees and biting mosquitoes are very common in the forests. Lions in the mountain caves, galloping deers, elephants in rut and river-water crocodiles are known to attack humans.

Sītā: Who said animals are always inclined to attack? I am attracted to deer and you are friendly with monkeys. Our prajā sees the majestic lion and elephant in your gait. Above all, you carry your bow, and a quiver of arrows everywhere, vowing to protect your dear ones. Forget about these animals, in your presence no devatā can hurt me.

Rāma: When you can enjoy all comforts in Ayodhyā, why do you wish to invite suffering by accompanying me to the forests? Stay here happily, adhering to your dharma.

Sītā: Your definition of happiness does not comfort me. It is only your presence that I derive joy from. Whether I am in Ayodhyā or in the middle of Daṇḍaka forests doesn't matter to me, because it is your presence which adds joy to my life. Ayodhyā will seem like a blazing fire to me in your absence.

Rāma: Living in the forests means suffering.

Sītā: I have nothing else and nobody else in my thoughts. In case of separation from you, I will choose death over living. I will either consume the poisonous juice of karavīra or throw myself into a blazing fire or a flowing river.

Rāma: Again, I repeat, forest means suffering.

Sītā: Āryaputra, you broke the bow of Śiva, while you were carrying yours. My father, captivated by your valour, conducted my vivāha with you. My father firmly thought that you will stay by my side all through, like him who always backs my mother. His protection of Mithilā, and its prajā is equally well-known. In our fields of Mithilā, the farmers used to fix scarecrows with arrows in their hands, to guard their crops. I now realize that you are the scarecrow of Ayodhyā. My father did not recognize the fact that you were a woman, masquerading as a man.

73

Lakṣmaṇa, the Dutiful Follower

After uttering those words out of inconsolable grief and desperation, Sītā fainted. Ūrmilā and Lakṣmaṇa rushed into the apartment. The latter brought some water, and sprinkled it on Sītā's face. She slowly regained consciousness, and Rāma placed her on a seat. She cried profusely for having spoken mean words to Rāma, and helplessly foresaw a future without his company.

'Sītā, without you, neither will I accept the Ayodhyā rājya nor will I walk the Daṇḍaka forests. Distribute your jewels among the poor brāmhaṇas, and provide food to the sannyāsīs outside our bhavana. You may give away the clothes to your maids,' said Rāma. Taking permission from Sītā and Rāma, Ūrmilā left the apartment to make arrangements for the charity. Lakṣmaṇa, with tears rolling down his cheeks, held the feet of Rāma. He slowly looked at the daṃpati and said, 'I shall accompany the two of you to the Daṇḍaka forests.'

Rāma said, 'You are very dear to me. You are obedient as well. You will know that taking care of Kausalyā and Sumitrā in my absence is your responsibility. "The eldest brother equals the father" is a dictum of Vaivāsvata Manu. You will need to exemplify this by staying back in Ayodhyā. This is your dharma indeed.'

Lakṣmaṇa implored with folded hands, 'Kausalyā and Sumitrā will support each other. Bharata, our dear brother, will take care of their needs. I shall walk ahead of you both, clearing the path of any thorns. I shall carry a bow and quiver of arrows to keep the wild animals away from you. I will carry a crowbar to dig Bhūmi and a basket to collect the tubers, which are consumable to tapasvīs. I shall hold your clothes while you bathe in the river waters. I shall cook food, the way you both like. I shall accomplish all of this, as both of you take pleasure walks on the mountain slopes. You are my eldest brother, thereby my father. Sītā is my mother. Serving my parents is my dharma.'

After performing sandhyāvandana in the noon, Suyajña started towards Rāma's bhavana. Noticing the ṛṣi enter their apartment, Sītā and Rāma rose to welcome him. They performed pradakṣiṇā to the ṛṣi, and offered him a seat. Suyajña said, 'I bless the both of you with a peaceful life ahead. I am sure that both of you will want to perform Varāha ārādhanā, and listen to his greatness.'

While the daṃpati stayed quiet, Lakṣmaṇa narrated all that had transpired to Suyajña. Ūrmilā brought the jewellery in various caskets, and placed them in a row. Rāma gave them away to Suyajña. He also requested that Śatruñjaya, the elephant gifted to him by his maternal uncle, be taken care of till he returned from Daṇḍaka forests. Rāma ordered that the cows in the shed be distributed amongst poor brāmhaṇa*s* like Agastya, Kauśika and Trijaṭa. He instructed that the granary be emptied to the vaiśyas and śūdras.

74

Yayāti and the Pursuit of Pleasures

Vālmīki brought the flowers meant for the daily ārādhanā. He sat in front of Jaladhivarna, his family mūrti. Nārada, too, finished his morning duties, and witnessed the ārādhanā that was performed. With immense respect, Vālmīki prostrated at the feet of Nārada. The ṛṣi blessed him, and asked, 'Do you wish to ask me any question?'

Vālmīki smiled.

Nārada asked, 'Why this smile?'

Vālmīki said, 'How are you able to read my mind every time I am on a quest for answers?'

Nārada smiled this time, and gestured that the questions be asked.

Vālmīki wanted to know the life history of Nahuṣa and Yayāti. Nārada immediately obliged and began the narration with great zeal.

In the lineage of Atri, Soma, Budha and Purūrava came Āyu. He had a son called Nahuṣa, who eventually married Virajā, and produced a son called Yati. As a young boy, Yati chose celibacy and left the rājya. Nahuṣa trusted his other son, Yayāti, to take reins of the administration and performed his paṭṭābhiṣeka joyously. Nahuṣa meanwhile learnt that Indra had earned the curse of bramhahatyā by killing Vṛtra. He developed a salacious interest in Śacī, Indra's wife. Bṛhaspati attempted to stop Nahuṣa from approaching Śacī. The latter propitiated Upaśruti, a form of Pārvatī, to overcome the impending calamity. Her prayers fructified when Agastya arrived in Amarāvatī. Instead of respecting this revered ṛṣi, Nahuṣa ordered that Agastya along with other ṛṣis lift his śibikā. The ṛṣis agreed gracefully and carried out the order accordingly. Agastya being a dwarf could not match the pace of the other ṛṣis. Nahuṣa in his hurry to meet Śacī, asked them to hasten, and sarcastically asked if they were delaying the meeting by making serpentine movements. His hanging feet touched the jaṭā of Agastya accidentally. The ṛṣi was unusually enraged by Nahuṣa's nasty behaviour. He cursed that Nahuṣa will fall from his position, and will be subject to multiple births which would culminate in the form of a python.[1] Meanwhile, Indra performed prāyaścitta through an Aśvamedha yajña, and finally united with Śacī.

In the forests, Śukra was blessed by Śiva with the sañjīvanī mantra. Practising this mantra helped Śukra revive those asuras who suffered from severe wounds, and were staring at death's door during wars. The devas urged Kaca, the son of Bṛhaspati, to acquire the knowledge of sañjīvanī mantra from Śukra. Heeding their request, Kaca became a śiṣya to Śukra. He mastered the mantra with the grace of his teacher. Devayānī, who was Śukra's daughter, fell in love with Kaca. She evinced her interest in him, but he politely declined the proposal. Devayānī cursed Kaca saying that he would forget the sañjīvanī mantra and its prayoga in due course of time.

On the following day, Devayānī left for the lake for bathing. She found a few other women bathing in the waters too. One of them erroneously draped herself in Devayānī's clothes. When questioned by Devayānī, the woman replied, 'I am Śarmiṣṭhā, the daughter of

---

1 *Rodagrapādārpaṇena Tiryagbhūtaṃ Suragaṇapatiṃ Bindusapyaṃburāśiṃ Yasyeśāno Muniparīśadam Kumbhayoni: Purodhā: Śucitayā Citayā Dhanasaṃpadā Rahitayā*

Talavaipuram copper plate inscription from the Pāṇḍya dynasty (9th century CE) refers to Agastya's curse on Nahuṣa

a rājā called Vṛṣaparva. I don't consider you as an equal to even quarrel with.'

The maids who had accompanied Śarmiṣṭhā, angered by Devayānī, pushed her into quicksand and left the forests. Yayāti, who was on a hunt, heard Devayānī's voice crying for help. He extended his right hand and rescued her. Upon Devayānī's request, Śukra married her off to Yayāti, and on her vengeful insistence, asked Vṛṣaparva that his daughter Śarmiṣṭhā be made Devayani's maidservant.

Yayāti with Devayānī produced two sons and named them Yadu and Turvasu. Captivated by Śharmiṣṭha, he embarked on a secret relationship with her and produced three sons with her and called them Druhyu, Anu and Puru. This discreet relationship of Yayāti with Śarmiṣṭhā angered Devayānī and her father. Śukra cursed that Yayāti should turn into a decrepit old man. Yayāti, startled by this curse, did not want to give up his youthful state. He asked any one of his sons to take upon himself the father's curse of decrepitude through a yajña.

Yadu, the eldest of his sons said, 'To a habitat of brāmhaṇas I have made many promises. If I become frail and weak by accepting the curse pronounced on you, I will be unable to fulfil them.'

Yayāti's other sons also cited one reason or the other to refuse their father's request. Finally it was Puru who agreed to be the recipient of Yayāti's unexpected senility. Yayāti blessed this obedient son of his plentifully.

Yayāti performed many Aśvamedha yajñas and marched to Amarāvatī to stake claim to the throne of Indra. His eyes fell on an apsarā who was playing with her friends. Her name was Viśvācī. He made advances, and ended up in a dalliance with her.

Indra, who was averse to sharing his throne with anyone, hatched a plan to get rid of Yayāti. He approached and asked, 'Yayāti, you must have accrued a lot of puṇya to reach this state. Do you see anyone who can match your status?'

Yayāti who was bemused by this praise from an unexpected quarter said, 'I don't see anyone in this current world who can match the puṇya that I have gathered.'

The devas, in no time, declared that Yayāti had lost his puṇya by this unwarranted boast, and banished him from Amarāvatī. Yayāti's grandsons made arrangements to send him back to Amarāvatī. But Yayāti evinced no interest in going to Amarāvatī. He bestowed his youth back to Puru, and became a sannyāsī. His words of wisdom were passed down to later generations and advised, 'Desire for sensual enjoyment is like ghee that is poured into a blazing fire. It only keeps increasing. The man who learns to keep his senses under control, like a tortoise controls its limbs, is the one who can seek peace.'

75

An Unrepentant Rānī and an Honourable Son

As Sūrya set in the background, Daśaratha heard Rāma's footsteps and noticed him entering the apartment. The rājā rose from his bed and staggered forward to welcome Rāma with open arms. As he was about to fall, Rāma braced him up for support, to the shrieks of Daśaratha's three-fifty wives in the background. Rāma, in measured words, so as to not inflict any further wounds on his father, said, 'I am set to leave for the Daṇḍaka forests with Sītā and Lakṣmaṇa who insisted that they will join me. We have come to seek your blessings.'

Daśaratha in a helpless tone said, 'Throw me into the prison. I am the cause of your suffering.' Rāma wiped the tears of his father, and said, 'You have always taught us the power of truth. I don't want to act against your teaching. I vow to return to Ayodhyā after fourteen years.'

'One more day, please. Can you stay back to please Kausalyā and me?' pleaded Daśaratha.

Rāma, with a brief smile, said, 'Staying back in Ayodhyā for another day will only be tantamount to disobeying Kaikeyī and your command. I have given away all my wealth in charity. Let my dear Bharata administer Ayodhyā happily.'

Noticing Daśaratha in a depressed state, Sumantra's eyes reddened in anger. Gnashing his teeth in futile anger he looked at Kaikeyī and said, 'You have killed your husband by letting him go against the tradition of making the eldest son the next rājā. But your behaviour comes as no surprise to me. Many years after your mother's vivāha to Aśvapati, she once noticed your father smiling to himself, while they were retiring to the bed. She asked him the reason for smile, to which your father said, "I found the conversation between the two ants near our bed very entertaining. I can't disclose the reason though. This boon of understanding the animal language was bestowed upon me by the ṛṣis. But the rider is, it will bring me death if I spell out these conversations to anyone around me."

'You know what your deceitful mother flippantly said with a guffaw? "Disclose the details, and then die!".

'Soon realizing your mother's evil nature, Aśvapati expelled her from Kekaya.

'Similarly, your stay in Ayodhyā has brought no improvement to your inherited evil nature. You still resemble your mother in temperament. True that neem leaves don't turn sweet just because they are soaked in honey.'

Sumantra couldn't stay in the apartment any further, and left on the pretext of getting the chariot ready for Rāma's departure.

Daśaratha said, 'Rāma performs agnihotra without fail. He may want to perform yajña in holy kṣetras. Let a large stock from our granary, and a large amount from our treasury be sent with him.'

In a tone of disagreement, Kaikeyī said, 'If drunkards enjoy vāruṇi, and leave the last few drops for an innocent, wouldn't the latter be called a fool? Similarly, you want the entire riches to be with Rāma even in exile, while you want Bharata to administer with an empty treasury?'

Daśaratha noticed Siddhārtha walking into the apartment. He looked at Siddhārtha and said, 'Rāma will need the help of our soldiers in hunting animals. Send a cavalry with Rāma, and also some guides who know the safe paths in the forests.'

Kaikeyī said, 'Did Sagara who exiled Asamañja send an army along?'

Daśaratha said, 'You are indeed my biggest enemy. I am already burdened by granting your boons, and now you want Rāma to suffer in the forests? While seeking boons, did you ask that the army should not be sent to the forests?'

Before Kaikeyī could retort, Siddhārtha said, 'Sagara received complaints of Asamañja throwing babies in the torrential waters of Sarayū. As a mark of displeasure, he exiled Asamañja, his son. To the best of our knowledge, there is no flaw in Rāma, leave alone complaints. Let Rāma stay in Ayodhyā.'

Daśaratha dissuaded Siddhārtha from persuading an adamant Kaikeyī on this for he knew it would be futile.

Rāma, with folded hands, said, 'Imagine giving away a well-fed and a well-trained royal elephant in charity, but retaining the rope that was used to tie it to the pillar. Similarly when I have relinquished my comforts, of what use is the army to me? I will live as a tapasvī for the next fourteen years. Lakṣmaṇa, make sure you carry a crowbar and a basket with you.'

The sly Kaikeyī who was in agreement with Rāma's views handed over valkala to Rāma, Lakṣmaṇa and Sītā. The rājakumāras discarded their silk clothes and were soon dressed in forest attire. Rāma, who realized Sītā's ineptitude in draping herself in valkala, took her aside, and assisted her.

As Sītā was struggling to hold the valkala tight, Vasiṣṭha entered the apartment. He was appalled to behold the sight in front of him.

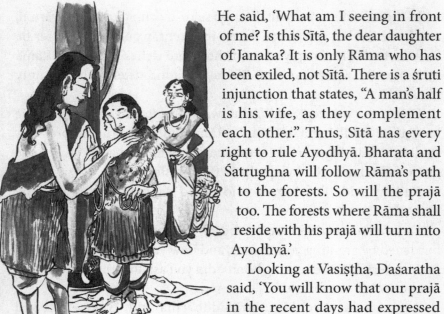

He said, 'What am I seeing in front of me? Is this Sītā, the dear daughter of Janaka? It is only Rāma who has been exiled, not Sītā. There is a śruti injunction that states, "A man's half is his wife, as they complement each other." Thus, Sītā has every right to rule Ayodhyā. Bharata and Śatrughna will follow Rāma's path to the forests. So will the prajā too. The forests where Rāma shall reside with his prajā will turn into Ayodhyā.'

Looking at Vasiṣṭha, Daśaratha said, 'You will know that our prajā in the recent days had expressed concerns about the widespread flowering in bamboo plants. I was equally worried that the flowers may end up destroying the bamboo. But nature had its peculiar way of telling our prajā that their rājā was destroying his own rājya by making irrational promises. I must have separated many children from their parents in my past births. That is why, I am ending up punishing my virtuous son. But you are right. Why should Sītā suffer? I hereby command that she is draped in the best of silk garments, and that the valkala be discarded. I also command Arthasādhaka to keep as many silk clothes and jewellery ready for Sītā's stay in the forests for fourteen years.'

Vasiṣṭha exited the apartment while Kausalyā was entering. Rāma asked that his mother be taken very good care of in his absence. With folded hands, the trio performed a pradakṣiṇā around Daśaratha and Kausalyā.

76

Sisterly Bonding

'Fetch those earrings studded with diamonds, and those armlets laced in ruby stones,' said Ūrmilā to a maid.

'Why do you ask for all of this?' asked Sītā in amazement.

'Daśaratha has commanded that you should be decked well,' replied Ūrmilā.

'It will seem out of place when Rāma and Lakṣmaṇa are dressed like tapasvīs and I am decked in jewellery,' said Sītā hesitatingly.

'It will not, Sītā. In fact you had promised to live like a tapasvinī to Rāma. It is your resolve that will make you live like one, not your attire. In fact, Daśaratha has asked you to be decked as always, even in the Daṇḍaka forests. I suspect our father-in-law doesn't want his reputation tarnished in our father's opinion and in his kingdom. Maybe he wants every passer-by to say "Daśaratha was always caring of his daughters-in-law", said Ūrmilā in a sarcastic tone.

Sītā flashed a look at Ūrmilā, and in no time, the sisters burst into infectious laughter.

'I will miss you so much, Ūrmilā. I don't even know if I have ever been without you,' said Sītā, while resting her cheeks on Ūrmilā's palms. Ūrmilā requested Sītā to narrate the greatness of Varāha avatāra, and Sītā immediately obliged.

Nārāyaṇa cast his lotus-petal like eyes on Bhūmi devī, his consort who was yet another manifestation of Lakṣmī, after waking up from a deep state of dhyāna. He noticed tears in her eyes, and asked, 'Bhūmi, you are revered by the ṛṣis for your matchless forbearance and compassion towards all creatures whatsoever. But what brings you tears?'

Bhūmi devī said, 'Paramātmā, there is nothing which is unknown to you. Mokṣa is unfathomable for the jīvātmā without seeking asylum in you, and without propitiating you. You are the consort to Lakṣmī who is the repository of all knowledge forms like madhu vidyā. You are thus revered as Mādhava. I am also your consort, and as a result the ṛṣis call me Mādhavī. With the increasing weight of hills, and the sudden rise in sea levels, many portions of Bhūmi have become submerged in deep waters. Remaining areas have been subsumed into rasātala. Many creatures have suffered death, and those who have managed to survive are in a miserable state. You have protected this Bhūmi many times. Please come to my rescue this time as well.'

In no time, Nārāyaṇa assumed the form of a multi-hooded snake called Ananta and pushed her submerged hills upwards using his hoods. Ṛṣi Marīchi was surprised at Bhūmi being restored to her earlier glory. He, along with the other ṛṣis, pleaded to paramātmā to give them a view of Himself alongside Bhūmi devī. In that very spot, a gigantic wild boar appeared. Between its tusks that looked like the crescent-shaped Candra was seated a coy Bhūmi devī. With folded hands, Marīchi said, 'You supported Bhūmi in your avatāra as Ananta, the multi-hooded snake from beneath. You held her between your tusks in your avatāra as Varāha to show your absolute concern for her. Your form as Varāha instils the knowledge of yajña in all of us. The grunt with "ghar" and "ghur" sound reminds me of the Sāma veda chants. The materials in a yajña such as the srak, sruvaḥ, ida, camasa, praśitra, graha, are personified in your tongue, nostrils, belly, ears, mouth and throat. Your body hair is as holy as the kuśa grass, and your eyes are solidified ghee. The different stages in a yajña are seen as your tusks. The four positions in a yajña, like the hotā, adhvaryu, udgātā and bramhā, are your four limbs. The retas is the soma extract while the body joints are the rituals like kratu that uses them.'

From then on, Varāha was meditated upon by the ṛṣis led by Marīchi.

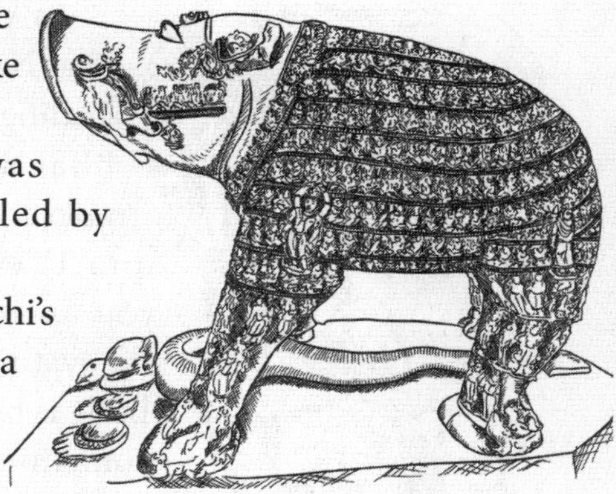

Varāha's appearance in Khajuraho (Madhya Pradesh) sculpted in the Candela dynasty (9th-10th century CE)

In due course of time, Marīchi's lineage continued with Kaśyapa and later with Hiraṇyākṣa. The latter with evil intent wanted to see Bhūmi suffer like in the times of yore. He summoned Varuṇa, the devatā supervising the water bodies, for a duel. Varuṇa cleverly directed Hiraṇyākṣa to a marshy land infested with wild boars. Enraged on seeing that animal form of paramātmā who alleviated Bhūmi devī's pain, Hiraṇyākṣa started tormenting creatures living on her. One day, a tiny boar with lotus-like eyes popped out of Bramhā's nostrils. Even before Bramhā could identify the avatāra, the incomparable Varāha was gone into the marshes to join the other boars with no qualms about being identified as just another boar. Smeared in the muddy waters, the boars looked dirty. Showing repugnance on his face, Hiraṇyākṣa walked on the swamp with his mace mercilessly attacking the boars. The Varāha form of Nārāyaṇa became furious and grunted heavily against the tyranny of Hiraṇyākṣa. He speedily rushed towards the asura with his sharp tusks that were infused with the power of Sudarśana, the most powerful discus. In one clash, Hiraṇyākṣa fell dead. The boars that had managed to survive the massacre attacked the body of Hiraṇyākṣa and left it in a mutilated state. Yet again, the ṛṣis propitiated the Varāha form, for having relieved Bhūmi of another asura.[1]

---

1 *Punyāpyāyanārthamesha Bhagavato Varāha Murtterjagatparāyaṇasya Nārāyaṇasya Śilāprāsāda: Svaviśayesmin Airikine Kāritah Svasyastu Gobrāmhaṇa purogābhya: Sarvvaprajābhya*

Eran Varāha inscription of Toramāna from Huna dynasty (6th century CE) refers to Varāha

Varāha restores the dignity of Bhūmi in Badami (Karnataka) sculpted in the Cālukya dynasty (6th century CE)

In Vaikuṇṭha, Bhūmi devī, who was near Nārāyaṇa, asked, 'For our children leading human lives, you have professed bhakti yoga as a means to obtain mokṣa. Given its limitations of sustained practice and a mandate to remember you as a repository of attributes when the jīvātmā is readying to exit the mortal body is an arduous task. Can you suggest something easier for them to follow?'

Nārāyaṇa said, 'Bhūmi, I am inseparable from Lakṣmī. We are venerated as the divya daṃpati. To those who perform prapatti to us while their body and mind are healthy, I grant mokṣa. Even if they are as immobile as a wooden log or a stone piece unable to internalize my attributes, I shall grant them mokṣa.'

Bhūmi, like a gratified mother, thanked paramātmā for being benevolent and accommodating to her children.

~

'How beautiful of paramātmā to come to Bhūmi's rescue everytime!' said a gratified Ūrmilā when the narration was over.

'Wouldn't you miss Lakṣmaṇa, dear?' asked Sītā.

With tears rolling down her cheeks, Ūrmilā said, 'While he is in the forests, he will think of me. I will also be lost in his thoughts. Is physical proximity the only parameter to a relationship, Sītā? I know he will cherish serving the both of you. He has told me on multiple occasions that he sees you both as his parents. Why should I stop him from enjoying what he loves the most?'

Sītā said, 'You are younger to me in age but in wisdom, you are older and wiser in manifold ways.' The sisters hugged each other, aware that their next meeting would be after fourteen full years.

77

An Exemplary Mother

Sumitrā was seated in dhyāna, with her mind fixed on Nārāyaṇa's lotus-like feet of Gayā kṣetra. Lakṣmaṇa went close, knelt down and said, 'Mother, I am leaving for the forests now. I need your blessings.'

Sumitrā rose from her seat, and embraced him tightly. She kissed him on his forehead and said, 'Lakṣmaṇa, I am the happiest person to know that you are leaving with Rāma and Sītā to serve them in the forests. You are thereby understanding the purpose of your birth and existence. I am happy to learn that your kaiṅkarya to your brother is not limited only to his prosperous days but also in his adverse times. You are in no way acting against any of our established practices. Following the path traced by one's eldest brother, providing charity to as many as possible and dying while fighting a war have been venerated in this vaṃśa. You must go. I am saying this wholeheartedly. But do not get lost in Rāma's beauty and his majestic gait. Your sole purpose is to render kaiṅkarya.'

Lakṣmaṇa, who listened to her words with rapt attention, had tears of joy rolling down his cheeks. He received her blessings and was leaving the apartment, when Sumitrā said, 'Wait.'

She went closer to him and said, 'There is a smṛti injunction that "One's eldest brother needs to be treated like one's own father." Treat Rāma as Daśaratha, your father. Sītā, his wife, should be treated the same way you treat me, your mother. Like your father who listens to Kaikeyī's words, one day Rāma may ask you to obey Sītā's commands, even if they are a bit unreasonable. But that shouldn't deter you from rendering kaiṅkarya. After the exile, Rāma and Sītā shall return to Ayodhyā. Bharata, who will never comply with Kaikeyī's plans, will make arrangements for Rāma's paṭṭābhiṣeka. Till such things happen, the forests of Daṇḍaka shall remain Ayodhyā to you. From my academic discussions with Vasiṣṭha, I somehow fathomed a secret that "Rāma is Nārāyaṇa and Sītā is Lakṣmī." My dear son, for another fourteen years, the forests of Daṇḍaka should be regarded as Vaikuṇṭha.'

Lakṣmaṇa said, 'Mother, I persuaded Rāma and Sītā that I shall accompany them to the forests of Daṇḍaka. I performed prapatti to them. I promised to serve them throughout their exile, immaterial of whether they were awake or asleep. Suyajña overheard this, and asked me, "Did you just recite the dvaya mantra?" I didn't understand what he said. Will you please explain it to me?'

Sumitrā explained that a mantra called dvaya was handed over by the ṛṣis in Kaṭhaśruti and Praśna saṃhitā to be recited by those who perform prapatti to the divya daṃpati. While it was inferred from the śāstras that divya daṃpati meant Lakṣmī and Nārāyaṇa, it was also known to the ṛṣis that Sītā and Rāma were their avatāras. So, when Lakṣmaṇa performed prapatti to them, and volunteered to render kaiṅkarya in the forests, he was actually exemplifying the purport of dvaya mantra, she said. Lakṣmaṇa felt immensely blessed and left the apartment. Sumitrā, who had controlled her emotions till then, shed copious tears on his departure. She was a mother, after all.

78

A Rājya in Distress

Rāma, looking like a tapasvī, walked out of Kaikeyī's apartment with a contented face. Sītā, adorned in jewellery and silk clothes, looking like the rising Sūrya, walked out of Ūrmilā's apartment. This daṃpati was led by a brisk Lakṣmaṇa, who was seen exiting Sumitrā's apartment. Sumantra, with folded hands, stood near the chariot with gold inlays, and fastened to sturdy horses. He looked like Mātali who awaits Indra's arrival in Amarāvatī. He looked at Rāma, and said, 'Please mount the chariot. Your first day in your exile period has already begun. Clothes and jewellery for Sītā, a pair of resplendent bows gifted by Varuṇa,

Sītā and Rāma in a chariot sculpted in the Gupta dynasty (6th century CE)

quivers of arrows, armours covered in leather and swords that shine for Lakṣmaṇa and you are already placed in the chariot. Tell me, where I must take the three of you, I shall.'

'Banks of river Gaṅgā,' said Rāma.

The chariot started moving slowly amidst a sea of prajā that had gathered to bid farewell to their most cherished person, Rāma. The latter asked Sumantra to move fast while the prajā asked him to slow down. One of them said, 'While we are still unconvinced about Rāma's exile, how does Kausalyā still survive?'

Another said, 'Sītā is fortunate to follow Rāma to the forests like Sūrya who is accompanied by his rays everywhere. Lakṣmaṇa is even more fortunate for he alone shall be cherishing Rāma's countenance for another fourteen years.'

Sītā, Rāma and Lakṣmaṇa in a chariot in Prambanan Yogyakarta (Indonesia) in the Sanjaya dynasty (9th century CE)

Rāma's friends, who wished him good, were upset about his exile but they lacked the strength to bid him farewell. They were prostrated by grief and could not even rise from their beds while Daśaratha rose, lurching forward with hands on Kausalyā's shoulder.

Mantrapālā, one of the mantris, said, 'We wish to see Rāma come back to Ayodhyā soon, just like you. Don't follow him for a long distance, thus.'

'Why are you warning us, Mantrapālā?' asked Daśaratha.

'Vāmadeva noticed a grahaṇa-like feature in the wee hours of the morning alongside placements of Bṛhaspati, Budha and Aṅgāraka which are not very favourable to the rājā. Despite the rise of Sūrya, the skies don't seem clear. Brāmhaṇas couldn't offer any havis in their regular agnihotra rituals, as the fire wasn't burning bright. I also heard that mothers aren't nursing their newly born children,' said Mantrapālā with a worried face.

Only the inconsolable wails of the wives of Daśaratha could be heard. The rest was silence. Kaikeyī sat by his side and ran her fingers through his hair. Daśaratha, sensing the touch of Kaikeyī, said, 'Like an eagle that runs down on snakes, you have taken away my cherished children. I renounce all the responsibilities that I was to fulfil as a husband when I held your hand during the pāṇigrahaṇa ritual during our vivāha. You cease to be my wife, I declare. In case Bharata accepts this rājya gleefully, let the tarpaṇa he performs upon my death not reach me.' Kaikeyī left the apartment while Kausalyā remained by Daśaratha's side.

Daśaratha said, 'Kausalyā, like the sky that is bereft of nakṣatras and Candra, so is our bhavana without our sons, and Sītā. I can't smell anymore. I can't see anymore. I can't walk any further. But my eyes are following Rāma's footsteps, like the jīvātmā that advances towards the paramātmā. Hold my hands in yours.'

Kausalyā said, 'Ārya, I have heard that an Āhitāgni, a brāmhaṇa who protects the fire of his yajña, by sheer negligence at times, offers the havis to asuras. Similarly, your misplaced promises to Kaikeyī have cost us our happiness. Separation from my son is agonizing, and is burning me up like Sūrya who dries up ponds during summers. Rāma, who is now twenty-five years, has left Ayodhyā. I don't know how long I must wait to see him?'

Sumitrā approached Kausalyā and as an act of consolation, embraced her. She observed that Rāma's adherence to dharma was his strength. She said that even Sūrya wouldn't scorch his body while Candra would only embrace him with his cool rays. She reminded her of an incident that occurred after Rāma's vivāha to Sītā, involving the son of Śambara, an asura in Vaijayanta.

In order to avenge the death of Śambara, his father, he challenged Daśaratha to a battle. Rāma, representing Daśaratha, fought the asura heroically, and received Bramhā's blessings in return. She added that Rāma was ably assisted by Lakṣmaṇa. She assured Kausalyā that Rāma and Sītā would safely return to Ayodhyā after fourteen years, and that Kausalyā would herself be witness to his paṭṭābhiṣeka.

79
Leaving Kosala Behind

'Why are you holding these umbrellas above me? I have promised to relinquish my comforts,' said Rāma to the brāmhaṇas who were running behind the chariot.

As Sumantra slowed down, the brāmhaṇas said, 'These were presented to us in the vājapeya yajña. They are not royal possessions any more. We can hold them for you.'

'But shouldn't you be engaged in adhyayana of the vedas instead? Your wives will be waiting for your arrival in your houses,' said Rāma as a reminder to them.

'Vedas reside in our memory and hearts. In the forests too, we can carry out adhyayana which is rigorous learning and adhyāpana which is diligent teaching. And as to our spouses, they are capable of protecting themselves. Rāma, they are supported by the power of their pātivratyas too,' replied the brāmhaṇas. Some of them who were greying and elderly even prostrated on the ground in an attempt to stop Rāma from proceeding any further. Smeared in dust, they looked like the haṁsa birds of pristine white-hue, rolling over sand. Rāma dismounted and started walking on foot. The brāmhaṇas were thankful to Tamasā, the river which flowed across, forcing Rāma to halt by its banks.

Rāma and Lakṣmaṇa left along with the brāmhaṇas to perform sandhyāvandana as Sūrya was about to set. After completion, the duo walked towards the chariot. As they heard a distinct cry of the birds, Rāma wished everything was well with Daśaratha. Though marred with worries about his old father, his fears were allayed when he thought of Bharata, whom he believed was the personification of virtues.

'Rāma, I will fetch some fruits and tubers to be cooked for this night,' said Lakṣmaṇa.

'You may cook them for Sītā and you. I consider this night very auspicious as our exile has begun on the banks of river Tamasā. To me, staying by her bank is akin to staying in a kṣetra. I will thus survive on her waters tonight,' replied Rāma.

While Sumantra attended to the horses, the brāmhaṇas happily made the banks of Tamasā their beds. To prepare a bed for Rāma and Sītā, Lakṣmaṇa gathered some fresh leaves. As he sat down to stitch them together, Sumantra asked if he could join. Sumantra said, 'Whenever I see the both of you, I am reminded of Nara and Nārāyaṇa.'

Lakṣmaṇa asked, 'Is that so? I have heard vague references to the duo, but I haven't had the opportunity to know more. Would you care to tell me about them?'

Sumantra, with a smile, said, 'Dakṣa married his daughter Mūrti to a ṛṣi who was always engaged in yajñas. The ṛṣi was called Harimedhas and popularly known as Dharma. The daṃpati settled at the foothills of Himālaya. They were blessed with a pair of sons. Nārada noticed that the chests of the boys were characterized by a Śrīvatsa-like mark. Their palms carried the cakra and śaṅkha marks. Nārada informed Dharma that his sons were the avatāra of paramātmā. They were lovingly called Nara and Nārāyaṇa.

Nara was fair-complexioned while Nārāyaṇa was dark. Both of them took up intense tapasyā by the banks of Alakanandā. Their only source of nutrition was the juice of badara fruits. Thus, their residence was called Badarikāśrama by the ṛṣis. Over a period of time, Nara and Nārāyaṇa grew into handsome men whose faces oozed radiance. Once, Indra seated on the majestic Airāvata, and followed by many apsarās, walked by the āśrama of Nara and Nārāyaṇa. The duo who were engaged in dhyana, did not notice Indra pass by. This was misconstrued by Indra as arrogance. He asked the apsarā women to lure them by making sensual advances. Despite their efforts, the apsarā women could not trap Nara and Nārāyaṇa. While they were wondering if someone more beautiful than them was keeping the brothers unmoved, they noticed a movement in one of the brothers. Nārāyaṇa, with his characteristic smile, placed his hand in the dhyāna mudrā on his lap. No sooner did the apsarā women hear the jingling of anklets from the inside of the āśrama, than a woman of enviable beauty walked out. Nārāyaṇa introduced her as Ūrvaśī to Indra. The latter was made aware of his folly. Indra prostrated at the feet of the brothers. He asked that Ūrvaśī be made the chief of

Nara-Nārāyaṇa in Deogarh Temple (Uttar Pradesh) sculpted in the Gupta dynasty (6th century CE)

the apsarā women, and the duo fulfilled his request. An asura who was flush with boons, each of which was like an armour to him, lived in the vicinity. He was called Sahasrakavaca, the one with a thousand armours. He was not kind to the people in the region, and they hence performed prapatti to Nārāyaṇa, for their protection. Nārāyaṇa fought Sahasrakavaca fiercely and vanquished him in the battle. Meanwhile, a rājā called Daṃbhodbhava heard about the death of Sahasrakavaca, the valiant asura. He who was longing for an equal in combat, reached the āśrama of the brothers. He repeatedly invited the brothers to battle. Nara finally decided to put an end to this unscrupulous rājā. He induced a mantra into iṣīkā grass blades, and released that as an astra towards Daṃbhodbhava. The rājā died in this battle. The ṛṣis still hail Nara and Nārāyaṇa, for their steadfast loyalty to aṣṭāṅga yoga, the eightfold system to attain sākṣātkāra.'

~

Lakṣmaṇa thanked Sumantra for the captivating narration. The night passed for the both of them discussing paramātmā's auspicious attributes.

80

Awaiting a Friend beside the Gaṅgā

'We have been hoodwinked, my friends!' exclaimed one of them. The prajā, lying asleep on the banks of Tamasā, woke up. They could neither spot the trio nor Sumantra. They found no traces of the wheel marks and horses' hooves on the ground. One of them said, 'How did Rāma leave us behind while walking into the forests, like a father who abandons his children while becoming a vānaprastha? From such altruistic care by Rāma, we have been left to the mercy of Bharata, like an animal that is well-decorated and left to the care of a butcher. How can we imagine living in Ayodhyā without him? Wouldn't immolating ourselves in a blazing fire be best suited for us?'

As the prajā trod northwards and reached Ayodhyā, their family members were equally dejected about Rāma not being brought back. But the women folk were of a slightly different opinion. They said, 'Rāma is our protector, well-wisher and friend. It is immensely depressing for us, no doubt. But while we lost the opportunity to witness Rāma adorn the golden crown, the forests have presented him with a crown of colourful flowers. Every mountain and forest that our Rāma walks past shall pay its praṇāmas to him. Even if it is not the season to flower, there will be a flood of flowers from every direction to celebrate Rāma's stay in the forests. Bharata should not be made our target for he is also a victim to Kaikeyī's avarice, as Daśaratha and we are.'

Meanwhile, Sumantra led Rāma, Lakṣmaṇa and Sītā to the outskirts of Kosala. They spent that night by the banks of river Vedaśruti.

The next morning, Rāma and Lakṣmaṇa performed sandhyāvandana by the banks of river Gomatī. Sumantra rode the chariot further till the northern banks of river Syandika which marked the southern boundary of Kosala. Further down were the vassal provinces to Kosala. Rāma offered praṇāmas to Nārāyaṇa, his family mūrti, to Kosala, the prosperous province and to Ayodhyā, its vibrant rājadhānī.

As they were crossing the forests with many animals, Rāma said, 'I am not that interested in hunting.'

Lakṣmaṇa countered, 'Is hunting prohibited?'

Rāma said, 'An animal could be hunted to be used as an offering in śrāddhas by some communities. Restoring peace in human habitats by hunting wild animals is the duty of a kṣatriya. Some rājarṣis even consider hunting as a leisure sport, but I definitely don't.'

They drove further south and heard the thunderous sound of flowing waters. Sītā asked, 'What is this sound?'

'She stays in the kamaṇḍalu of Bramhā, brushes the lotus-like feet of Nārāyaṇa, gushes out of Śiva's jaṭā, and nourishes our Bhūmi in totality. Her name is Gaṅgā.' Even as Rāma completed his response, their chariot was on the very banks of Gaṅgā.

Sītā's eyes were filled with wonder at the massive river she saw for the first time, which was in full flow. She immediately prostrated herself at Gaṅgā multiple times. Rāma was delighted to see Sītā happy. He looked at Lakṣmaṇa and said, 'We shall remain by her banks tonight. There should be an Iṅgudī tree spread with its rich fruits closeby. We can spend our time there, and let the horses be directed to the tree as well. I am expecting his arrival anytime. He will lead us from here.'

Rāma and Sītā took a stroll by the banks of Gaṅgā while Lakṣmaṇa started making arrangements for the dinner. He ran into the woods to collect fruits and tubers. Sumantra was amazed at Lakṣmaṇa's speed of working, but was also doubtful about what Rāma had just said. He asked Lakṣmaṇa as to how Rāma knew about the Iṅgudī tree, and also asked about the person whose arrival he hinted at. Without slowing down for even a second, Lakṣmaṇa kept answering Sumantra with alacrity. He narrated how in their younger days they were under the tutelage of Vasiṣṭha. He said that they used to walk this far to try their archery skills. On one such occasion, while Rāma and Lakṣmaṇa rested by the shade of the Iṅgudī tree at noon, they were trapped in a net laid by the children of vyādhas, the hunters and nāvikas, the boatmen.

As the rājakumāras struggled to disentangle themselves, a well-built individual approached Rāma. He was in a trance while his friends tried to bring him back to senses. The awe-struck person looked into Rāma's eyes with tears flowing from his own. As he gazed at Rāma's face, neck and chest, he instantly fell at his feet, exclaiming the word 'daiva'. In no time, his friends followed suit and uttered the same word with reverence. Upon enquiry, he disclosed that Rāma was exactly like the mūrti that they worshipped in the forests. Eventually, he became Rāma's closest friend. Rāma wouldn't let go of any opportunity where he could meet this friend in the forests. Sumantra was speechless on realizing that he was unaware of something as significant as Rāma's priceless friendship with the vyādha.

Lakṣmaṇa had set up a bed of leaves, soft and fresh, for the daṃpati to relax, even as he conversed with Sumantra. Fruits were gathered, washed and peeled. Tubers were cooked and mashed. As he looked at Sumantra, he sensed an element of disapproval. He asked, 'What is bothering you?'

Sumantra said, 'Are the kṣatriyas allowed to befriend the vyādhas and nāvikas of the niṣāda jāti, a community whose ancestors were the descendants of a tyrant rājā?'

Lakṣmaṇa with a sheepish smile said, 'Sumantra, you have been Daśaratha's mantris, charioteer and confidant for many decades now. You have had plenty of conversations with Vasiṣṭha, Vāmadeva and Suyajña. Nothing that I am going to speak is new to you or something you are unaware of. Yet, I would like to submit whatever little I know from our śāstras.'

Lakṣmaṇa continued, 'In the lineage of Dhruva came a rājā called Aṅga. He performed an Aśvamedha yajña seeking progeny. Eventually, Aṅga was blessed with a male child who was named Veṇa. To everyone's shock, Veṇa as a little boy derived pleasure in killing one deer after another. He used to secretly carry newborn babies and throw them into river waters. Like Asamañja, he, too, was abhorred for such inhumane habits. Aṅga, who failed miserably in guiding his son on the path of dharma, abandoned his riches and became a vānaprastha. Veṇa designated himself the rājā, and began his reign filled with bloodshed and injustice for the prajā. Brāmhaṇas could no longer profess the essence of the vedas and anything even remotely associated with dharma was prohibited. A secret yajña was conducted beside the river Sarasvatī to bring about Veṇa's death. The tyrant rājā fell terribly sick and died and thieves started plundering houses of citizens thereby adding to their woes. It was imperative for Veṇa's lineage to continue. Veṇa's retas was posthumously extracted and the rānī was impregnated. She bore two valiant sons in the coming months.

The brāmhaṇas who were entrusted to nurture them noticed their abilities. The elder son of short limbs, flat nose, large jaws and coppery hair was adept in hunting animals and rowing boats. He left for the forests. His descendants became vyādhas and nāvikas. They were collectively called the niṣād jāti. Pṛthu, the younger son, was inclined towards solving the problems of his prajā. In contrast to his father, Pṛthu's actions adhered to dharma, and his demeanour was a solace to the prajā. The brāmhaṇas saw auspicious signs of Pāñcajanya and Sudarśana in the palms of Pṛthu, thereby regarding him as an avatāra of Nārāyaṇa. It is true that the niṣāda jāti made the forests their home. It is true that their practices are different from kṣatriyas now. But that doesn't detach them from our shared ancestry. How can children bear the brunt of their parents' criminal acts? If niṣādas are frowned upon for being Veṇa's descendents, shouldn't that judgement be extended to Pṛthu and his descendants as well? There is a śruti injunction that a rājā who conducts a yajña should invite the chief of niṣādas, and keep him by his side.[1] I remember Vasiṣṭha mentioning the chief of niṣādas then, while participating in the Aśvamedha yajña, that Daśaratha conducted. Paramātmā is venerated as the "one who is the forests; one who resides in the forests; one who is the chief of forests; one who holds the bow and a quiver of arrows; and one who is the thief in the forests as well."[2] Rāma's friendship with the current chief of niṣādas transcends any jāti restrictions. He is very dear to Rama. In fact, Rāma treats him as his very ātmā. As regards my view, whoever respects and adores Rāma, I am that person's servant.'

Sumantra asked, 'That chief of niṣādas, what is his name?'

'Guha' came the answer, as the two of them turned to notice Rāma and Sītā returning to the tree.

---

1 *Nishadasthapatim yajayet.*

2 Sri Rudram.

81

Guha

Guha was spotted at a distance, accompanied by his mantris and announced by a fanfare of blowing conches and instruments made from buffalo horns. As they began crossing the waters of Gaṅgā, Guha couldn't hold his excitement any further. He ran like a

warhorse, with his long legs hitting and splashing water everywhere. Sītā who heard this increasing noise, nudged Rāma. The latter in a spirited voice said, 'Guha.'

Guha continued running on the fine sands of Gaṅgā, getting covered by the fine river sand and dust. He stood awe-struck in front of Rāma, and fell at the feet of Rāma, like a stick falling on barren ground. He was immediately lifted, and Rāma, teary-eyed, firmly held his shoulders. He said, 'Guha, you are my friend. My best friend. Do friends prostrate at each other's feet? They only embrace each other.'

Rāma gave a heartfelt embrace to Guha, completely unaware that all the sand dust on Guha's body would adhere to his body now. Guha's tears were uncontrollable. As he slowly noticed Sītā, he moved out of the embrace, and prostrated at her feet. Rāma said, 'Sītā, bless this good friend of yours immensely. He deserves your grace and protection.'

Sītā acknowledged this wish of Rāma with a smile.

'What are all these?' asked Rāma, pointing to many baskets that were placed on the ground by Guha's mantris. 'Rāma, these are for you, fruits, tubers, freshly caught fish, and honeycombs,' replied Guha. Rāma politely declined the offerings citing the reason that the brothers had just not dressed as tapasvīs but had vowed to live simple lives like them. Rāma asked Lakṣmaṇa to fetch the Gaṅgā waters for their consumption, but assured Guha that Sītā and Sumantra would consume the fruits and tubers brought by him.

'Rāma, please consider Śṛṅgaverapura, our habitat, as your Ayodhyā. Rule over us with your knowledge and experience,' pleaded Guha.

Rāma, with his characteristic smile, said, 'Guha, you're the chief of niṣādas. I should neither interfere nor exercise any unwarranted power over your prajā. You are their biggest asset.'

Crossing a thin stream of Gaṅgā waters on foot, they entered Guha's habitat.

Lakṣmaṇa rolled up the mats made of fresh leaves, and carried them along. He spread them at a place pointed out by Guha's mantris and requested the daṃpati to sleep. Looking at Rāma showing no signs of discomfort about sleeping on the leaf-mat on bare ground, and Sītā relaxing without any ado, Lakṣmaṇa's respect for them only increased manifold. He kept a strict vigil over the daṃpati, while holding a sharp arrow to fling at any poisonous insects approaching them. Guha was worried that Lakṣmaṇa would be harmed, and so he in turn kept a vigil over the younger brother. The mantris were in turn awake waiting for orders from Guha, their chief. Sumantra's observant eyes noticed all of this and said to itself, 'This daṃpati's aura can diligently ignite the spark of sādhanā even in the minds of niṣādas. Guha showing bhakti to Rāma and Sītā is akin to that of Śiva's son Guha who meditates on Lakṣmī and Nārāyaṇa.'

The next morning, Rāma woke up to the chirping sound of kokila birds. As he got up, he saw Lakṣmaṇa standing and resting his head on his bow. Rāma walked towards him, and caressed his hair. He said, 'Dear Lakṣmaṇa, we need to cross the mighty Gaṅgā today, don't we?'

Lakṣmaṇa immediately opened his eyes alongside feeling embarrassed that he had dozed off. He took a dip in the Gaṅgā waters, while noticing the rugged Guha move the boat out of the pier. After performing sandhyāvandana, Lakṣmaṇa presented himself to Rāma, who was talking to Sumantra. Rāma said, 'Sumantra, I have already conveyed to you what I have wanted to submit to my mother and father. Bharata and Śatrughna have been away in Kekaya for many years now. Daśaratha is physically weak. Lakṣmaṇa and I were guarding Ayodhyā like the snakes that guard the river waters. We, too, have left Ayodhyā, carried away by our vidhi, like Garuḍa that carries the snakes away. Our enemies will fish in these troubled waters. It is my opinion that Bharata be installed as the rājā at the earliest. This will also be assuring to Kaikeyī.'

Sumantra said, 'What should I tell Kausalyā? The pleasant untruth that you are happily settled in your maternal uncle's house or the unpleasant truth that you are walking in the dense forests of Daṇḍaka?' Rāma convinced Sumantra that his decision to return to

Rāma in jaṭā in Tirucherai Temple (Tamil Nadu) sculpted in the Cola dynasty (10th century CE)

Ayodhyā only after fourteen years was unchanged. He asked Lakṣmaṇa to fetch the milky latex of nyagrodha tree closeby, and used them to tie his hair as a jaṭā. Lakṣmaṇa followed suit. Sumantra blessed Rāma and Sītā for a peaceful stay in the forests, while wishing that they conquer the world like paramātmā who did so as Trivikrama. He also prayed that Lakṣmaṇa received more opportunities to serve the daṃpati, as he was already doing. Sumantra finally left for Ayodhyā in the chariot.

82

An Auspicious Start to the Exile

'Gaṅgā, help us cross your waters safely,' said Rāma and Lakṣmaṇa to themselves as they sipped the river waters. Sītā, too, sipped Gaṅgā waters and prayed to her that they safely return to Ayodhyā after the period of fourteen years. She promised to offer many pots of meat and barrels of toddy to Gaṅgā as prasāda, and to distribute it among niṣādas on her return. She vowed that she would give brāmhaṇas in Ayodhyā cows, clothes and food. She wished to visit the Maṇikarṇikā tīrtha in Aṅga upon her return.

The boatman slowly rowed the boat to the spot where the three of them were standing. Lakṣmaṇa jumped into the boat, and helped the daṃpati get in. Guha took the oar from the boatman and ferried the boat himself, crossing the vast waters of Gaṅgā. They all arrived on the other side of Gaṅgā. Rāma, like a doting father, encouraged Lakṣmaṇa to guide the daṃpati to the āśramas of eminent ṛṣis. Meanwhile, with tears trickling down his eyes, Guha bid adieu to Rāma, and his family.

Guha helps the trio cross Gaṅgā in Nageśvaran Temple (Tamil Nadu) sculpted in the Cola dynasty (9th century CE)

As the three of them entered Vatsa deśa, Lakṣmaṇa asked Rāma and Sītā to rest for sometime, while he went hunting. After a muhurta, he returned with the bodies of a wild boar, deer of the ṛśya, pṛṣata and mahāruru species on his shoulders smeared with their blood. Muttering a certain mantra, he slowly peeled the animal skins and let the blood ooze out. The deer hides were washed in Gaṅgā waters and spread on grass for drying. He carefully extracted the vapā portion, a peritoneal membrane guarding the abdomen, from these animals. He ignited a fire and offered the vapā to the devas. As a small portion of the vapā got consumed in the fire, he took the remaining burnt portions and placed them on a leaf. He washed the blood off the pieces of meat and skewered them on a medhya stick and cooked them on the fire before placing them on the leaf. Lakṣmaṇa respectfully offered them to bhūtas, those guardians of the forests, and to pitṛs, the representatives of one's forefathers.

Rāma and Sītā came to the spot where Lakṣmaṇa was conducting the sacrifices to the devas, the pitṛs and the bhūtas. They, too, joined Lakṣmaṇa in the prayers but were visibly taken aback at the carcass in one corner and the dried animal skins. Lakṣmaṇa placed the charred vapā, and the cooked medhya on a leaf and presented it to the daṃpati. Rāma and Sītā looked at each other confused, when Lakṣmaṇa said, 'These are prasāda offerings, bereft of any pāpas. It wouldn't be contradictory to the commitment you have made to Daśaratha.' The daṃpati found Lakṣmaṇa's justification corroborated by a śruti injunction, and thus consumed the prasāda with reverence.

As they sat on the ground, Rāma initiated a conversation with Lakṣmaṇa. He said that Kausalyā had nurtured a pair of birds in her apartment. One was a myna and the other was a parrot. These birds were extremely attached to Kausalyā. Once while Kausalyā was feeding these birds mashed rice in milk, the parrot noticed a cat sneaking towards the vessel. The parrot raised an alarm to the myna saying, 'bite his foot'. Kausalyā immediately noticed the cat and remarked to herself about how smart and grateful the birds were.

Rāma felt that he was not as protective of his mother as the birds were. He was also wary of Kaikeyī's treatment of Kausalyā and Daśaratha after his departure to the forests. He urged Lakṣmaṇa to head back to Ayodhyā to set things right. But Lakṣmaṇa refused to heed Rāma's advice. He said, 'Without you by my side, I don't wish to see Daśaratha, Sumitrā or even Śatrughna. Whom does Candra shed cool rays for and why is the candana paste so fragrant? It is only to delight us. I am born only to serve, and to serve only the two of you. A fish that is removed from its waters doesn't die instantly. It dies only after the waters that have seeped between its scales dry up. Till that moment, it suffers. Similarly, I may manage to survive only till I reach the ramparts of Ayodhyā, if I were sent back.'

As an endorsement to Lakṣmaṇa's view, Sītā remarked, 'My state will be no different either.'

Rāma's move to dissuade Lakṣmaṇa did not succeed. As Sūrya was about to set, the brothers performed sandhyāvandanā. The trio retired to their leaf mats with the dried deer skins as blankets.

83

A Home in Citrakūṭa

'What is this deafening noise?' asked Sītā.

'We are nearing Prayāga which sees the confluence of two mighty rivers, Gaṅgā and Yamunā. Sarasvatī, too, joins them in this kṣetra. Sītā, I am seeing you in this confluence,' said Rāma.

'How?' asked Sītā, in bewilderment.

'The Yamunā waters look like your hair tresses, the Gaṅgā waters are akin to the mallikā strands that decorate them and the Sarasvatī waters resemble the kuṅkuma on your forehead,' said Rāma to a bashful Sītā.

Lakṣmaṇa asked, 'Why are the waters of Yamunā dark?'

Rāma said, 'Śiva couldn't withstand the separation from Sati. He wandered in the Himālaya mountains, and reached Kalinda. Blossoming flowers in the spring season made him lovesick and bereft. His body was burning like molten fire, as a result. He jumped into the waters of Yamunā that was originating from Kalinda mountain. She gracefully absorbed the heat and melancholy and is said to have

Yamunā on a tortoise in National Museum (Delhi) sculpted in the Gupta dynasty (5th century CE)

turned dark from then on. She is called Kālindī for her association with Kalinda. She is called Yamunā as she is the daughter of Yama.'

The niṣādas in Śṛṅgaverapura were sending logs of wood downstream on the Gaṅgā waters for the yajñas performed by the ṛṣis living along the Prayāga. The trio noticed the brāmhaṇas unloading the logs by her banks. Lakṣmaṇa noticed the setting of Sūrya. He erected a square vedikā in no time, and the daṃpati performed the agnihotra in it. Noticing smoke arise from close quarters, Bharadvāja came out of his āśrama. He saw Rāma, Sītā and Lakṣmaṇa in his neighbourhood. He welcomed them to his āśrama. The animals in the āśrama mistook Rāma and Lakṣmaṇa for hunters, thereby running helter-skelter. Bharadvāja offered a lavish treat of tubers and fruits to the three of them. He asked if the trio could stay in his āśrama for the remaining period of exile. Rāma politely declined stating that the prajā of Ayodhyā would find it easy to keep visiting him, thereby making his commitment to Daśaratha meaningless. Bharadvāja expressed appreciation of Rāma's commitment to dharma. He also appreciated the attention paid to detail by Rama during the donation of cows to the brāmhaṇas in Ayodhyā, unlike the times of Nṛga. Rāma asked Bharadvāja for a place that would be conducive for tapasvīs and would at the same time bring pleasure to Sītā. Bharadvāja recommended that Rāma walk towards Citrakūṭa.

Upon taking permission from Bharadvāja, the trio left for Citrakūṭa the next morning. Lakṣmaṇa constructed a raft with bamboo canes, covered them with soft grass and requested the daṃpati to board the raft.

While crossing the waters, Sītā prayed to river Yamunā for a safe return from the forests after fourteen years. She promised to donate cows to the brāmhaṇas, and barrels of toddy to the niṣādas on her return.

As they walked by the Yamunā banks, Sītā paid her praṇāmas to Śyāma, a nyagrodha tree whose leaves were strikingly dark-green.

Then, they entered the Citrakūṭa valley surrounded by tall mountains. Evergreen trees covered their slopes. Many rivulets carrying cool waters were seen emptying into the Mandākinī river while on the rocks, ṛṣis were seen performing kapālāsana, an upside down yogic posture. Lakṣmaṇa constructed an āśrama the roof of which was stitched in leaves while Rāma and Sītā were bathing in the river waters. The daṃpati commenced the gṛhapravēśa ritual with the vāstu ceremony. By chanting mantras, Rāma prayed to the devatās to grace his dwelling. He invoked the blessings of Nārāyaṇa, his family mūrti, and performed the vaiśvadeva ritual. He then performed a ritual to propitiate Rudra, also known as Īśāna, the mūrti guarding the north-eastern direction.

Having propitiated Rudra, Rāma undertook the customary avabhṛtha ritual by bathing in the river waters again. The daṃpati again sat to perform the last of the rituals called the bhūtabali, as was decreed, to please bhūtas, the forest guardians. Towards its end, Lakṣmaṇa brought the cooked meat of a blackbuck that was recently hunted, to be placed as naivedya for bhūtabali. After the rituals, the daṃpati expressed their appreciation for Lakṣmaṇa's building skills. The trio spent their night describing the ravishing Citrakūṭa, their new home.

84
Preceptors Meet

'Come in, Bharadvāja, you are welcome,' said Vālmīki.

Bharadvāja, with folded hands, entered the āśrama and prostrated at the feet of Nārada and Vālmīki.

'A fortuitous visit indeed as I was writing about Rāma's visit to your āśrama during his exile,' said Vālmīki.

Bharadvāja described the occurrence as serendipitous as Rāma and Sītā had graced his āśrama at the commencement of their exile, and again at its culmination.

'But I was later told that Rāma who refused to eat the offerings by Guha, his dear friend, gracefully consumed whatever I offered to him. Which dharma did Rāma adhere to in this instance to explain the disparity in his actions?' asked Bharadvāja. Nārada volunteered to explain this dichotomy in Rāma's behaviour.

'Bharadvāja, you will be aware of the śruti injunction that calls a scholar as accomplished, only if he has sought refuge under an ācārya. You have been fortunate to be under the tutelage of Vālmīki, your ācārya. Guha received no such initiation under an ācārya. Even if he was Rāma's close friend, Rāma did not find it suitable to consume his offerings for this sole reason,' said Nārada.

Bharadvāja continued to show his partial disapproval for this justification since it was not Guha's mistake not to have been associated with an ācārya. Nārada said that Guha had never proactively sought an ācārya for guidance and instruction. This was a deterrent to the acceptance of his offerings by Rāma. Nārada noted that this did not in any way hinder Guha from being a recipient of Rāma's grace, though.

Vālmīki said, 'Bharadvāja, after visiting your āśrama in Prayāga, the trio visited my āśrama in Citrakūṭa. They offered their respects to me. I stayed in Citrakūṭa for a few years, and shifted my āśrama to the banks of Tamasā. Little did I know then that I would get to take care of a pregnant Sītā.'

Vālmīki then probed into Bharadvāja's passing reference to Nṛga in his conversation with Rāma at his āśrama. Bharadvāja thus narrated an incident that occurred involving Nṛga, the brother of Ikṣvāku. Nṛga had once donated a cow to a brāmhaṇa and many days later the cow had mistakenly joined Nṛga's herd. Unaware of this, Nṛga donated the same cow to another brāmhaṇa. This gaffe led to a tussle between the brāmhaṇas who landed in the court of Nṛga for a solution. A cowardly Nṛga avoided offering a settlement to the brāmhaṇas. For his lackadaisical attitude, Nṛga was cursed with multiple births as a lizard. Bharadvāja wanted to be sure that Rāma hadn't committed any such mistake like Nṛga, when he heard of Rāma's donation of cows to brāmhaṇas like Agastya, Kauśika and Trijaṭa in Ayodhyā.

Vālmīki was proud of Bharadvāja's attention to detail while Nārada was pleased to witness a conversation between scholarly luminaries. Before departing, Bharadvāja quietly paid his praṇāmas to Sītā, who was five months pregnant then.

85

A Rājya Mourns

Sūrya, known to the residents of Ayodhyā as Vivasvān, must have been extremely angry at this treatment meted to Rāma, his famed descendent. His scorching rays had dried up the lakes, and the Sarayū river too. Despite it being springtime, trees had started shedding their leaves and not a single bud blossomed into a flower. The women were shedding copious tears, while the men showed no inclination to work. The elephants and horses in the stables showed little interest in eating. On hearing even a faint sound of chariot wheels, the prajā climbed up their roofs to check if there was the faintest chance of Rāma returning. Even the week-long separation was heart-wrenching for them. Sumantra's chariot drove past the houses and streets engulfed in stillness.

'Sumantra wishes to meet you, do we let him in?' asked Kausalyā to an infirm Daśaratha. The rājā gestured that he be allowed.

Sumantra, with folded hands, entered the apartment and paid his praṇāmas to Daśaratha. He said that he had stayed back in Śṛṅgaverapura for three days until Guha's spies, who had secretly followed the trio, returned to inform Sumantra of their safe stay in Citrakūṭa. He also elaborated on the places visited by them, the food they ate and their resting places at night. Daśaratha could not hold back his tears when listening to the ordeals faced by his sons, and his daughter-in-law. He made some frail movements with his fingers. Sumantra, in no time, grasped that the rājā wanted to know the parting message of Rāma.

Sumantra answered in the affirmative and duly expressed the messages that Rāma wished to convey.

To Bharata, 'Execute the orders of Daśaratha dutifully. Respect all our mothers equally. Treat Kausalyā like your mother as she will see her son in you. Adhere to the dharma that a rājā is enjoined to follow.'

To Kausalyā, 'The paṭṭābhiṣeka of Bharata needs to be conducted with grandeur. You must make suitable arrangements for the ceremony as if your very son is being anointed. You must also accompany my father when he performs agnihotra.'

To Daśaratha, 'I offer my praṇāmas to you. Please take care of your health.'

The women in the apartment let out a wail that only increased Daśaratha's sorrow.

Daśaratha asked Sumantra if there was any parting message from Lakṣmaṇa. The intelligent mantris hesitated to speak any further, but Daśaratha insisted that he divulge Lakṣmaṇa's message. Sumantra mustered some courage and conveyed Lakṣmaṇa's message: 'What mistake did Rāma, the one loved by all, commit to deserve this treatment? Why should Rāma be the victim of Kaikeyī's greed? If these boons were promised during the war with Śambara, why were they not intimated to the mantris at that very moment? If granting the boons sought by a mulish Kaikeyī was deemed as dharma, then who will adhere to the smṛti injunction which states that "the eldest son can never be isolated from his rājya"? Āryaputra, you have neither respected the prajā's emotions nor have you taken the smṛti injunction seriously. I have heard that an arrogant person who is bereft of wisdom and is steeped in bad habits, needs to be abandoned, even if the person were one's father. I don't wish to call you my father.

Rāma, my eldest brother, who loves me like a doting father, will be my father from now on. Sītā and Rāma, the divine daṃpati, shall be my sole protectors.'

As Sumantra finished, the apartment was suffused in stark silence. Even the tear drops of Kausalyā that fell on her bangles made no sound. But there was only one person smiling. It was Daśaratha. It seemed to Sumantra that Daśaratha was proud of Lakṣmaṇa and his message, however stern it was.

Kausalyā inquired about Sītā's state to which Sumantra stated that Sītā was choked with emotions and was at a loss for words. She then asked if Sītā had anything to state about Kaikeyī. Sumantra evaded that question by speaking about the rhythmic tinkling of Sītā's anklets as she walked, and her matchless grit. He then took leave of Daśaratha as he left the apartment.

To his surprise, Sumitrā was standing outside, posturing as if she was waiting only for him. 'What did Sītā say about Kaikeyī that you did not want Kausalyā and Daśaratha to know?' asked Sumitrā. Reassured of her discretion, Sumantra said, 'You will be aware that Kaikeyī wanted Bharata to be anointed the rājā. But she cleverly asked that Rāma should go to the forests. Was she interested in seeing Bharata as the rājā or did she want to see Rāma in valkala? She was worried that Rāma and Sītā may end up having children, who in due course could end up challenging Bharata's succession. So she implored that Rāma be sent to the forests. It was shocking to her that Sītā was allowed to accompany Rāma to the forests. Yet, she let it happen because she knew that a beautiful Sītā would be a feast to the eyes of the rākṣasas in the Daṇḍaka forests. Her instinct said that some harm may occur to Sītā, and Rāma would end up giving up his life for Sītā's sake. It was therefore in her interest that Sītā was accompanying Rāma.'

'Did Sītā tell you all this?' asked Sumitrā in dismay.

'No, her eyes conveyed a myriad of thoughts. Her tears spun this narrative. Rāma's tears and his pitiable look at her only ratified the narrative,' replied Sumantra.

86
Kaikeyī's Path to Redemption

Sumitrā reached the temple of Nārāyaṇa, and sat in a worried state. Vasiṣṭha, who was present in the temple walked towards Sumitrā and asked, 'What is the cause of your worry?'

Sumitrā said, 'How did Kaikeyī turn selfish all of a sudden? Is there a way for her to become a better person? Is there a way that such bigoted people, too, receive the paramātmā's grace?'

Vasiṣṭha said, 'Kaikeyī did not turn selfish all of a sudden. She has always carried the traits of her mother who was notorious for throwing tantrums at Aśvapati. But this self-centred nature of Kaikeyī did not manifest itself earlier because she had focussed her attention on Rāma and his auspicious attributes. This had kept her occupied and calm all through these years. I am unable to fathom the identity of the person who could have drastically brought this wicked trait in Kaikeyī to the fore.'

While Sumitrā listened intently to Vasiṣṭha's words, her eyes were focussed on the mūrti of Nārāyaṇa, their family mūrti. Vasiṣṭha took notice of Sumitrā's bhakti towards the paramātmā and felt a sense of tranquillity all around. Taking a deep breath, he said, 'To relinquish this evil nature, Kaikeyī must delve deep into the nature and attributes of Nārāyaṇa. The first step to achieving this goal is to savour his name, and keep repeating it. A kṣatrabandhu can be redeemed of his pāpas by reciting the name of Govinda. Even a fallen Ajāmila can seek redemption by reciting Nārāyaṇa's name.'

Sumitrā, whose eyes shone in hope, and who still wished for Kaikeyī's welfare said, 'Ācārya, please tell me about how the names of Govinda and Nārāyaṇa changed the lives of Ajāmila and a kṣatrabandhu?' Vasiṣṭha agreed and began the narration.

~

In the lineage of Haryaśva was born a child who was named Vimati. From his young days, he exhibited only bad behaviour. His birth in a kṣatriya vaṃśa brought no sense of responsibility in him to protect his subjects. On the contrary, his acts were against the very nature of a kṣatriya and the welfare of his rājya.His people sarcastically referred to him as kṣatrabandhu which meant the 'friend of kṣatriyas'. Unable to tolerate his antics, the people sought his banishment from his rājya. He wandered in the forests, killing animals and consuming the raw flesh. Accidentally he came across an immobile ṛṣi, who looked famished. Taking pity on the ṛṣi, he brought some water to drink, and a few lotus tubers to eat. The ṛṣi was impressed with Vimati's demeanour but was shocked to know from him that he was called a kṣatrabandhu. To redeem him from his pāpas, the ṛṣi said, 'Vimati, the paramātmā rescued Bhūmi from the hands of the tyrant Hiraṇyākṣa, thereby being praised by the devas through their śruti chanting. He is therefore revered as 'Govinda'. Keep reciting this name, as this will lead you on the path of bhakti.'

Vimati practised bhakti, and continued his sādhanā in the next birth as a brāmhaṇa by being a jātismara, a person with memories of his previous lives. He attained mokṣa, eventually.

~

A brāmhaṇa named Ajāmila lived in Kanyākubja. He was learned in the śāstras, and eventually married a noble woman. Once, his father asked him to fetch samidh and kuśa from the forests for their daily rituals. In the forests, he saw a śūdra woman in coitus with a man, under the influence of vāruṇi, out in the open. He fell in love with the śūdra woman. He employed her as a maid in his house, and abandoned his wedded wife. His carnal nature with the śūdra woman made him indisciplined, and resulted in producing many children. Forgoing his duties as a gṛhastha, he even refused to retire to the forests as a vānaprastha. At a ripe age, he had a son who as an infant smiled when he was surrounded by the waters. Ajāmila, named him Nārāyaṇa only for this reason and not for his devotion to paramātmā. He enjoyed the pranks of his son, and developed an intense attachment to him. As age advanced, he couldn't move out of his bed, but kept thinking about his dear son. As he closed his eyes, he had a vision of Yamadūtas, the messengers of Yama, holding a noose ready to be thrown at him. In fear of death, he muttered the name of Nārāyaṇa, his cherished son. In no time, he saw the charming faces of the Viṣṇudūtas, the messengers of Nārāyaṇa, on the scene. In no time, the Yamadūtas and the Viṣṇudūtas engaged in a tussle, as to who must take custody of Ajāmila. The former stressed on Ajāmila's fallen habits and a life smeared in adharma. The latter insisted that Ajāmila had taken the name of Nārāyaṇa. They further said, 'Even if the name of paramātmā were taken jokingly, the person still receives his grace. Like a medicine that cures the disease even if consumed by the patient with little faith in its curative properties, so is the name of Nārāyaṇa that yields fruits to the person who recites it. Like the fire that burns the dry grass into a heap of ashes, so does the name of Nārāyaṇa that absolves one of his pāpas.'

Ajāmila's eyes opened, but to his surprise the Yamadūtas and Viṣṇudūtas were not to be found. He had learnt his lessons. He asked that he be taken to Haridvāra, and engaged in austerities as a prāyaścitta for his past activities. Despite his inabilities, he performed upāsana towards Nārāyaṇa, and as he was resting besides some temple pillars, he saw Yamadūtas in his vision. In a respectful tone, they said, 'Yama has strictly advised us to stay away from the bhaktas of Nārāyaṇa. We apologize if we have hurt you in the past.'

In no time, the Viṣṇudūtas arrived and escorted the jīvātmā with its subtle body, when it left Ajāmila.

~

Sumitrā offered her praṇāmas to Vasiṣṭha and prayed that Kaikeyī developed an urge to correct her adamant attitude. As they were speaking, a rakṣaka entered the temple, and conveyed news of the ailing state of Daśaratha. Both of them rushed to the bhavana to attend to the rājā.

87

A Grieving Rājā Dies

Daśaratha was lying on the floor muttering Rāma's name in a feeble tone. His eyes were swollen and his weak body could barely even crawl forward. Kausalyā, with dishevelled hair, was seated near his head with one hand holding her head. Drowning in the sorrow caused by Rāma's separation, she said, 'Āryaputra, Sītā will be struggling to chew the wild rice and Rāma will be lying on the forest ground with his arm as his headrest. I am fully convinced that Bramhā has designed my heart out of a diamond. You know why? Because any other mother's heart would have exploded on thinking about the distress of her children. When will I get to see those lotus-petal like eyes of my son? Should I wait for fourteen years? Do you think Bharata will hand over the rājya to Rāma? Do you think Kaikeyī will let him give away? It is said that to please the pitṛs, one must invite brāmhaṇas for the śrāddha ceremony. Ṛṣis like Āpastamba and Bodhāyana prescribe that the invited brāmhaṇas be scholars, holding good intentions for the host. But this is seldom practised as only relatives and friends are invited, which is at odds with Manu's injunction. In fact, the relatives are fed, and the brāmhaṇas are called only if the need arises. Brāmhaṇas don't entertain such invitations. Similarly, Rāma who was qualified to be the next rājā was sent to the forests for no fault of his.

But on his return, he will not accept the rājya that is ruled by Bharata like a tiger that refuses to consume the leftovers of a jackal.'

Breathing heavily, Kausalyā knotted up her messy hair into a bun and said, 'Like a mother fish that eats her little ones, you have smashed the future of our son by exiling him to the forests. Learn the truth however bitter it is. My father who nourished me is no more. My husband who is supposed to have been my pillar of strength was always spotted in my co-wife's apartment. My son who was intent on serving me has been banished to the forests. Where will I go now? You have ruined all our lives.'

Daśaratha, in a feeble voice said, 'Kausalyā, I am the root cause of this catastrophe. I have done injustice to Rāma. I have done injustice to Sītā. I have done injustice to Lakṣmaṇa. Even fathers with devilish sons don't abandon them. On the contrary, I have abandoned the crest jewel of my vaṃśa. But see how he has rewarded me. Without expressing any displeasure, he has left Ayodhyā. I never deserved a son like Rāma, the best among men. He, too, never deserved a father like me, the worst of men.'

Kausalyā immediately held Daśaratha's head on her lap and asked for forgiveness. In no time, Sumitrā and Vasiṣṭha rushed into the apartment. Sumitra placed the feet of Daśaratha on her lap with Vasiṣṭha's eyes fixed on Daśaratha's fading aura. The rājā could hear the faint voice of the tapasvī's father who had cursed him to die of sorrow caused by his son's separation. He said, 'I will not survive to see Rāma's return to Ayodhyā. Like Śukra's return to his exalted state ushers in happiness, so will Rāma's return be joyous. But only you will be fortunate to see him successfully return from exile.'

He looked upwards and said, 'Yamadūtas, the messengers of Yama have arrived. They are asking me to hasten.' He kept gazing at the ceiling, whispering only one name, 'Rāma.' Vasiṣṭha knew that the rājā was nearing his final moment. With none of his four sons by his side, as Sūrya was setting, the jīvātmā in Daśaratha's body was also readying its exit.[1]

---

1 24 December, 5091 BCE, Pramoda saṃvatsara, Caitra, Śuklapakṣa, Pūrṇimā tithi, Hasta, Saturday.

88

An Ignorant Crow Meets Its End

Nārada asked, 'I have heard that Indra's son assaulted Sītā even on their very first day in Citrakūṭa. Can you explain the incident in detail?'

Vālmīki said, 'I shall narrate whatever I have heard ṛṣis telling me at my Citrakūṭa āśrama, and the additional information that Sītā revealed to me, the previous week,' and he commenced.

~

Lakṣmaṇa sought permission from Rāma to proceed into the forests to fetch wood for cooking purposes. Rāma, after consenting, walked with Sītā by the stream of Mandākinī gazing at the sweet-smelling flowers and the deer grazing on the grass. They walked back towards their āśrama, and sat under the shade of a tree. Rāma rested his head on Sītā's lap. She ran her fingers through Rāma's hair slowly. In no time, she saw Rāma asleep. She wondered at his undiminished beauty even while asleep. She was equally worried that someone would cast their evil eyes at his splendour that rivalled that of Lakṣmī, the mūrti of prosperity. Sītā, too, rested by leaning on the tree trunk. There was peace all around.

As mandated by Manu, Rāma had performed the bhūtayajña, by placing cooked rice on a banana leaf under the same tree for the fauna to feed on, like any other day. A murder of crows arrived at that spot, not very far from where the daṃpati were resting. One of the crows, instead of feeding on the rice, was looking only at Sītā. Her feet and toes that were as tender as the lotus petals and carried the hue of pomegranate seeds were thought by the crow to be chunks of flesh. He started pecking at her foot, and when she withdrew her leg, the crow nipped her toe. Sītā, who didn't want to disturb Rāma, threw clods of mud scattered near her at the rogue bird. The bird ignored the mud, and kept pecking at her foot. Sītā removed and held her golden girdle in her hand, like Durgā who held the sword in her war against Mahiṣāsura. Though at a striking distance, Sītā resisted from hurling it at the crow, out of benevolence. Her upper garment slid down in no time, and the crow could not resist his hunger looking at her bosom. It scurried to her bust and pecked off a piece of flesh from her cleavage, and flew away.

A bleeding Sītā was visibly in withering pain. The crow that managed to savour her flesh sat on the tree branch under whose shade the daṃpati were resting. Blood drops from his beak fell on Rāma's face who woke up in shock. Like a snake that hisses when its female is attacked, so did Rāma's eyes turn red in anger. With his bow and quiver of arrows in the āśrama, and Lakṣmaṇa away in the woods, Rāma didn't want to waste any further time. He looked around and plucked a blade of darbha grass. He meditated on Bramhā pleading that the darbha blade turn into an astra, and released it upwards aiming at the crow. The crow couldn't propel itself any further as iṣīkā, the heat emitting astra chased it at a lightning speed. Hit by the astra in his breast, the crow instantly dropped to the ground. This crow, which had been tamed and nourished by Indra as his very son, thought that his foster parents would come to his rescue. He did not comprehend the enormity of his heinous act of hurting Sītā, the very avatāra of Lakṣmī who was the embodiment of compassion. Indra, who constantly prayed for Lakshmi's grace could not have offered any support to Lakṣmī's offender, even if it was his own son who had erred. Śacī, Indra's wife could not have provided asylum to the bird that had hurt Lakṣmī who was the paragon of all virtues. The ṛṣis, too, who were witness to the daṃpati's peerless demeanour, refused to help the bird. The other crows did not come to his rescue either, petrified of Garuḍa's anger, if the latter got to know of their culpable act. Abandoned by one and all, the crow, battered and bruised, fell at Rāma's feet. Sītā, like a true mother, asked that the crow be spared of his life.

Rāma, in order to honour Sītā's appeal, scooped the crow's right eye, like a caring father who punishes his disgraceful son. The daṃpati decided to not narrate this ordeal to the unselfish Lakṣmaṇa, who already was serving them tirelessly.

~

Nārada asked, 'Why did Rāma spare the life of the crow, whose acts were bloody and unpardonable?'

Vālmīki said, 'I, too, asked Sītā about this. She said, 'The very act of the crow falling at our feet, was in itself treated as prapatti. It is said that when a person who has killed his mother and as a result acquires mātruhatyā, performs prapatti, that remorseful act still needs to be accepted. In the case of the crow, he had only assaulted out of ignorance. So I insisted that his life be spared. But to release an astra in the name of Bramhā and then to render its actions ineffective was not advisable. So Rāma took away the crow's right eye.'

She innocently asked if Rāma's act rendered all the crows single-eyed? I laughed saying that all crows have two eyes, but to overcome the hindrance of their beaks impeding their vision, they only employ one eye to spot their target.'

Nārada said, 'I can sense another reason for Rāma's forgiveness to the crow.'

Vālmīki said, 'What is that?'

Nārada said, 'Long ago, to conduct śrāddha for his pitṛs, Ikṣvāku advised his son Vikukṣi to head to the forests, and fetch him suitable flesh. Vikukṣi killed a variety of animals like deer, hare and others. As it was night time, and he was hungry, he cooked a part of the hare, and ate it. The following morning he reached Ayodhyā, and in the śrāddha, Ikṣvāku had invited Vasiṣṭha, their purohita to participate in the ritual. The hare was cooked and served to Vasiṣṭha. The brāmhaṇa found out that the served meat was a leftover, and it wasn't medhya, the pure meat. He refused to eat, and sarcastically declared that Vikukṣi would be called Śaśāda, 'the hare-eater' from then on.

Śaśāda, had a valorous son who was invited by the devas to fight the asuras. To help Śaśāda in the war, Indra induced his energy in a bull and asked the rājā of Ayodhyā to stand on the bull. Śaśāda stood on the hump of the bull known as kakud, fought ferociously and emerged victorious against the asuras. He earned the name Kakutstha as a result. From the time of Kakutstha until Daśaratha's times, the rājās of Ayodhyā shared a cordial relationship with Indra. To value this alliance, Rāma decided to spare the life of the crow, who was like a foster son to Indra.'

Vālmīki immensely thanked Nārada for the insight and continued writing verses of the incidents that he perceived through his divine eyes.

89

An Empty Throne Beckons Bharata

'In the illustrious lineage of Vivasvān who spreads his rays, of Ikṣvāku who held the sceptre of dharma, of Kakutstha who fought the asuras valorously, of Hariścandra who spoke only the truth, of Bhagīratha who brought the Gaṅgā waters to Bhūmi, of Raghu who performed a viśvajit yajña, comes our beloved rājā, Daśaratha. He who cared for us like our parents is not with us anymore. The jīvātmā in his body has left seeking the realm of peace.'

As this passage was being sung by the bards and panegyrists outside the apartment of Daśaratha, the cries of his wives echoed in the bhavana. Kausalyā holding Daśaratha's head and Sumitrā his feet were visibly sorrow-stricken and tired. As Kaikeyī joined her co-wives in expressing her sorrow, Kausalyā said, 'Like a person who can understand the intense bitter taste in a bitter gourd only when he tastes it, Daśaratha, too, understood your evil intentions only after his vivāha with you. Needless to say, your friendship with Mantharā, an effigy of crooked thoughts, has brought a catastrophe to our rājya. Rāma is gone to the forests. Daśaratha has been escorted by the Viṣṇudūtas. When Janaka gets to know about how much turmoil Sītā is going through, it is unfathomable how much he will lament.

I too have decided to enter the funeral pyre of my husband. What more do you desire?'

As Kausalyā burst into tears, Sumitrā held her tight and convinced her not to take such a drastic step. Like a gloomy day that barely sees Sūrya, and like the night sky that is bereft of its nakṣatras, so was the bhavana of Daśaratha in his absence, filled only with the wails of his sobbing wives.

The industrious mantris of Daśaratha's council arrived in no time. As they sat down for a discussion, Jayanta said, 'We will need to perform funeral rites to Daśaratha's body.' Siddhārtha asked, 'What do you mean by saying "we will need"?

Jayanta said, 'We will need to perform the funeral rites as none of his sons are here.'

'This doesn't sound right to me. We must summon Rāma to Ayodhyā which is the only solution,' said Vijaya. They all looked at Sumantra who with a straight face said, 'Rāma will not come.'

'What do we do when the eldest son refuses to come?' asked a worried Driśti.

'We must call the next son,' replied Aśoka.

'It will surely take time to bring Bharata from Rājagriha. In the interim what do we do with Daśaratha's body?'asked Arthasādhaka to which there was stark silence among the council of mantris.

'An oil trough,' boomed a voice as the mantris noticed Vasiṣṭha walk into the apartment. They all paid their praṇāmas to the purohita. Vasiṣṭha asked Mantrapāla to arrange for the trough with herbal oil for the body of Daśaratha to be preserved in till Bharata's arrival. The council of mantris left the apartment to make arrangements when the ṛṣis wanting to meet Vasiṣṭha entered. The ṛṣis took notice of the women helplessly crying over Daśaratha's body.

Kātyāyana mournfully said, 'Daśaratha of Ikṣvāku vaṃśa was as loving as a mother and as caring as a father to his prajā. He guarded them like the eyelids of the eyes. Like fire that is inferred from smoke, so was Ayodhyā's prosperity attributed to Daśaratha's adherence to dharma. His majestic pose on the throne of Ayodhyā was reflected in the victorious fluttering of the flag atop his chariot.'

Mārkaṇḍeya said, 'The sons of Daśaratha whose bodies are smeared with the fragrant candana and aguru paste are away from the rājya. Ayodhyā which used to be a vibrant rājadhāni is lacklustre and now akin to a fully flowing river that has gone dry.'

Suyajña said, 'Ayodhyā is without a rājā now. If this situation persists, the brāmhaṇas will not be motivated to conduct yajñas, and even if they did, there is no one to offer them commensurate dakṣiṇā. The devas who won't receive their share of havis through yajñas will be reluctant to shower timely rains. The festivals that used to be conducted on the arrival of rains will slowly fade out. The farmers would be wary of cultivation fearing the robbers who will run away with the produce.'

Vāmadeva said, 'I fear that the bhaktas will not be motivated to string garlands for mūrtis in the temples. In such a gloomy atmosphere, neither will women sport jewellery nor will their spouses be energised to show them around in their chariots. The archers who will lose touch with their weapons won't be ready to guard the rājya when the need arises. As a result, the army will face defeat in case of attacks from adversaries.'

Jābāli said, 'I fear that the conclaves meant for deliberating the śruti and smṛti injunctions will lack participation. Neither scholars adept in elucidating the qualities of paramātmā nor an audience that can respectfully receive it will be found. I won't be surprised if a person ignorant in the Bṛhaspati sutras would call himself a cārvāka, and flex his muscles on selfless sannyāsīs.'

Vasiṣṭha right away realized that Ayodhyā was in arājaka, a state where the prajā is bereft of its rājā. He also knew that such instances were propitious for rival rājās to declare wars. He summoned the rājadūtas asking them to hasten to Rājagriha and bring Bharata to Ayodhyā. They were asked to not speak of Rāma's exile to the Daṇḍaka forests and not reveal the news of Daśaratha's death. The rājadūtas left Ayodhyā with the hope of seeing their rājadhāni in her previous glory.

90

Ill Omens and Premonitions

'Don't jump, don't jump …,' muttered Bharata.

Māṇḍavī, who heard the disturbed voice of Bharata, woke him from sleep and asked, 'Did you have a dream?' Bharata nodded positively and ordered the rakṣaka to bring Śatrughna to his apartment at once. Śatrughna and Śrutakīrti entered Bharata's apartment. They noticed Bharata seated on the floor with teary eyes and a petrified look.

'Brother, what brings sadness to you? Did someone hurt you? Did Mantharā utter despicable words at you or Māṇḍavī?', asked a concerned Śatrughna.

'Śatrughna, I am not able to look at you properly. The scenes that I saw in my dream are still hanging in front of my eyes. My throat is dry and my voice is choking up,' said Bharata.

'What dream was it?' asked Śatrughna.

As Māṇḍavī and Śatrughna were lending their ears, Bharata said, 'Śatrughna, I saw the Sarayū river bed with its waters dried up, the trees whose leaves had also dried, and forests fires at distant mountains. I saw a rākṣasī in red clothes guffawing and dragging a man on a street with scattered pieces of elephant tusks. That man was draped in black clothes and adorned in an iron garland strung with reddish flowers. He, whose body was smeared in dust, suddenly escaped from the rākṣasī and ran in a dishevelled state. He jumped into a lake that was formed of cow dung. He swam across to its banks and hurriedly ate rice balls mixed with sesame seeds. A chariot drawn by donkeys took him away in the southern direction.'

Śrutakīrti asked, 'What does this dream imply?'

Śatrughna said, 'None of these nimittas individually translate into anything inauspicious, though a combination is a bit worrying. It is said that the funeral shall be performed soon to the man whose chariot is pulled by the donkeys in the southern direction.'

Māṇḍavī said, 'Āryaputra, why do you fear of Ayodhyā's safety when Daśaratha, the rājā who adheres to dharma, presides?'

Bharata said, 'My worry is not about Rāma, who is paramātmā to my eyes and mind. It is not about Kausalyā who strives for dharma and Sumitrā, an expert in the smṛti texts either. But my concern is about Kaikeyī, my mother. She thinks she is more intelligent than others. She is concerned only about herself and her own welfare. She is irascible and adamant about her choices.'

Śatrughna asked, 'The person whom you saw in your dream, was it Daśaratha, our father?' Bharata's tears confirmed this. None wanted Bharata to reveal the rākṣasī's identity. They guessed who it could have been. They didn't want to wound Bharata any further as he was already battling a melancholy.

Śatrughna recommended that they walk towards the place in the outskirts of Rājagriha where Dīrghāyu, the revered ṛṣi of Ayodhyā was camping. On their way to his tent, Māṇḍavī enquired about Mantharā who was not traceable. Śrutakīrti replied that her attendants had spotted a short woman covertly leaving Rājagriha in a merchant cart that was carrying emeralds to Aṅga. This raised an alarm in Māṇḍavī's mind since she knew about her mother-in-law's long association with Mantharā.

The rājakumāras and their spouses reached the place where Dīrghāyu had camped. They paid their praṇāmas to the ṛṣi and

Bharata narrated his dream yet again. The ṛṣi who heard him out patiently said, 'It has long been recommended by ṛṣis that listening to the story of Gajendra, the bruised elephant, obtaining mokṣa through the grace of Nārāyaṇa shall help alleviate the effects of bad dreams.' Therefore, Dīrghāyu began his narration.

91
Gajendra Mokṣa

In the widespread Draviḍa deśa was a lineage of devout rājās called the Pāṇḍyas. Their pristine devotion to paramātmā was unparalleled. They ruled from its rājadhāni called Kavāta whose borders were earlier believed to have been protected by snakes. Indradyumna, the rājā, delivered flawless justice and excellent governance to his prajā. He was equally loved for his other qualities. The rājā spent much of his time conversing on vedānta, with Agastya ṛṣi, who now lived south of the Vindhya mountains after witnessing the vivāha of Śiva and Pārvatī in Himālaya. Agastya deemed Indradyumna to be capable of being initiated into bhakti yoga. He taught him a stotra which was a hymn praising the paramātmā's qualities. It read thus, 'Vāsudeva, I meditate on you who is revered by the ṛṣis as Nārāyaṇa and whose body is the entire universe that comprises both the sentient and insentient matter. Pervading this creation through your splendour, you are the sole cause of all their existence while having nothing that has birthed you. You are the 'causeless cause'. You are witness to the activities of jīvātmās that are housed in material bodies, yet you remain untainted by the flaws committed in due course of time. Like a performing actor whose real identity is masked by his attire, similarly your true nature isn't fully comprehensible in your avatāras, that appear ordinarily human. The kalpaka creeper that is entwined to the pārijāta tree is known to fulfil one's material desires. Similarly you, a storehouse of riches, have the ability to grant mokṣa which is the priceless state of transcending the vicious karma. I perform prapatti to you, for helping me attain you through bhakti yoga.'

The rājā, who wanted to dedicate the rest of his life to sādhanā, retired to the base of the Malaya mountain. As a tapasvī in a jaṭā, he took to mauna, the vow of silence. Agastya, on the other hand, spent his time discussing the grammatical nuances of a language that he had learnt from Śiva. This language was known among the scholars of Kavāta who called it the Tamiḻ language. Draviḍa deśa was also popularly referred to as Tamiḻakam accordingly. With his śiṣyas, Agastya authored a grammatical treatise on the Tamiḻ language called Agattiyam. To spend more time in tapasyā, he wanted to retire to the peak from where the river Tāmraparṇī originated. On his way, the disciples informed the ṛṣi about Indradyumna's āśrama in the vicinity. Agastya who was eager to see the rājā turned tapasvī went to his āśrama but was shocked that he was not accorded a ceremonial welcome. Indradyumna, engrossed in dhyāna, was unaware of the ṛṣi's arrival. This behaviour attracted the ire of Agastya who said that the rājā would be an elephant in his next birth, who would aimlessly wander in the forests. Uttering the curse, he angrily left the place.

Meanwhile, the ṛṣi called Harimedhas, who had fathered two sons, called Nara and Nārāyaṇa, came to Draviḍa deśa. He fell in love with Hariṇī, a young lady in the forests. The daṃpati eventually had a son who was called Hari. While the daṃpati retired to Himālaya, Hari, who was fond of animals, stayed back in Tamiḻakam. He occupied the same āśrama that had once housed Indradyumna, the bhakta of paramātmā. He, too, was engaged in tapasyā like his older brothers. A young elephant that used to wander in the nearby forests started developing a bond with him. He would visit the nearby lake, and then pay a visit to Hari's āśrama. In the next decade, he grew into a large elephant thereby leading his herd everywhere. Hari used to call him Gajendra, the 'chief among elephants'.

On a day when the breeze from the Malaya mountain carried the smell of areca palms, betel leaves, cardamom creepers and candana sticks, Hari was deeply engrossed in dhyāna. As he opened his eyes, he realized that the day was gone, and that Gajendra hadn't paid his customary visit. He walked towards the lake where the elephant would normally come with his friends. To his surprise, the lake sand was smeared in blood. The elephant had fallen on the ground, and his limb was severely bruised. In the lake waters was the mutilated body of a crocodile. Hari rushed to his āśrama and brought some medicinal paste to the lakeside. He applied the paste on the affected areas of the elephant's limb while also shedding tears for his dear friend. The elephant managed to rise by himself, but looked visibly tired. Hari, who realized that it was a conflict between the elephant and the crocodile, couldn't grasp how the crocodile's head was sliced as if a sharp weapon was deployed. Agastya, along with his śiṣyas, on his descent from the Malaya peak was heading to Kavāta. He spotted Hari, and the limping elephant getting ready to move into the forests from the lake. He noticed the lake waters that had turned red, and the floating torso of the crocodile. Hari, who took notice of the ṛṣi, paid his praṇāmas and the elephant nodded his head as a sign of reverence. The ṛṣi patiently heard Hari's queries and closed his eyes in dhyāna. He then said, 'Hari, by the grace of paramātmā, I shall narrate all that transpired during the day. Gajendra and his herd of elephants made their visit to the lake. They sprayed water on each other with their trunks, and remained in a playful mood. Gajendra plucked one of the lotus flowers in style and held it in his trunk, to the backdrop of his friends trumpeting for him. As he was getting out of the lake, his limb was caught by this ferocious crocodile that we see here. Unable to shake off his predator, the elephant cried in pain. The crocodile lost no time in further pulling the wounded elephant into the lake water. Gajendra, the elephant became a jātismara thereby being reminded of his previous birth as Indradyumna. He repeated the prayer that I had taught him and performed prapatti to Nārāyaṇa, asking for immediate cessation of pain. Realizing that the call of the elephant for the 'causeless cause' was aimed at the paramātmā, Śiva and Bramhā excused themselves. Nārāyaṇa, seated on Garuḍa, prodding him to fly faster reached the lake. Sudarśana, his never failing discus, rushed at lightning speed to slice the crocodile's head, providing instant relief to Gajendra. Nārāyaṇa came close to the elephant, and gracefully accepted the crushed lotus, as if Gajendra had plucked the flower intending to offer it to him. Realizing that you were heading to the lake, Nārāyaṇa seated on Garuḍa disappeared from the scene.'

Gajendra mokṣa in Deogarh Temple (Uttar Pradesh) sculpted in the Gupta dynasty (6th century CE)

Hari asked Agastya of the crocodile's antecedents, and the reason for paramātmā's disappearance. Agastya said that the crocodile was a gandharva by name Hūhū who had insulted a ṛṣi called Devala. He was thus cursed to be a crocodile in his subsequent birth. His encounter with Gajendra was fruitful for he inadvertently held a bhakta's limb and, as a result, his jīvātmā was released from the crocodile's body by Nārāyaṇa himself. On the other hand, Agastya expressed his happiness that Indradyumna who had engaged in sādhanā in his previous birth also performed prapatti in the present birth as an elephant. He prophesied that the jīvātmā in Gajendra's body would attain mokṣa eventually, exemplifying paramātmā's commitment to granting mokṣa to every being.

He also divulged that Hari was an avatāra of Nārāyaṇa, and that his purpose was to engage in tapasyā for the larger good of the world. It was thus pertinent for paramātmā to disappear from Hari's sight. The ṛṣi took leave of Hari as he was to attend the Aśvamedha yajña being performed by a Pāṇḍya rājā who came in the lineage of Indradyumna. Hari, who realized the purpose of his birth, engaged in rigorous tapasyā from then on while Gajendra attained mokṣa by the end of his life. 'Gajendra mokṣa' henceforth, became a testimony for the ṛṣis, of paramātmā's mercy.

92

Bharata Returns

'Ācārya, a few rājadūtas of Ayodhyā have stopped by our āśrama. They wish to meet Bharata at once,' said one śiṣya. Dīrghāyu granted permission while Bharata who was worried looked at Śatrughna praying that everything was fine in Ayodhyā.

'Victory to Bharata' said the rājadūtas in a boisterous tone as they entered the āśrama. Bharata ran towards them and asked, 'Is the rājā keeping good health? Is everyone in Ayodhyā doing well?' The rājadūtas looked at each other, and one of them said, 'All of them are keeping well. Lakṣmī, the consort of Nārāyaṇa, seated on a lotus, showers immense grace on you. Vasiṣṭha seeks your presence in Ayodhyā.'

Bharata, who was in a confused state, paid little attention to what the rājadūtas had said. Dīrghāyu, on the other hand, deciphered from the statement of the rājadūta that Daśaratha was dead. He offered to accompany the rājakumāras and the rājadūtas to Ayodhyā. Bharata took leave of Aśvapati, his ailing grandfather, and Yudhājit, his doting uncle. The retinue of Bharata and Śatrughna with their consorts, and Dīrghāyu left for Ayodhyā in four-wheeled chariots.

After travelling for seven nights, Bharata reached Ayodhyā. He entered the rājadhāni through Vaijayanta, her western gate. He saw the streets that were once bustling with activities, and filled with the jubilant prajā were now sporting a deserted look. The customary welcome that used to be accorded for the rājakumāras was missing. Bharata was worried that his bone-chilling dream had turned true. He rushed to his mother's apartment where his father would usually be spotted. He offered praṇāmas to Kaikeyī. She beheld her son, whom she was meeting after many years, and kissed him on his forehead. She said, 'My dear rājā of Ayodhyā, how is my father doing? How is my brother faring?'

Bharata was startled on being addressed as 'rājā'. He enquired about his father at once, to allay the fears caused by his recent dreams.

Kaikeyī said, 'Bharata, you will know that the jīvātmā has to depart from the material body at a destined time. It is true for me, and you as well. Your father treated our prajā as his own children. He was revered for his knowledge and valour. He used to propitiate agni through yajñas saying, "O Agni, lead us in the path to prosperity, and bestow upon us the state of bliss." Those prayers have fructified, and he too has departed to the abode of his ancestors.'

Bharata swooned upon hearing the news of his beloved father's death while Kaikeyī held him immediately. In a panic-stricken tone, she said, 'Bharata, Bharata, open your eyes.' Like a person who regains consciousness after being bitten by a snake, Bharata gently opened his eyes. While still lying in Kaikeyī's lap, he asked, 'I knew something was wrong in our bhavana, when my father, who is usually present to welcome us, was not found at the entrance. How was I not informed earlier? Shouldn't Rāma have held back the funeral rites of Daśaratha who was also my father?'

Kaikeyī with a firm face looked straight ahead and said, 'He doesn't know of it.'

'Doesn't know what?' quipped Bharata.

'Of your father's death,' came Kaikeyī's retort.

Bharata was confused, depressed and angry at the same time.

Kaikeyī said, 'As soon as I heard about the news of Rāma's paṭṭābhiṣeka, I thought it would be more appropriate for you to occupy the throne of Ayodhyā. I requested your father to allow you to become the rājā. He immediately acceded.'

Bharata gathered some energy and sat up. He asked, 'Where is my brother now? I need to meet him. I need to inform him of Daśaratha's death, and we need to perform the funeral rites.'

Kaikeyī fumbled for a moment and said, 'Rāma isn't in Ayodhyā. He has left to the Daṇḍaka forests with Sītā and Lakṣmaṇa.'

Bharata said, 'To the forests? I wish to know if Rāma seized the wealth of a rich person out of jealousy or that of a poor brāmhaṇa who struggles to make his ends meet? Did he forge a relationship with another person's wife? Did he kill the developing foetus in a mother's womb? Did he kill a brāmhaṇa who is called a bhrūṇa for having mastered the vedas, for being composed and exercising caution over his emotions? It is only acts like these that demand banishment to the forests.'

Kaikeyī maintained silence.

Bharata said, 'Please tell me what blunder Rāma committed to receive this punishment?'

Kaikeyī said, 'Rāma committed no mistake. I wanted to secure your position in Ayodhyā as her rājā. This demanded Rāma to stay away from this nagarī, and live in the forests. In fact, I sought these boons from your father.'

Copious tears were running down the cheeks of a stupefied Bharata, while Kaikeyī continued, 'Hasten to perform the funeral rites of your father, and take control of the rājya at the earliest.'

93

Bharata's Fury

'You have not requested for Rāma's exile to the forests, rather you have insisted. My father, who was helpless in front of you, gave in to your demand, and must have died thinking of Rāma's separation. You have explained the situation as if Rāma's departure to the forests and Daśaratha's death were unrelated incidents. I knew you were cruel, but never thought that you could potentially cause my father's death. What harm did Daśaratha cause to you to receive a death sentence at your hands? He was a righteous rājā who was very caring to his prajā and immensely devoted to Nārāyaṇa. He was committed to fulfilling promises, and you, like a crafty fox used this to your advantage. He was innocent enough to not realize that he was embracing a piece of burning, red charcoal whenever you got close to him. By marrying you and bringing you to Ayodhyā, my father must have dreamt that the rājya would be blessed by Lakṣmī, without realizing that you were Alakṣmī who is the personification of inauspiciousness. I am unable to fathom how you could send Rāma to the Daṇḍaka forests. Did you not know that rākṣasas have stationed themselves in large numbers there? Or was it a part of your plan to see him defeated and dead? You are an expert in such evil designs. Rāma would always visit your apartment, more than that of Kausalyā. Do you know why? That is because he saw you as his mother. Kausalyā was never hurt by this for she treated you as her sister. As a mother, doesn't the pleasing countenance of Rāma that is akin to Candra and his eyes that look like lotus-petals flash before your eyes? What pleasure did you derive in seeing Rāma as a tapasvī, clad in valkala going to the forests? I can imagine how the entire bhavana must have burst into tears seeing him in that state, and how you must have smiled like a witch. I asked you if Rāma committed the act of killing a bhrūṇa to deserve such an intense punishment. I now realize that it is you who has engaged in such a crime by sending Rāma to the forests. In fact you must be banished to the forests like your mother, for an evil animal like you doesn't fit well amidst the kind hearted prajā of Ayodhyā. Don't you know that the eldest son always becomes the heir-apparent? This is the tradition in the vaṃśa of Ikṣvāku. This is also the tradition in your land of Kekaya. By deciding to make Rāma the heir-apparent, Daśaratha wasn't acting against tradition. Instead, you wanted me to be the successor to Daśaratha.

How foolish of you to have concluded that I will happily accept your decision? Had you only observed me since birth, you would have realized my bhakti for Rāma! He is not just my brother, he is my father, my friend and my devatā who is worthy of worship. The news of Daśaratha's death has wounded me, and the news of Rāma's exile is akin to rubbing salt over it. I can't imagine how much pain Kausalyā must be enduring to see her son away in the forests. I can't face Sumitrā whose one son is serving Rāma in the forests, and the other son has been a pillar of support for me. I seriously doubt if you are the daughter of the noble and pious Aśvapati. Well, how can you be generous if you are perennially under the influence of that hunchback friend of yours, who is truly a rākṣasī. I have heard Vasiṣṭha say that the "fruits of one's pāpas need to be borne by his relatives". Today, I realize the purport of my ācārya's words for I am the victim to your sinful deeds. I may be disappointing you, but let me now announce that I will be bringing Rāma back to Ayodhyā. I will be his eternal servant. How can I live in an Ayodhyā that is bereft of Rāma?' said Bharata in Kaikeyī's apartment.

Māṇḍavī, Śrutakīrti and Śatrughna were shell-shocked to see Bharata roar like a lion.

Kaikeyī did not expect Bharata to react this strongly and hurl such unpleasant words at her. She walked to him, and extended her arm as if to console him. But Bharata was in no mood to be cajoled. He swiftly moved away, rejecting her efforts to pacify him. He continued, 'Kāmadhenu, the divine cow of Amarāvatī once shed tears looking at the bulls toiling on farm lands. If a mother cow with many children can sense their pain, I can't imagine what Kausalyā must be enduring. A mother looks at her son and utters a śruti statement that says, "My son, your limbs are just like mine, and your birth is straight from my heart. I see my ātmā in you. May you live a hundred years." Will Kausalyā be able to say these things to Rāma again? Will she survive till his return? You are my enemy in the disguise of my mother. I was recently rendered fatherless, and from now, I am motherless too. You must hang yourself from one of the trees or jump into blazing fire,' blurted Bharata at a dispirited Kaikeyī. He left the apartment with a resolve to never see her again.

94

A Tormented Rājakumāra

'Rānī, salutations to you! Bharata desires to meet you,' said the rakṣaka to Kausalyā. She nodded in approval and Bharata was let in. He walked in like a calf that had lost its way and found his mother. He fell at Kausalyā's feet. In a sombre tone she said, 'Your mother has worked hard to fetch this rājya of Ayodhyā for you. You are extremely fortunate to have a mother like Kaikeyī. She blessed me with an opportunity to see my son clad in valkala and walk to the Daṇḍaka forests as a tapasvī. This hard-fought rājya is all yours now. You should arrange for your paṭṭābhiṣeka at the earliest. Meanwhile, I shall ask either Vasiṣṭha or Vāmadeva to carry the sacred agnihotra fire preserved by Daśaratha and lead me to Citrakūṭa forests. The mantris will help me carry the mortal remains of Daśaratha that is currently preserved in the oil trough. If Śatrughna permits it, I will take Sumitrā also along. Rāma, who is unaware of his father's death, should at least perform the funeral rites of his father. Vasiṣṭha in the past has pointed at Rāma's navel that is distinctly gold-hued, and has said to me, "This son of yours is Hiraṇyanābha. He is no ordinary man." It has been days since I have seen my Rāma. If he permits, I shall stay in Citrakūṭa for the remaining exile period.'

Bharata cried his eyes out, and banged his head multiple times on the floor. He said, 'Vasiṣṭha has taught us the nuances of śruti and smṛti so that their injunctions guide us in our lives. But all of what I have learnt from him shall dissipate from my memory *if I have* schemed for Rāma's banishment from Ayodhyā. When a brāmhaṇa is promised dakṣiṇā for a yajña but it is not given upon the yajña's completion, he goes back broken-hearted. I shall incur the same pāpa as the one who has caused this pain *if I had* wanted Rāma to stay away from Ayodhyā. When the respects accorded to a learned brāmhaṇa is forcefully stopped or a calf that is less than ten days from birth is not allowed to consume his mother's milk, a mountain of pāpas is incurred. I, too, shall suffer them *if I had* wanted Rāma to live in the forest. It is ordained to offer a pāyasa that contains milk, jaggery, sesame seeds and slices of goat meat as naivedya to the devas and the pitṛs. Then, it is distributed among families. I shall incur the pāpa of doing neither *if I had* wanted Rāma to suffer in the forests. A rājā is said to incur pāpa for not rewarding those who serve him tirelessly and for inducing diffidence in his army by running away from the battlefield. The rājā is abhorred by his prajā when he over-taxes his subjects. I, too, shall endure that same pāpa *if I had* wanted Rāma to walk in the rugged path of Daṇḍaka. The prajā, too, incur pāpa when they plot to kill a noble rājā, and that pāpa I shall undergo *if I had* wanted Rāma's feet to be pricked by the Daṇḍaka thorns. A man who refuses physical congress with his good-natured wife while he harbours carnal feelings for another woman incurs a terrible pāpa. I shall endure the same *if I had* wanted Rāma to become a tapasvī. A man who either abandons his family or supports their needs through trade of liquor, poison and meat bears the pāpa which I too shall, *if I had* wanted Rāma to languish in the forests. It is wrong to defecate in broad daylight, and heinous to kick a sleeping cow. Let me be subservient to the man who has committed both these errors *if I had* wanted Rāma to suffer in the forests. Pāpas are incurred by a person who attempts suicide, who indulges in a sexual affair with his ācārya's wife, who least values the virtue of gratefulness, who enjoys sleep in the sandhyā time, who poisons the food and burns the dwelling of the righteous, who refuses to serve water to the thirsty and who pollutes the water bodies making it unpalatable for the prajā. I will shoulder all these pāpas *if I had* wanted Rāma to relinquish his comforts and stay away from Ayodhyā.'

Sumitrā, Śrutakīrti and Śatrughna stood like statues while their brimming eyes overflowed. Māṇḍavī ran to Bharata and held him tightly. She wept at the pitiable state of her beloved and his reinless lament. He continued, 'My riches should be robbed. I should wander everywhere like a demented man with a begging bowl. I should be afflicted with diseases. I should have no children. I should never enjoy the full human life. I should never be able to see Rāma, my devatā anymore in my—' and collapsed.

95

Bharata, 'He Who Bears'

Vasiṣṭha deliberated with Kausalyā and Sumitrā about antyeṣṭi, the funeral rites and rituals to be performed for Daśaratha's mortal body. When Vasiṣṭha raked up the issue of Daśaratha's order that wouldn't allow Bharata to perform the final rites to his father, Kausalyā asserted that Bharata who was endowed with all auspicious attributes should be permitted for the same. Sumitrā, too, seconded Kausalyā's viewpoint by praising Bharata's resolve to bring back Rāma to Ayodhyā. After a consensus on this, Vasiṣṭha ordered Sumantra to take Daśaratha's body out of the oil trough, and place it on a śibikā. Bharata and Śatrughna led the procession[1] to the chanting of pitṛmedha sūkta that said, 'We hereby invoke the blessings of our pitṛs, those who are eligible to sit on kuśa grass and consume the soma juice in the yajñas, to bless us. We, who have imbibed the grace of Trivikrama in us, invoke the blessings of our pitṛs, to accept the havis that we are offering, and remove all the affliction from us.'[2]

1 5 January, 5090 BCE, Pramoda saṃvatsara, Caitra, Kṛṣṇapakṣa, Caturdaśī tithi, Friday.

2 Rig Veda, 1.10.15.1–14.

Daśaratha's funeral in Prambanan Temple sculpted in the Sanjaya dynasty (9th century CE)

Scholars trained in sāma veda recited verses to alleviate the pain of the prajā. The fire of agnihotra, that was maintained by Daśaratha was carried to the banks of Sarayū. Precious gems were strewn on the path by the prajā as if to bid a royal farewell to their beloved rājā. Kausalyā, Sumitrā, Māṇḍavī, Ūrmilā, Śrutakīrti and the other women performed apradakṣiṇā, the anti-clockwise movement around the funeral pyre. Then the gathered people, who were experiencing an explicable grief, returned to their houses. Vasiṣṭha advised that the descendents of Ikṣvāku vaṃśa should observe aśauca. This was the period of impurity arising out of the birth or death of a family member that doesn't allow performing of vaidika rituals was followed. This period for the kṣatriyas lasted for twelve days, and as it got over, on the thirteenth day after the first son's birth, Dasaratha performed the naming ceremony for his newly born sons. But upon observing the dedication with which Bharata was conducting himself, Vasiṣṭha reduced the impurity period to ten days in accordance with an injunction by Parāśara who had incentivized this for the sincere. On the twelfth day, piṇḍīkaraṇa, the ritual of offering food balls to one's ancestors was conducted by Bharata. He donated clothes, goats, cows and houses to various sections of his prajā, including the brāmhaṇas. On the thirteenth day, Śatrughna escorted Bharata to the funeral area by the banks of river Sarayū. They picked the bones from the ashes, when Bharata screamed, and said, 'My brother is gone to the forests. You, too, have left us father. Why have you both abandoned us? Who will now guard us? Should I retire to an āśrama or jump into a blazing fire?'

While Śatrughna consoled Bharata and walked him back to Ayodhyā through the eastern gate, they noticed a pair of guards dragging a person to their presence. It looked as if a monkey was being pulled by its master to perform pranks amidst people. They came closer to the rājakumāras and said, 'Āryaputra, we noticed this lady whose body was smeared in sandal paste, draped in silk clothes and decked in precious ornaments, trying to secretly escape our attention.'

The brothers could barely see her face. Śatrughna signalled to Bharata about her prominent hump. A shocked Bharata said, 'Mantharā, is it you?' Śatrughna seized her by her neck, as the place echoed with her shrieks. He dragged her to the bhavana, while the maids ran helter-skelter fearing Śatrughna's wrath. Bharata was appalled by his brother's rage, and his treatment of Mantharā could not be condoned. He held Śatrughna's hand and indicated that she should be freed. This led to a squabble between the brothers.

Śatrughna: It is because of this lady who is cruel by nature that our father is dead and our dear brothers are away. Śrutakīrti had already warned us that a short woman had escaped Rājagriha to Aṅga. But this little evil has instead come to Ayodhyā. She is the sole cause of our calamities.

Bharata: Mantharā is not the cause of our problems.

Śatrughna: Kaikeyī shouldn't have succumbed to the whims of this hunchback lady. It was least expected of the daughter of Aśvapati to act in such a selfish manner but being her mother's daughter, such bad behaviour was a part of her inheritance. She is the cause for our hardships.

Bharata: Kaikeyī is not the cause of our problems.

Śatrughna: Even if Mantharā had manipulated Kaikeyī, and the latter had sought boons, it was mandated upon Daśaratha to have judiciously decided and then granted the boons. Either intense lust for Kaikeyī or senility made him take such ill-advised decisions. Daśaratha has caused distress because of his ineptitude.

Bharata: Daśaratha is not the cause of our problems.

Śatrughna: Rāma shouldn't have ceded to Daśaratha's orders. He should have revolted against such diktats. Lakṣmaṇa should have restrained our father from being ruthless. Sītā should have coaxed her father-in-law to revert to his original order of Rāma's paṭṭābhiṣeka. The trio found it easier to leave Ayodhyā, I suppose.

Bharata: The daṃpati or Lakṣmaṇa haven't caused our problems.

Śatrughna: Bharata, are you speaking sensibly? If Mantharā, Kaikeyī, Daśaratha, Rāma, Sītā or Lakṣmaṇa aren't the cause of the current state of affairs, then who is? I am all ears to listen to you.

Bharata took a pause, and said, 'I don't know which Bharata, the son of Ṛṣabhanātha or the son of Duṣyanta, inspired Vasiṣṭha to name me as Bharata! I know that my name is derived from the word 'bharaṇa' that means 'to bear'. My mother must have thought that I was born 'to bear' the rājya of Ayodhyā as her rājā while my ācārya must have thought that I would 'bear' the rājya of servitude to Rāma. I will never become Ayodhyā's rājā and Lakṣmaṇa has stolen my opportunity to serve Rāma by walking to the Daṇḍaka forests. Now, I truly realize the meaning of my name. I am bearing the brunt of my mother's avarice and my father's indecisiveness. I am bearing the bitterness of my prajā. I am the 'Bharata' in every sense. Mantharā, Kaikeyī, Daśaratha, Rāma, Sītā or Lakṣmaṇa caused none of our problems. It is simply my existence that has caused hurt to so many people around me. It is simply me, simply me!'

Knowing how deeply hurt Bharata was, Śatrughna hugged him for his frank yet evocative submission. Like a crane looking to escape from its hunter's noose, Mantharā too waited for the apt moment, and when the brothers were immersed in emotions, she quietly crawled into Kaikeyī's apartment seeking asylum.

96

Journeying to Bring Back Rāma

Bharata entered the assembly hall that once resembled Sudharma, the resplendent hall of Amarāvatī, when Daśaratha ruled. He offered his obeisances to Vasiṣṭha who was seated on a chair gilded in gold. Vasiṣṭha acknowledged him by raising his palm and said, 'My dear rājā, may you live long! Long ago, when your father had conducted the Aśvamedha yajña, I was commanded to administer this rājya. I was again forced to do the same, because of the passing away of your father. This responsibility feels to me like hanging a tala fruit around a sparrow's neck. I wish to relinquish this.'

'To whom?' asked Bharata worriedly.

'To you, of course! Daśaratha gave this prosperous Kosala rājya to you, and Rāma left for Daṇḍaka forests to fulfil his promise made to your father. Your paṭṭābhiṣeka will make this rājya secure. Rājās ruling the rājyas in the far north, the east, west and south including the yavanas and islanders will offer gifts to you. Even those who aren't rājās will offer their praṇāmas to you.'

In a melancholic voice akin to a haṁsa bird in distress, Bharata said, 'Purohita, you are called by this name for a reason. It is to guide us on the right path, and thereby desire our welfare. Kindly contemplate if it is justified for me to undergo the paṭṭābhiṣeka.

You are my ācārya too. You have taught us that this prakṛti, the material world, and the jīvātmās are subservient to paramātmā. In that case, shouldn't Ayodhyā and this miserable son of Daśaratha be subservient to Rāma?

'How can I rule Ayodhyā? Rāma learnt śrutis and smṛtis under you. He is devoted to his duties. He is the eldest and the most capable son of Daśaratha. He alone should rule Ayodhyā. I have asked Sumantra to create a path to Gaṅgā by clearing the stones, thorny creepers and shrubs. I will bring back Rāma to Ayodhyā. In case he refuses, I will stay back in the forests, and serve him for the remaining fourteen years with Lakṣmaṇa.'

As Vasiṣṭha was listening to Bharata with rapt attention, different musical instruments played in the background. Bharata had asked that the day be called nāndīmukha, a day of joy marking the festival of Rāma's return and eventually his paṭṭābhiṣeka. He also asked the prajā to call it abhyudaya, a momentous occasion to pray for Rāma's return, his rise and prosperity.

The next morning, a procession comprising of ṛṣis, mantris and the army left for Gaṅgā. Kausalyā, Sumitrā, Māṇḍavī, Ūrmilā and Śrutakīrti joined Bharata and Śatrughna in their journey. At the gateway, they spotted Kaikeyī standing with her hands extended towards Bharata, as if she was asking for forgiveness. Bharata did not relent, but Vasiṣṭha felt that the plea of Kaikeyī, who was the daughter of Aśvapati and the wife of Daśaratha, should not be disregarded. He arranged a śibikā for her as well. As the entourage reached river Gaṅgā, Bharata bathed in her waters and offered tarpaṇa to pitṛs keeping Daśaratha, his dear father, in mind.

Guha, who was standing on the other bank of Gaṅgā, wondered: 'Who could this warrior be? Who could the other warrior standing behind him, as if waiting for his command, be? They look like Rāma and Lakṣmaṇa who are in Citrakūṭa now. I see multiple flags bearing the emblem of Kovidāra tree indicating that it could be the Ayodhyā army, and the two men in the Gaṅgā waters could be Bharata and Śatrughna. Even after being allowed to be the rājā, what more does this son of Kaikeyī want? Can't he let the trio live peacefully?'

He ordered his men to be ready with boats and weapons that could prevent Bharata's army from marching further to Citrakūṭa. Meanwhile when Bharata rose after offering tarpaṇa, he noticed a powerfully built forester at a distance, and asked Sumantra about him. He learnt that Guha was the chief of niṣādas who was also an old friend of Rāma. This brought happiness to Bharata, who ran across the flowing river to meet Guha. This enthusiasm that was visible on Bharata's face brought some respite to Guha's apprehensions.

When Bharata stood in front of him, panting for breath, Guha hesitantly asked, 'Āryaputra, I hope all is well with you. I pray that you won't harm Rāma.'

With teary eyes, and a blanched face, Bharata said, 'No.'

Guha said, 'Śṛṅgaverapura is your house. Bless us with your stay.'

Guha's men brought fruits and dried fish for Bharata, and for his entire army that had accompanied him. The rānīs, who took to fasting till they had met Rāma, refused to eat anything that was offered. As the nakṣatras were slowly becoming visible in the sky, Guha led them to their resting spots.

97

Guha Endorses Bharata

'What is this place that is fenced? Why are so many flowers strewn on the ground?' asked Bharata. Guha said, 'Āryaputra, this is the place where Sītā and Rāma slept while they visited our land. Rāma slept on a bed made of leaves and kuśa grass. You can notice the impressions formed by his sleeping and the bed has dried completely. You can spot a few gold grains that fell off Sītā's jewellery, and silk threads from her clothes that were entangled in the sharp grass. I can't comprehend the words that ācāryas like Vasiṣṭha use to explain matters to you. Of course, I have heard words like paramātmā and bhagavān in such scholarly discourses. To us, Rāma is our ācārya. To us, the daṃpati we hosted is the paramātmā that you all lecture about. So we decided to fence this spot, and offer our praṇāmas through flowers. We pray that we haven't transgressed the śāstras?'

Bharata bent to offer praṇāmas at Guha's feet and Guha jerked his feet back swiftly saying, 'Āryaputra, you shouldn't be doing this.' Bharata said, 'What is the harm, Guha? Though not trained in the śāstras, your understanding of the paramātmā is unambiguous. It is your wisdom which is praiseworthy.'

Guha said, 'Your mother waged a war with your father to claim the rājya of Ayodhyā for you. But you are here today to return the position to Rāma. I was surprised at Rāma's composure, and I am stunned by your sacrifice. I wonder if a thousand Rāmas can match a Bharata!' He hugged Bharata. They drenched themselves in each other's tears.

Bharata asked, 'Where did Lakṣmaṇa sleep?'

Guha said, 'Lakṣmaṇa, your brother, would fetch water in lotus leaves for the daṃpati, lay the bed of leaves for them, and after they had slept, he would perform pradakṣiṇā around them thereby keeping close vigil for their safety. When I insisted that he, too, should sleep, he would say with sadness, "Do you think I can sleep when I see Sītā and Rāma lying on this bare ground?"

'He predicted that Daśaratha would not survive long, on being separated from Rāma. He called you fortunate, as he believed that you would get to perform your father's funeral rites. But I am sorry that I disclosed all this.

'How is Daśaratha, your father?'

Bharata informed Guha about Daśaratha's death. In turn he thanked Guha for sharing his experiences with Lakṣmaṇa. Like an elephant that is wounded by the aṅkuśa used over it repeatedly, Bharata was hurt by thinking of Rāma's agony. He deliberated on Lakṣmaṇa's qualities and said to himself, 'There is one brother of Rāma who follows him everywhere, and serves him all the time. There is another brother of Rāma who has only given him misery'.

Bharata, with others from Ayodhyā, spent the night at Śṛṅgaverapura.

98

Bharadvāja's Āśrama

Bharata said, 'Wake up, my dear Śatrughna! I wish Daśaratha's death and Rāma's exile to Daṇḍaka forests were a dream. But sadly, it isn't one as I can sense the rays of Sūrya falling on me. I atleast wish to see Rāma, whose complexion is like the blue-lotus and whose eyes overflow with mercy. You will need to have Guha accompany us as only he can help us cross these bottomless waters of Gaṅgā.'

Śatrughna woke up, and brought Guha at once.

Kausalyā, seeing the three of them speak from a distance, also joined them. To Guha who was standing with folded hands, Bharata said, 'O rājā of niṣādas! We were treated by you with so much love and reverence. I would like you to lead my entourage to the āśrama of Bharadvāja. I have heard there are two routes to reach there. Could your men lead us there?'

Guha informed Bharata that Rāma, Sītā and Lakṣmaṇa were staying in Citrakūṭa. He added that Bharata could be taken directly to the banks of Mandākinī instead of heading towards Prayāga. But Bharata insisted that he visit Bharadvāja and seek his blessings.

In no time, Guha ordered his men to keep svastikas, the boats, with good bells, flags and white sails, ready. Vasiṣṭha, who knew that Ayodhyā was bereft of its defending men, thought that she could be an easy target for enemies. He did not want to leave any trace of their stay at Śṛṅgaverapura which otherwise could tempt the rival rājyas. He ordered that the tent materials be burnt, which in itself also achieved an established practice of praying for the dear ones to be back at their native land.

Bharata requested Vasiṣṭha to brief him about Bharadvāja's ancestry and birth. Vasiṣṭha happily agreed to narrate Bharadvāja's antecedents.

Bṛhaspati in the British Museum sculpted in the Eastern Gaṅgā dynasty (13th century CE)

Aṅgiras, the son of Bramhā, produced many sons. The eldest of them was called Utathya who was married to Mamatā. When Mamatā was pregnant, Bṛhaspati, Utathya's younger brother, tried to force himself on her. She resisted Bṛhaspati's sexual advances citing her pregnancy. Bṛhaspati felt insulted and cursed that the child in her womb would not see the world. As cursed, the little one was blind at birth, and was called Dīrghatama, the one sunk in 'perpetual darkness'. Again, when Utathya was away from his āśrama, Bṛhaspati forced himself on Mamatā. Fearing the state of her blind son, Mamatā fell victim to his venereal pleasure. When the child was born, Utathya refused to accept the child, and Mamatā spurned him too. Considered a burden by both Utathya and Bṛhaspati, he was called Bharadvāja.

Maruts, on the other hand, took mercy on the child, and nourished him as their very own. The devas convinced Bṛhaspati to tutor the necessary śāstras to Bharadvāja, a demand which he finally acceded to. Bharadvāja, being the son of Bṛhaspati and later the śiṣya to Vālmīki, had gathered knowledge meticulously from the both of them. He was older than other ṛṣis both in years and in tapasyā. He was fondly referred to as 'maharṣi'.

Bharata was very eager to meet Bharadvāja, in whose āśrama the trio had stayed. Guha requested them all to embark on the boats. In five hundred svastikas, the family of Daśaratha, his mantris, the ṛṣis, and the army with their horses, elephants and weapons were ferried to Prayāga on whose banks was the āśrama of Bharadvāja. Leaving his army at a distance and bidding farewell to the kind Guha, Bharata discarded his ornaments and weapons, dressed himself in plain silk clothes, and asked Vasiṣṭha to lead him to Bharadvāja, as was the established norm.

99

Lokāyata Philosophy

'What a fortunate day it has been, to see a bramharṣi in our āśrama, accompanied by Bharata and Śatrughna. May this arrival of yours at the maitra muhurta bestow auspiciousness on you all,' said a reverential Bharadvāja to the trio. After offering them arghya and pādya, Bharadvāja laid seats for them. Despite being a maharṣi who was completely cognizant of Bharata's true nature, he asked, 'You rule Ayodhyā, yet you found time to visit our āśrama. I was told that you are heading to Citrakūṭa. I hope you don't intend to cause any harm to Rāma, your brother.'

Bharata, though visibly vexed by this provocative insinuation, said in a sad voice, 'I will never agree with what my mother did to Daśaratha or Rāma. But all of this happened in my absence. I have come to take Rāma back to Ayodhyā as a prāyaścitta for the pāpas committed towards Rāma. I shall don a jaṭā, wear valkala, live on fruits and roots, and sleep on earth from today. I shall complete the fourteen years in the Daṇḍaka forests that Rāma had promised Daśaratha.'

Bharadvāja smiled at Bharata and patted him approvingly on the back. The sage also appreciated Bharata's wisdom in leaving his cavalry at a distance so as to not hamper the tranquillity of the āśrama. He entered his agnihotra chamber to invoke the blessings of devas to serve the army with lavish food. Meanwhile, Bharata saw a grand throne readied for his seating. He did a pradakṣiṇā around it and sat on the ground near its footstool, looking at the throne as if Rāma was seated on it with Sītā. The guests to the āśrama savoured the food varieties and drinks. But Bharata was not tempted by the feast that was laid in front of him for his mind was fixed on meeting Rāma at Citrakūṭa. He went to the chamber where Bharadvāja was seated in dhyāna. He offered his praṇāmas to the maharṣi and said, 'I have heard from ṛṣis in Ayodhyā that Bṛhaspati, your father, in his younger days had professed a set of heretic tenets which became popular with a small group of people. Though your father himself refuted those tenets later, by then I have heard that its believers had already called it lokāyata, the "philosophy for the common man". Those who work to propagate its principles are called carvakas, the soft-spoken people, is what many say. Vasiṣṭha has shrugged off my plea to be briefed about the lokāyata tenets. If you can enlighten me on the same, I shall remain grateful.'

Bharadvāja, with a smile, began to expound the controversial philosophy.

~

The sperm from the father fertilizes the ovum in the mother at the right time, and that leads to the birth of a human. A human body is a conglomerate of four of the bhūtas, namely air, fire, water and earth. This gives rise to intelligence.

To be emotionally attached to one's mother and father is senseless. Like a traveller who isn't attached to his night halts, so should one remain with parents. If a human dies, his body is cremated. There is no jīvātmā as one can't perceive jīvātmā with naked eyes. If one insists on its existence, then it is to be treated as the human body itself. To conduct rituals like aṣṭaka and śrāddha for one's pitṛs is a waste of food as there is no jīvātmā in the first place. Even if there was one, how will the food reach the jīvātmā that has left the body? If piṇḍas, the food balls offered to one's pitṛs, at one place can fill their stomachs who are far away, then travellers will not feel hungry because their relatives will eat for them.

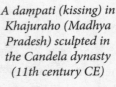

A daṃpati (kissing) in Khajuraho (Madhya Pradesh) sculpted in the Candela dynasty (11th century CE)

Puruṣārthas are a farce. There can be no dharma that can bestow a non-existing mokṣa. Pocketing wealth by all means and living for bodily pleasure are the means for a happy life. To give up on pleasure is advised by some scholars citing the pain that accompanies actions. If this is well thought-out, then will a person give up on consumption of grains just because he finds them covered in husk and dirt?

Learning the Vedas is a sure means to livelihood and nothing else. Performing agnihotra, applying the ūrdhvapuṇḍra or becoming a sannyāsī by holding the tridaṇḍa is nonsensical. A scholar who adheres to the karma-kāṇḍa portion of the Vedas spends his time in performing elaborate yajñas but rejects the existence of paramātmā. There are scholars who believe that the jñāna-kāṇḍa portion of the Vedas that profess the existence of paramātmā disregard the need to read the karma-kāṇḍa portion. Scholars of the two schools point to their actions that elevate the jīvātmā to the state of mokṣa. But these scholars are indeed idiots as neither the jīvātmā's existence has been proven nor has anyone known how it feels to receive mokṣa. Mantras with risible words like jarbharī and turpharī, and yajñas that guarantee that the sacrificed animals attaining svarga are often told by such idiots with conviction. These halfwits keep insisting that every born individual has debts to the devas, ṛṣis and pitṛs. This is plain hogwash. Alternatively, one can borrow ghee from a vaiśya, enjoy sweets made of it, and upon his death, leave behind his descendants with such debts.

Bharata was stupefied that such a baseless philosophy could exist and thrive. He asked, 'Is there a prominent lokāyata teacher even now?'

'Jābāli' came the answer.

While Bharadvāja looked, Bharata turned to check who it was that had answered.

It was Vasiṣṭha, the bramharṣi.

100

The Rise and Fall of Mahiṣāsura

Spending the entire night in the āśrama, Bharata woke up[1] with the prayer to see Rāma in Citrakūṭa. He abandoned his silk clothes and wore valkala. With the milky latex of the nyagrodha tree brought by Śatrughna, Bharata sported the jaṭā.

Kaikeyī, who saw this, started crying. Bharadvāja, who heard the cry, came out of his āśrama. She, who spotted the maharṣi, ran to clasp his feet. She kept crying.

Bharadvāja said, 'Rise Kaikeyī! You are a rānī. You shouldn't lie on the ground this long. Rise.'

Bharata said, 'Let her cry, maharṣi. Her arrogance over her looks and brains has cost us the life of Daśaratha. Her greed for the throne has resulted in Rāma's exile to Daṇḍaka. She is the biggest curse on the Ikṣvāku vaṃśa.'

Bharadvāja said, 'Bharata, Kaikeyī is firstly a woman and importantly your mother. Mahiṣāsura had erred in underestimating a woman's prowess which ultimately led to his death in the hands of Durgā, a revered devatā.

---

1 22 January, 5090 BCE, Pramoda saṃvatsara, Vaiśākha, Śuklapakṣa, Prathama tithi, Svāti, Monday.

'The revered Āpastamba maharṣi has declared that a "mother does very many sacrifices for her child, which in itself makes the child indebted to her for lifetime, and serving her is mandatory, even if she is promiscuous." Daśaratha's death was in conformity to his vidhi. Rāma's exile on the contrary will usher in happiness to the devas, ṛṣis and the rākṣasas. So don't humiliate her any more.'

Bharata respected the maharṣi's views and started to Citrakūṭa. Intrigued by Bharadvāja's reference to Durgā, Bharata on his way, requested Vasiṣṭha to narrate the feat of Durgā killing the wild Mahiṣa.

In Danu's vaṃśa came asuras called Rambha and Karambha who undertook tapasyā by the Sindhu river. Karambha, who was immersed in the river, was eaten by a crocodile while Rambha continued his tapasyā in pañcāgni on one leg with raised hands. Agni devatā took immense mercy on Rambha and granted him a boon that the asura would have a valorous son. The asura, who felt invigorated, proceeded to the land of yakṣas. On his way, he saw a pair of buffaloes mating, which excited him. He pulled a helpless yakṣa woman who was passing through the forests, and forced himself on her while his mind was still fixed on the buffaloes. As he ejected his retas into her, he got up and charged towards the animal pair. The male buffalo saw a danger in Rambha, and killed him with his horns. Eventually, the yakṣa woman delivered a son who was radiant and strong. The yakṣas spotted the vigour of an asura and the power of Mahiṣa, a buffalo, in the child that gave him the name Mahiṣāsura.

He was nurtured as the leader of both yakṣas and asuras. He performed tapasyā like his father, and obtained the boon from Bramhā that no one but a woman could cause his death. He seized Amarāvatī from Indra by force, and to remind the devas of his buffalo sap, he sported a head gear of buffalo horns. He prohibited brāmhaṇas from conducting yajñas and killed those who transgressed.

The devas, who were perturbed by Mahiṣa's tyranny, pleaded to Nārāyaṇa for a way out. A little baby girl with an unmissable aura was spotted by Kātyāyana near the āśrama. Finding no claimants, he raised her as his daughter and called her Kātyāyani. She grew into a stunning woman with kṣatriya traits.

One day, Mahiṣāsura, who was passing by the āśrama, noticed this pretty woman sharpening her trident. He was infatuated by her looks and his usual disdain for women was hidden well. Meanwhile, the ṛṣi was walking towards his āśrama carrying the necessary wood for his yajña. Annoyed that the ṛṣi was acting against his decree, Mahiṣa kicked Kātyāyana and raised his sword to behead him. Kātyāyani came running and held the hand of Mahiṣa. The devas, yakṣas, asuras and even the beasts gathered in no time to witness the momentous battle. The ṛṣis were invoking chants from the Vedas to fetch victory for Kātyāyani. The brāmhaṇas said to themselves, 'Like the fortress that protects its prajā, so is she to us. She is invincible, and her grit, unattainable. She is Durgā to us.'

Durgā kills Mahiṣāsura in Mahabalipuram (Tamil Nadu) sculpted in the Pallava dynasty (7th century CE)

A lion that was in awe of her braveness, ran to her and offered to be her vehicle. She jumped over the lion, and asked him to run towards the asura. The asura attacked Durgā with sharp weapons. She stood unfazed while the asura was getting weaker with every blow. At one point, she pushed, and squashed his chest with her foot. As he raised his head, Durgā pierced the trident in Mahiṣa's body. The frightened yakṣas and asuras ran helter-skelter. The devas called her 'Mahiṣāsuramardinī', the one who vanquished Mahiṣāsura.

Mahiṣāsura being slayed in Pattadakal (Karnataka) sculpted in the Cālukya dynasty (8th century CE)

Bharata said, 'Our march to Citrakūṭa is sanctified by listening to the greatness of Durgā.' Vasiṣṭha added that her abode[2] that was close to Bharadvāja's āśrama was frequented by girls who were seeking suitable grooms. Bharata's retinue which was crossing the Yamunā river waited to behold Mandākinī.

2 Vindhyavasini Temple in the Indian state of Uttar Pradesh.

101

Bharata Reaches Citrakūṭa

'Āryaputra, enough, don't splash any more water on me,' Sītā said as she held out her palms like a shield. Rāma paid no heed to her warnings while he continued to splash the Mandākinī waters on her. Sītā put her hands down, cupped some water and threw it at Rāma who was delighted to see Sītā happy. They paused for sometime and sat on a rock amidst the waters.

Rāma gazed at Sītā and held her hand on his chest. He said, 'Sītā, I swore on the smṛti texts to spend a hundred autumns with you.[1] We may end up spending many autumns here. By the way, is Citrakūṭa bringing you some delight?'

She said, 'Āryaputra, it of course does. Aren't kṣatriyas ordained to be vānaprasthas in order to experience such ecstasies? Anywhere I turn I spot ṛṣis draped in antelope hides, standing on one leg with raised arms and engaged in tapasyā. The trees that sway in the breeze shed their flowers and those streams that carry them appear as if gems were scattered into them by the devas from the hills. With you by my side, the beasts seem like our prajā, this river like Sarayū and Citrakūṭa like Ayodhyā.'

---

1 Śaunaka smṛti 1242 and Laghu-Āśvalāyana smṛti 15.33.

As they got out of the water, Rāma realizing Sītā's hunger, quickly got some meat. He grilled them on a fire, and raised the medhya portion to Sūrya who was shining in the sky. He then asked Sītā to savour the food to her satisfaction. They strolled to their āśrama, holding each other's hands. Wishing for Bharata's fame, hailing Lakṣmaṇa's assiduity and praying for the prajā's prosperity, they walked. Rāma stopped by a campaka tree, looked at its branches stooping with sweet odorous flower bunches and buzzing bees hovering around them.

He said, 'Sītā, don't they look like the chignons of drāviḍa women adorned with flowers?'

Sītā chuckled at Rāma's witty observation. As the daṃpati reached their āśrama in the noon to perform agnihotra, Lakṣmaṇa had kept the chamber ready. A sudden trumpeting of the elephants was heard and the trio looked at each other. Rāma immediately asked Lakṣmaṇa to ascertain the cause. The obedient brother climbed a sāla tree, and in the northern direction, saw an army with kovidāra emblem flags. He shouted, 'Rāma, discontinue the agnihotra. Let Sītā be hidden in the chamber itself while you take up your bow and quiver of arrows.'

The confused daṃpati got out to look for themselves. 'It is surely that evil Kaikeyī's gambit upon the advice of her unholy maid to get you killed. Her plan was to deny you the right to rule Ayodhyā, and to eventually see your death in her son's hands. But all her plans will be foiled by me. I shall kill Bharata, Kaikeyī and Mantharā. You will be back to ruling Ayodhyā as her rājā.'

Rāma stayed silent. Lakṣmaṇa asked, 'Aren't you ready?'

Rāma said, 'My promise to Daśaratha is real. I won't go back to Ayodhyā till my exile period is over. I swear by Kodaṇḍa, my bow, that I will not desire any wealth that is ill-gotten. Do you think I can ascend the throne of Ayodhyā by slaying my own brother? Any victory that is obtained by me without my brothers, is a worthless bauble. Bharata must have understood from Sumantra that I have left Ayodhyā sporting a jaṭā, in an antelope skin. He must have held his mother responsible for my exile, and taken our father's permission to fetch me back to Ayodhyā.'

Lakṣmaṇa heard Rāma patiently but refused to get down from the tree and welcome Bharata. 'Has Bharata ever hurt you or any of us in the past? Should you say such harsh words about your brother? In case you desire Ayodhyā's throne, I will ask him to relinquish it for you,' said Rāma with reddened eyes. Lakṣmaṇa slid to the ground, and sought Rāma's forgiveness for speaking pungent words against Bharata, their brother and a supreme devotee.

102

An Emotional Reunion

'Citrakūṭa is finally here! Look at this picturesque place! Kubera could mistake this Citrakūta for his famed garden called Caitraratha. I can see some smoke over that peak which is covered in sāla trees. I suspect Rāma and Sītā are performing agnihotra, as it is noon time. I am waiting to see the Candra-like face of Rāma, and his lotus petal-like eyes. I can't be at peace until I hold Rāma's feet that bear the marks of dhvaja, aṅkuśa, vajra, the amṛta pot and a lotus flower over my head. I am waiting to offer my praṇāmas to his pair of pādukās. Paṭṭābhiṣeka will be soon performed for Rāma, who is the only one eligible to sit on the throne of Ayodhyā,' said Bharata to Śatrughna as he asked his army to stay back with the elephants and horses. He requested Vasiṣṭha to escort the rānīs to the āśrama, once their śibikās arrived.

As Bharata climbed the hill, he noticed kuśa grass knots tied to trees. He understood that they were direction indicators fixed by Lakṣmaṇa to lead Lakṣmaṇa and Rāma to the āśrama. He also saw wooden sticks fixed to the trees that served as torches to keep the beasts away in the nights. He saw a heap of dried dung balls of deers and buffaloes, meant for small fires on cold nights. He saw the āśrama slowly revealing itself with every step he took, and on a platform, he saw Rāma seated in vīrāsana, a posture with the left leg extended and the other leg folded.

Seated very close to him was Sītā, and on the ground was Lakṣmaṇa, both whose eyes were fixed on Rāma. Wearing an antelope's skin, sporting a jaṭā, and a chinmudrā pointed towards his chest, this Rāma's form, though new, was riveting to Bharata's eyes. Rāma resembled Dakṣiṇāmūrti, a unique form of Śiva, who seated under the shade of a vata tree, dispenses knowledge of the śrutis to Sanaka and his three brothers. But with the effulgent Sītā by his side, the dark complexioned Rāma was akin to the monsoon sky lit by lightning streaks.

Lacking the courage to face Rāma, Bharata ran like a long lost calf that had found its way back to his mother. He prostrated at Rāma's feet and refused to get up. Śatrughna couldn't stand Bharata's pain, and along with Lakṣmaṇa, he lifted Bharata who was losing consciousness. Bharata was shedding tears, and was choked with conflicting emotions.

Taking pity on Bharata, Rāma took him by his arm, and seated him on his lap like Nārāyaṇa did to Dhruva. He brought Bharata's wet cheek close to his, and said, 'Is Ayodhyā's prosperity that is attributed to a multitude of yajñas such as puṇḍarīka, Aśvamedha and vājapeya performed by Daśaratha, being preserved? Are yajñas that please the devas being conducted now? Are ācāryas of different knowledge streams being felicitated? Are you performing agnihotra that exemplifies your tutelage under Vasiṣṭha? Is Suyajña, an expert in śrutis and smṛtis just like Vasiṣṭha, his father, your purohita now? Is he guiding you on maintaining the three holy fires called gārhapatya, āhavanīya and dakṣiṇāgni? Is Sudhanva, an expert in economics as well as dhanurveda, guiding you well?

'I hope you don't let brāmhaṇas with fatuous arguments, proudly calling themselves lokāyatas influence your thinking. It is better to have a few brāmhaṇas like Suyajña and Sudhanva guide you, than having a council of foolish lokāyatas pretending to do so. Are mantris who are incorruptible, valorous, hardworking and well-versed in the Vedas, being taken care of? Are decisions arrived at after due consultation with your mantris? Are they adept enough to guard administrative secrets, especially from vassal rājās? Are you careful in guarding the administrative and military secrets from the women in our family? Are you mulling over the veracity of your decisions at midnight as a rājā is advised to not succumb to excess sleep? It is said that a rājā deploys many functionaries to understand the developments in his own as well as his rival rājyas. Some of them include the senāpati; rakṣakas of the nobility, treasury and the ramparts; executors of the approved policies; advocates who fight for the poor, and those who deliver timely justice.

'The rājā is also updated on sensitive matters by his purohita, mantris, and the rājakumāras. Are you aware of this? Do you possess rājadūtas endowed with a sharp presence of mind and an ability to decipher nuanced statements coupled with adroit speaking skills? Is the senāpati you have chosen efficient and loved by his soldiers? Are the soldiers constantly incentivized for their earnest services? Are you watchful of enemies who return to your fold after being subdued in the past? Are those vaiśyas who tend to agriculture and cattle-rearing flourishing in Ayodhyā? Are productive tasks that guarantee superior fruits, with minimum efforts being hastened? Like a yājaka who is ridiculed by ṛtviks when he performs yajñas to seek emancipation from pāpas and like a woman who bedamns her molester, so does a prajā curse her rājā when he levies excess taxes.

'Are you being unreasonable with your prajā? Do you compromise on adhering to dharma in the garb of accumulating wealth? Do you squander your acquired wealth on sensual pleasures? Is your expenditure under control? Do you present yourself in the sabhā mantapa to the prajā every morning? Are you being cautious in taking punitive actions on the innocent for their tears can lead to a catastrophe? Do your mantris dispassionately conduct enquiry on disputes between the rich and the poor? I hope you are not sparing the life of the person who paints an honest servant in evil colours, or tries to cause death to an honest rājā. Are tasks being impartially assigned to servants, based on their capabilities? Neither remain inaccessible nor excessively attached to your servants. A calibrated approach will help you earn their trust. Are your servant wages paid without any delay? Minds of the young are captivated by polite words, of the elderly through care, and of the scholars through charity. I am sure you will walk the path of dharma, inspired by our forefathers.'

There was silence, total silence.

103

Rāma Mourns Daśaratha's Passing

'All that you have spoken applies to a rājā?' said Bharata.

'Aren't you the rājā of ...', said Rāma hesitatingly as he took notice of Bharata's jaṭā, deer skin and valkala.

'It is a tradition to perform paṭṭābhiṣeka for the eldest son. As you asked me to walk the path of dharma traced by our ancestors, I have rejected the throne. You need to take charge as the rājā of Ayodhyā, as you are the dearest son to our father. It is said that a rājā is seen as Nārāyaṇa in the eyes of his prajā, through his conduct,' asserted Bharata.

'Are you keeping our revered mothers happy? Are you serving our father well? Did you leave our ailing father in Ayodhyā, and come here? Is everything fine with Daśaratha?' asked Rāma in a worried tone.

'With his reputation at stake, Daśaratha regrettably granted the boons sought by my mother. You had hardly left Kosala rājya with Sītā and Lakṣmaṇa when our father, who couldn't handle his separation from you, left for svarga. I have performed the antyeṣṭi for him and come here,' said Bharata.

Like an axed tree that falls to the ground, Rāma collapsed. Sītā held him, while the brothers sprinkled some waters on his face. Rāma gained consciousness, and lamented over the death of his dear father. He expressed regret for being the underlying cause of his death and for not being by his side in his last moments.

In Daśaratha's demise, Rāma rued that he had lost a guide, a friend and an ācārya. He thanked Bharata for performing the antyeṣṭi, which the smṛtis state that a son is primarily meant for. He asked Lakṣmaṇa to fetch the fruits of Iṅgudī tree, and clothes to the river side. Adhering to the injunction that a "woman should lead the group that is to perform tarpaṇa", he asked Sītā to walk ahead, his brothers to follow her, and then he completed the line.

Sumantra helped Rāma get into the river. Facing south, Rāma held Mandākinī waters in his palms jointly, and offered them in tarpaṇa saying, 'My dear father, I am offering these waters to you and our pitṛs. Please accept them'.

He returned to her banks, sat on a mat made of kuśa grass, and offered piṇḍas made of Iṅgudī and Badara fruit pulp, while his brothers looked on. After piṇḍīkaraṇa, Sītā and Rāma with his brothers led by Sumantra trekked to the āśrama. They noticed that Vasiṣṭha had arrived with the rānīs of Ayodhyā. Like Indra welcoming Bṛhaspati, Rāma welcomed Vasiṣṭha. He offered his praṇāmas to him. He then sought the blessings of his mothers, and so did Sītā embrace her mothers-in-law. They expressed each other's feelings and mourned over the death of Daśaratha.

As the night was setting in, Sumantra had made stay arrangements for the rānīs in tents that were erected at the foothills of Citrakūṭa. On the contrary, the rānīs wanted to spend the night with Sītā, while the brothers agreed to sleep outside the āśrama. Sumantra and Vasiṣṭha let them enjoy their special moments, while choosing to retire to their tents.

'What is that?' asked Kausalyā pointing at the wound on Sītā's bosom. Sītā narrated the incident of how the crow had assaulted her and how Rāma punished him for his blunder. Kaikeyī wept loudly for having been the cause of all their misfortunes. Sītā said, 'Mother, I have understood from my father's teachings that the jīvātmā, which is the sentient matter that is housed in you, me and all of us, is subservient to the divine will of the paramātmā. There is no doubt that there is an empirical effect of its accrued karma, of both its current and previous births. There is also a strong belief that the jīvātmā does enjoy some free will. But all factors are subsumed by the paramātmā's sovereign power, which is irrefutable and unsurpassed. To many, it does appear that you were responsible for our exile. But Rāma and I are aware that this is a divine act for a purpose. Do not curse yourself. We will come back once we accomplish what Nārāyaṇa has entrusted us with.'

Kaikeyī, whose heart was filled with the pride of having such an eloquent daughter-in-law, hugged Sītā.

'Did you visit the āśrama of Atri and Anasūyā?' asked Sumitrā.

'No. But I have been wanting to, as it is not far from Citrakūṭa,' replied Sītā.

'You are a well-read person. Can you tell us about the greatness of Anasūyā?' asked Kausalyā, and Sumitrā happily consented.

Kardama and Devahūti had a daughter called Anasūyā. She was given in vivāha to Atri, a renowned ṛṣi. The daṃpati settled in the Kāmada forests that was close to Citrakūṭa. For many years at a stretch, there was no rain. The foresters, facing severe drought, sought the intervention of the daṃpati. Observing vratas like cāndrāyana and kṛcchra, Anasūyā's tapasyā coaxed Indra to duly shower rains in the region. The forests produced many fruits and tubers, thereby leaving no trace of famine. A river called Mandākinī carrying sweet waters like the Gaṅgā started flowing in the forests. Anasūyā made friends with a lady called Nālāyanī who used to come to Mandākinī to fetch water. Known for her good demeanour, Nālāyanī was called Śīlavatī by her friends. But her husband, Ugraśrava, lacked morality. He was addicted to sex and habituated to visiting prostitutes. He became a leper and thus a sign of ridicule in his neighbourhood. But Nālāyanī continued to render her services towards him. On Ugraśrava's insistence that he should be taken to a bordello, she carried him there. In the middle of the night, while passing through the forests, his foot hit a horn that was fixed to the ground. On the tip of the horn was seated a ṛṣi called Māṇḍavya. It was a retribution ordered on the ṛṣi by a rājā who had mistaken the ṛṣi for a robber. Despite the horn's tip piercing the ṛṣi, it did not cause the harm it was meant to mete out. The ṛṣi's fury was fuelled when Ugraśrava's foot struck the horn. Māṇḍavya pronounced a curse on Ugraśrava that the latter would die when Sūrya rose that morning. Nālāyanī sought forgiveness from the ṛṣi which he refused to accept. Angered by his denial, she pronounced a counter-curse that the world would not see the rise of Sūrya any further.

Atri, realizing that such bitter exchanges amidst the brāmhaṇas would not augur well for the society, sent for Anasūyā to bring about a reconciliation. As she approached the warring factions, she reminded Māṇḍavya of how ṛṣis had to hold their reins on anger, while she chastized Ugraśrava for being victim to sensual pleasures. She finally consoled Nālāyanī by stating that a wife was not meant to execute her husband's immoral desires, but to bring him to the path of dharma. When all of them were convinced of their flaws, Anasūyā invoked the grace of Nārāyaṇa to nullify the evil effects of their curses, and brought peace to the world.

Seeing her superior values, Nārāyaṇa was born to her as Datta. He was called Dattātreya to highlight the rich legacy of Atri. He was able to destroy the heretic arguments put forth by cārvākas, pāṣaṇḍas and their ilk, which were opposed to the message of the Vedas. To highlight the organic relationship of the paramātmā with jīvātmās and prakṛti, he became a sannyāsī holding the tridaṇḍa, a cluster of three bamboos.

Anasūyā later had a son whose radiance was infectious, and anger notorious. He wandered the forests as a ṛṣi whose presence was feared. He was called Durvāsa and was seen as a manifestation of Śiva. Later, a boy whose face was as brilliant as Candra was born. The daṃpati saw the grace of Nārāyaṇa and Śiva in him, and they believed that Bramhā had immensely blessed the child when prophecies assured the he would have a rich vaṃśa, emerge from him. He was named Soma. Anasūyā's adherence to dharma, made her a pativratā who was venerated amongst women.

~

'What are you thinking, Kaikeyī?' asked Sumitrā.

'If only Nālāyanī's curse could fructify now,' said Kaikeyī.

The women rose in a tizzy, and looked at Kaikeyī who was lying down looking at the āśrama roof. 'But why?' they asked.

'If Sūrya rises, we may have to start for Ayodhyā. And these conversations that we are having may never happen again. I wish I had realized the joys of bonding with you all earlier,' said Kaikeyī with teary eyes.

104

Honouring the Promise to Daśaratha

'Rāma, to a rājā, his first vivāha is with his rājya. Your vivāha with Ayodhyā rājya hasn't happened yet, but Kaikeyī wanted the paṭṭābhiṣeka for me. She wasn't aware that her son would incur the pāpa of being a parivettā, where he will be married while his elder brother isn't. Kaikeyī earned her widowhood, and is hell bent to keep the rājya a widow, too, by sending you away to the forests. Does she think I can match your stature? A donkey trying to copy the horse's speed is like a crow that aims to match the movement of Garuḍa. Both of these are never going to happen. I urge you to come to Ayodhyā, and become our rājā,' said Bharata and fell at Rāma's feet holding his feet, as an act of prapatti.

Rāma smiled and lifted Bharata. He placed his hands on his shoulders, and said, 'You must have crossed mighty Yamunā while coming towards Citrakūṭa. She is birthed by the Kalinda mountain, and flows towards the sea. Will she trace her path towards her source? Will the night that has just passed return? I have always believed that obeying father's words is my dharma. I wish to walk on the path clearly laid by our forefathers, and so should you. Daśaratha conducted yajñas with utmost sincerity and offered lavish dakṣiṇā to the ṛtviks. He treated his servants with respect, and protected his prajā like his own children. He deserves our respect even after his death. We need to honour his commands. You may start for Ayodhyā, while I will continue to stay in the forests.'

Bharata, adamant about his resolve to bring Rāma back, said, 'It is said that "on the verge of death, even wise minds falter." Daśaratha was no exception to this. His blind love for Kaikeyī has led us to this state. Excerpts of smṛti injunctions flash in front of my eyes which urge that one's mother be treated as devī, despite my mother deserving to be killed. It is only because of my devotion to you that I have refrained from matricide.

'Rāma, you are a repository of auspicious attributes. You treat elders with utmost respect, and you are equipoised, which was evident when you were asked to abandon the rājya that you were earlier promised. But this isn't that phase of your life where you should adopt vānaprastha. In fact, Gautama maharṣi has held the gṛhastha on the highest pedestal among the four āśramas for two reasons. One, it is this āśrama that allows the daṃpati to work towards progeny. Second, it is this gṛhasthāśrama that supports the livelihood of a bramhacārī, vānaprastha and sannyāsī. You are the all-knowing, sarvajña, and you are sarvadarśī, the one who is aware of all things of the past, present and future. Like Nārāyaṇa who has empathy for all, I fall at your feet seeking your grace, just as we propitiate Nārāyaṇa who has empathy for all. Please return to Ayodhyā.'

Rāma reiterated that to fulfil the promises made to Kaikeyī for her services during the war with Śambara, and to Kaikeyī's mother, Daśaratha was left with no option but to send him on exile. He said that Bharata, too, as a son was duty-bound towards his father and advised him to undergo paṭṭābhiṣeka at the earliest. He cited the legend of an asura called Gaya, who was killed by Viṣṇu by sitting on the asura. The kṣetra where Viṣṇu defeated the asura was called Gayā tīrtha from then on, and was frequented by people to perform śrāddha ceremonies for their pitṛs, he said. He added that the pitṛs wait to receive the piṇḍas offered to them in the name of one's ancestors at the Gayā tīrtha. He asserted that only such obedient offsprings are entitled to call themselves putra or putrī for they prevent their pitṛs from experiencing a dreaded abode called put.

As Rāma concluded that it was pertinent for Bharata to go back to Ayodhyā, a booming voice was heard entering the āśrama saying, 'Relationships are an absurdity, performing śrāddhas is purposeless. Enjoyment is the only essence of life.' It was the voice of Jābāli, a trusted brāmhaṇa in the council of Daśaratha, who was known to endorse the lokāyata philosophy, and wear his cārvāka heart on his sleeve. He vociferously listed its injunctions much to the repugnance of Vasiṣṭha and others who were present.

105

Sanātana, the Supreme Dharma

Rāma, the patient listener, heard the arguments put forth by Jābāli, which were rooted in the lokāyata school of philosophy.

Walking casually alongside a vociferous Jābāli, Rāma said, 'Long ago, it is said that the asuras had gained immense power to cause problems to sādhus, the innocent. Heeding to the prayers of the devas, Nārāyaṇa incarnated as a bhikṣu, a mendicant with a tonsured head, dressed in red robes and carrying a hand fan of peacock feathers. He approached the asuras who were in tapasyā by the Narmadā river. Rolling his fingers on his pot-belly that was as resplendent as a gem, with his bewitching eyes and tender speech, he caught the attention of the asuras. He freely stated how he abhorred adherence to practices rooted in dharma, and propagated heretical ones like consuming curd-rice balls at dawn, with unwashed teeth. He taught detachment from yajñas spoken of in the śrutis, and made fun of śrāddhas that were performed to please the pitṛs. Prefacing every line of his as he addressed his followers was prefaced with the word, "buddhyata" which meant "know". He was called "Buddha" for that reason, and his minions were "Bauddhas".

'He preached a muddled set of injunctions to another group of asuras, and called them "ārhatas" which meant "worthy of the doctrine". In no time, the "Bauddhas" and "ārhatas" professed this prattling of Bṛhaspati's youth, as being supportive of their tenets. So was born the lokāyata school that you keep raving about; founded on unsound grounds. If pratyakṣa, which is visual perception alone, is true, then it fails a man who mistakenly sees a snake as a rope, since what he sees is contrary to the truth. If anumāna, that is inference, isn't permissible, then a hungry person can never be fed as hunger isn't visible either. If śruti and smṛti decrees are unreliable, then lokāyatas should hold their belief in astrology and mantras at a distance, for such beliefs are ingrained in the Vedas. Nītiśāstra, a compendium that talks about means to accrue wealth, insists on following dharma. Kāmaśāstra, a compilation on sensual acts, too, aligns itself to dharma. Why else would ṛṣis talk about abstinence from sex on certain days? To say that "life is about wealth and sex" and to later preach such texts is contradictory in nature. A newborn baby that is deformed will find no explanation until the jīvātmā in his body is eternal, and his sufferings are attributed to his accrued karma.

Every rājya is embedded in dharma, the truth which is perpetual, Sanātana in nature. It is this Sanātana dharma which makes me hold on to the promise I made to my father.

Your arguments favouring the cārvākas hold no water. In fact, a person like you should have never been accorded such a high position in the rājya. An individual who doesn't believe in the authenticity of the Vedas, the presence of paramātmā, jīvātmā, and Vaikuṇṭha, the paramātmā's abode, is referred to by the scholars as a "nāstika". I have heard that a rājā called Śatadhanu, with his wife Śaivyā, while observing the fast on a purṇimā of the Kārttika month, spoke to a "nāstika" who was passing by. This detestable act of engaging with a nāstika led to a series of births for the rājā's jīvātmā before finally attaining mokṣa. Jābāli, what punishment will be pronounced on me for being an audience to a nāstika like you?'

Jābāli with folded hands said, 'Rāma, I am not a nāstika. It is true that I am versed in the Bṛhaspati sutras. It is true that I had a tryst with the cārvākas, but that didn't last long. My commitment to the Vedas is total, and your father was aware of it. Like ṛṣis who were once cārvākas, and later turned vaidikas and participated in the yāga conducted by Kaṇva, I am also a vaidika always desiring the welfare of Ayodhyā. My arguments were put forth to somehow bring you back to our rājadhānī.' After Jābāli's futile attempt, Bharata with a pitiable face looked at Vasiṣṭha with hope, his final recourse.

106

Filial Piety

'The eldest son is made the rājā. This is the tradition in Ikṣvāku vaṃśa,' said Vasiṣṭha.

'Of course yes. But to ascend the throne by being the eldest son is sāmānya dharma which is followed under normal circumstances. But the situation is a bit different now. Despite knowing that my paṭṭābhiṣeka was to be conducted, my father granted my mother her boon, and has asked me leave Ayodhyā. This dharma therefore overrides the previous one. This is viśeṣa dharma which is followed under unique circumstances. Being my ācārya, you must bless and allow me to follow this viśeṣa dharma,' said Rāma. Bharata, Lakṣmaṇa, Śatrughna, Sītā, Kausalyā, Kaikeyī and Sumitrā were watching the heated exchange between Vasiṣṭha, the eminent ācārya, and Rāma, his illustrious śiṣya.

Vasiṣṭha, who looked visibly disturbed, said, 'It is appropriate that you have referenced the viśeṣa dharma. Giving birth makes both the mother and the father gurus to a child because they become the reasons for his existence. Later, when the child comes under the tutelage of a guru, he imbibes the teachings of the śāstras in his śiṣya. It is the duty of a guru to dispel the flawed notions that exist in the mind of the śiṣya regarding the jīvātmā, paramātmā, and the relationship between them. This makes a guru more respected and pertinent. A guru's instructions thereby override anyone else's decree. Remember, I am not just your ācārya, but was your father's as well. So if you return, in no way will you become disobedient or ungrateful to your parents. In fact this will become your viśeṣa dharma.'

Rāma, with folded palms, replied, 'A woman with her man, performs many vratas to have a child. It is their prayers which grants them the status of parents. Will I ever be able to repay the love showered on me by Kausalyā and Daśaratha? I treat Kaikeyī no different from Kausalyā. Many ṛṣis such as you have told us that the "body is the means to fulfil our duties which adhere to dharma". In such a scenario, I, too, have a dharma, as a dutiful son. No one can ever deny the contributions of an ācārya. Whatever little I am is because of you. It is you who has taught us the importance of śrutis that instruct their followers to treat their mother, father and ācārya as paramātmā himself. If that is true, shouldn't I follow the words of my mother, father and ācārya, in that order? I do not refuse to return to Ayodhyā permanently. I will return, but only after fourteen years.'

Sumantra in a panic said, 'Bharata has decided to seat himself on a mat made of kuśa grass. He refuses to leave that position until you return to Ayodhyā. He has informed the ṛṣis that he will neither drink water nor eat food.'

Rāma took note of this, and went towards Bharata who was seated under the vaṭa tree. He said in a stern tone, 'Bharata, you should not take up such vows that are proscribed for kṣatriyas. This material body also belongs to paramātmā, as much as the jīvātmā does. We must abstain from causing any damage to it. I instruct you to break your vow at once. As prāyaścitta, touch the waters in the puddle next to you. This will be akin to doing ācamana. Hold my hands, and rise.' Rāma held the hands of his brother and promised to return in fourteen years.

Bharata innocently asked, 'Till then?'

Vasiṣṭha put his hands around Bharata's shoulders, and said, '*She* will come.'

107

A Rānī for Ayodhyā

As those who stood by watched, Sumantra carried a gem-studded casket on his head, to where Rāma and the others stood. Bharata had missed seeing this casket, and was surprised that it was brought to the āśrama, upon the order of Vasiṣṭha. Sumantra carefully placed the casket on a platform under the vaṭa tree. Bharata looked at Vasiṣṭha, puzzled. He wondered what was in the box. Vasiṣṭha smiled, and said to Bharata, 'Like the brāmhaṇa who sits at the doorstep of the person to whom he has loaned money, and who refuses to repay, so are you here refusing to return to Ayodhyā. But Rāma's reasons to fulfil the duties of a son are genuine, and we need to support his decision. He may well leave her, his trusted companion at all times, with you as a "security deposit". I am sure like any other smart lender, you will value her immensely. Rāma did give up his claim to the throne of Ayodhyā instantly, but he couldn't part with her when he left Ayodhyā. He carries the burden of protecting his prajā on his broad shoulders, while *she* supports him effortlessly. *She* clung to him when he left Ayodhyā. *She* will leave for Ayodhyā the moment he asks her to head back. *She* is more obedient than you, and your brother Lakṣmaṇa. With Daśaratha dead, Rāma refusing to return, and you, refusing to be anointed King, only *she* can lead the prajā now.'

Bharata wondered if it was Sītā to whom Vasiṣṭha was referring, while Sītā and her mothers-in-law were perplexed, wondering if Rāma had a mistress, whom he had never spoken about. There was a mix of suspicion, and surprise in the air. Vasiṣṭha gestured to Sumantra to open the casket.

A pair of pādukās, sandals, were lifted with both hands by Sumantra and displayed to those who had gathered. Gilded in gold, the pādukās had diamonds, rubies, emeralds, sapphires laid in different patterns, with alternate arrangements of coral and pearls dangling at the sides. Sītā cheerfully acknowledged them and said, 'These were gifted by my illustrious father to Āryaputra, during our vivāha.'

It was evident that Vasiṣṭha had asked Sumantra to secretly pack the pādukās. Meanwhile, to the surprise of many, three new personalities arrived on the scene. One was Janaka Sīradhvaja, the rājaṛṣi and karma yogī, Sītā's father. Second was Viśvāmitra, the bramhaṛṣi and third was Bharadvāja, the mahaṛṣi. Though, it was a dream come true to see Vasiṣṭha and Viśvāmitra in one frame, Bharata wondered at the sudden confluence of such luminaries. All of them paid their obeisance to the celebrity arrivals. Sītā embraced her father, and shed tears of joy upon seeing him after a long time. 'These pādukās were presented to Rāma by you, weren't they, Janaka?' asked Viśvāmitra. Sīradhvaja nodded positively.

'Someone here had preempted Rāma's refusal to return to Ayodhyā, and brought her here it seems!' said a sarcastic Viśvāmitra, glancing out of the corner of his eye at Vasiṣṭha. 'Like someone who knew that *she* would be arriving in Citrakūṭa, and has come to witness a special moment, isn't it bramhaṛṣi?' came a rejoinder from Vasiṣṭha. The bramhaṛṣis smiled at each other.

Bharata asked, 'Why is this pair of Rāma pādukās relevant to us now?'

Bharadvāja said, 'It has been our tradition to seek the blessings of the tried pādukās of ācāryas, that are worthy of ārādhanā. Rāma is your brother, your father, and from now on, your ācārya too. Rāma's absence shouldn't be felt by you, as you will have the pādukās in his place.'

Bharata felt a sudden current of energy passing through him. He felt relieved of his burden. He asked what should be done further. Vasiṣṭha advised Rāma to stand atop his luminous pādukās, and then step down and go back to wearing his normal ones. Rāma removed his feet from the pādukās and stood on the Bhūmi barefooted, for scarcely a few seconds. In no time, there was a gentle breeze carrying the smell of aśoka flowers, and that of mallikā. Some parched portions of Bhūmi saw grass blades emerge.

Bharadvāja murmured in the ears of Viśvāmitra, 'It seems as if Bhūmi Devī, who is mercy-incarnate was waiting to be united with the lotus-like feet of Rāma, and as his feet touched her, *she* couldn't control her excitement.' Rāma stood on those ornate pādukās with his eyes closed, appearing to receive energy from her to walk on the rugged paths of Daṇḍaka. Vasiṣṭha tied a silk cloth around Bharata's head like a tiara, and chanted along with the other ṛṣis, 'May Nārāyaṇa, the chief of all devas, grant the rājā, everything he desires, and keep him prosperous like Kubera, the son of Viśravas.'

Then Lakṣmaṇa took those pādukās, held her above his head, and transferred her next to Bharata's head. Tears rolled down Bharata's eyes, his voice choked while his heart filled. Kaikeyī couldn't control her tears either. She held the hands of Kausalyā and said, 'I had thought that the crown of Ayodhyā would bring happiness to my son. Today, I have seen that the pādukās have ushered in immeasurable joy to him. I don't think I have fulfilled the duty of a true mother. Instead, it is pādukās which have done so, like the cow that feeds her calf. Rāma has adhered to dharma, even now. By refusing to succumb to Jābāli and Vasiṣṭha's arguments, he has fulfilled his promise to Daśaratha. By coronating Bharata with pādukās, he has followed my words as well. He will forever remain a son whom I never birthed, but nursed and cherished.'

Janaka told Sītā, 'Bharata, donning a jaṭā, dressed in valkala, and carrying the pādukās looks like Śiva in Kailāśa, donning the jaṭā, dressed in elephant hide, and bearing the Gaṅgā waters. After all, Gaṅgā rises from Nārāyaṇa's feet, and so do these pādukās that have adorned Rāma's feet. Sītā acknowledged her learned father's observations with a smile. He added, 'Sītā, these pādukās signify Bhūmi to me. If Rāma chooses to send her along with Bharata, note the importance he attaches to his rājya and prajā. In case there is a situation where he has to choose you over someone, he will surely choose you. But if you were pitted against his rājya, he will only choose the latter as he believes he is foremost wedded to his rājya. In accordance to this, should your actions be as well. Do not insist on something that he doubts or detests, for he dons two hats: the hat of your husband, and that of Ayodhyā's well-wisher.'

There was the sound of musical instruments and drums in the background, as Śatruñjaya, the elephant walked royally to the āśrama. The place that was gloom-ridden a while ago, had turned sanguine and was radiating grandeur in all directions. Bharata, with pādukās on his head, sat on the elephant. Śatrughna sat close behind him, holding the umbrella with one hand, and cāmara in the other. Following the elephant closely was Sumantra's chariot. Sūrya's rays falling on the pādukās gave rise to variegated colour streaks, looking as if fans made from peacock feathers were suspended on either side of Śatruñjaya.

Viśvāmitra said, 'With Lakṣmaṇa handing over the pādukās to Bharata, with Bharata carrying her respectfully and with Śatrughna fanning her, I am convinced that this is a prāyaścitta of sorts.'

Bharadvāja asked, 'Prāyaścitta for what?'

'An incident must have transpired in Vaikuṇṭha that may have hurt the pride of pādukās. For having looked down upon her as mere footwear at some point, the servants of Nārāyaṇa must have done prāyaścitta this day with the avatāras of Ananta, Pāñcajanya and Sudarśana serving her religiously. There is no effect without a cause, afterall,' asserted Viśvāmitra.

Bharadvāja could not control his excitement which was visible on his face.

Vasiṣṭha said, 'This looks like an event of the past. To me, it seems as if a lion is sending back his prized cub with the lioness, fully confident of his capacity to destroy a rutted elephant alone.'

Bharadvāja was clueless about this comparison, and requested clarity. Vasiṣṭha revealed that the pādukās leaving with Bharata, were like the lioness accompanying her cub, and the rutted elephant was a certain rākṣasa tormenting the innocent for long. Bharadvāja wondered at the understanding levels of both Vasiṣṭha and Viśvāmitra on such a nuanced event.

Viśvāmitra borrowed no time, and said, 'Vasiṣṭha does know the greatness of pādukās, but there are only two people who know her the best.'

Bharadvāja pleaded to Viśvāmitra to reveal the names. Viśvāmitra said, 'Atri maharṣi, and I. Only either of us or our descendants can extol her distinction.'

After taking permission from each other, the ṛṣis left Citrakūṭa.

~

'Sumantra, you may arrange for the throne to be brought to Nandigrāma[1],' said Bharata, as his elephant lurched down from the Citrakūṭa hill.

---

1 A locality in the outskirts of Ayodhya, in the Indian state of Uttar Pradesh.

'Nandigrāma?' asked Śatrughna.

Bharata admitted that memories of Daśaratha would haunt him if he were to head to Ayodhyā. He believed that Rāma's resolve to not enter a paṭṭana, an inhabited city while in exile was his resolve as well. But Sumantra asked about the need for the throne, if he was not going to sit on it.

Bharata said, 'In the lineage of Marīci, Kaśyapa, Vivasvān, Ikṣvāku, Kakutstha, Māndhātā, Hariścandra, Sagara, Bhagīratha, Dilīpa, Raghu, Aja and Daśaratha, there is a rānī for the first time! Her name is Pādukā devī, and she is henceforth the rānī of Ayodhyā. We shall conduct her paṭṭābhiṣeka tomorrow.'[2]

2 23 January, 5090 BCE, Pramoda saṃvatsara, Vaiśākha, Śuklapakṣa, Dvitīya tithi, Vaiśākha, Tuesday.

108

An Unparalleled Bhakti

Vālmīki looked at Nārada and said, 'I was elated when I composed verses pertaining to Rāma's birth. I was happier when Rāma was married to Sītā. But as I am composing verses on Pādukā paṭṭābhiṣeka, words fail me.There can be no happier day in my life. I am unable to plumb the depths of the bhakti that Bharata, Lakṣmaṇa and Śatrughna have for Rāma, and how Pādukā's entry altered even this. Could you care to explain the nuances of what we have seen till now?'

Nārada said, 'A jīvātmā is endowed with the knowledge to discern the good from the bad. A sustained effort to nurture this ability leads to viveka, which is wisdom. When this viveka is laced with the blessings of an ācārya, it allows the jīvātmā to understand its true nature. What is that true nature? It is to be subservient to the will of paramātmā. Such subservience translates into servitude. The jīvātmā realizes that it needs to serve the paramātmā in very many ways, through the material body it is housed in. This makes the jīvātmā a śeṣa, the one who serves, and the paramātmā a śeṣī, the one who is the recipient of such services. The śeṣa aspires to serve the paramātmā at all times, everywhere. A clear example of this is seen in Ananta, the multi-hooded serpent in Vaikuṇṭha. When Nārāyaṇa sits, Ananta is His seat; when He walks, Ananta's body twirls to become His pādukās, and his hoods His umbrella; when He chooses to rest, Ananta is His couch, his moulted skin is His blanket, his body bulge is His pillow, his gem-like eyes, His torch and the tongues, His fan. Such unparalleled services fetched him the title "Ādi" śeṣa, the first and foremost of all śeṣas. As you know, Lakṣmaṇa is the avatāra of Ādi śeṣa, and his services to the daṃpati are no less. The ṛṣis have called his bhakti to the daṃpati as śeṣatva, the state of being a śeṣa. Such śeṣatva turns invaluable when the servitude is extended to Nārāyaṇa's bhaktas. To attain that state, one has to transcend the bhakti to paramātmā, and arrive at bhakti to His bhaktas. When this is attained, such śeṣatva becomes peerless.

Bharata carrying Rāma's pādukās in the National Museum (Delhi) sculpted in the Vijayanagara dynasty (14th century CE)

Śatrughna's bhakti to Bharata, who was Rāma's bhakta, was of this variety. But ṛṣis opine that there is something even more difficult to achieve than Lakṣmaṇa's śeṣatva to Rāma, and Śatrughna's śeṣatva to Bharata.' A bewildered Vālmīki asked, 'What is that?'

Nārada said, 'It is Bharata's bhakti towards Rāma. Let me explain. A jīvātmā with its discerning skill, is śeṣa to paramātmā, no doubt. But it is completely dependent on paramātmā for its existence. It is hence a paratantra, an eternally dependent entity. On the other hand, the paramātmā reigns as the sovereign power, all powerful. He is called svatantra, an independent entity, whose orders can't be transgressed.

'Bharata returned to Ayodhyā, when Rāma asked him to, though it was his desire to take Rāma along. But Rāma's order superseded his own wish. Such bhakti which never questions the daṃpati but blindly follows them is called pāratantrya, the state of being a paratantra. Bharata's pāratantrya lost out to the pāratantrya of somebody else towards Rāma, though.'

Vālmīki said, 'I can't believe my ears. Bharata is the foremost of bhaktas to Rāma. Who can surpass him?'

Nārada said, 'Bharata is, no doubt, a great bhakta. But his pāratantrya was not absolute as he did question Rāma's resolve to stay in the forests. It is only the pādukās that were totally subservient to Rāma. Her bhakti to Rāma is unparalleled.'

Vālmīki couldn't control his tears when he realized the attachment of the brothers and the pādukās to Rāma. He was immensely grateful to Bramhā and Nārada who had blessed him with the opportunity to write the Rāmāyaṇa.